The Gourmet's Guide to
FISH & CHIPS

The Gourmet's Guide to
FISH & CHIPS

PIERRE PICTON

Edited by Rod Harrod

Cartoons by Larry

ALAN SUTTON

PUBLISHER'S NOTE

The information in this book is presented in good faith. While every effort has been made to ensure that all details are accurate, the publishers do not accept any responsibility for errors in the information supplied, for changes subsequent to the book's printing or for printer's errors, etc. Readers should verify for themselves that prices, details and standards meet with their requirements.

First published in Great Britain in 1990 by
Alan Sutton Publishing Limited · Phoenix Mill · Stroud · Gloucestershire

First published in the United States of America in 1990 by
Alan Sutton Publishing Inc · Wolfeboro Falls · NH 03896–0848

Copyright © P&H Publishing 1990

British Library Cataloguing in Publication data

Picton, Pierre
A gourmet's guide to fish and chips.
1. Great Britain. Fish and chip shops
I. Title
647.9541

ISBN 0-86299-770-4

Library of Congress Cataloging in Publication data applied for

Cover by Marcus Wilson Smith (*photography*) *and* Dolly Meers (*Home Economist*)

Photoset Times 10/12pt condensed.
Typesetting and origination by
Alan Sutton Publishing Limited.
Printed in Great Britain by
The Guernsey Press Company Limited,
Guernsey, Channel Islands.

CONTENTS

FISHING FOR COMPLIMENTS

We would like to acknowledge, and thank, the following for their help, assistance and contributions towards the compilation of the guide:

The Potato Marketing Board
The Sea Fish Industry Authority
The National Federation of Fish Friers Ltd
Tony Rogers, V.A. Whitley & Co Ltd
Elsie Robinson, Yorkshire Press Agency
Rhys Watt
Shirley Mitchell

Don't forget – a little of what you fancy does you good!
And if fish be the food of love, fry on . . .

INTRODUCTION

So, what's a clown doing writing a guide to the country's fish and chip shops?

The answer is simply because I, and my fellow entertainers, probably eat more of our nation's traditional fare than most, journeying around the land, catching a bite where we can.

It all started in the 1960s, when I was performing with Bertram Mills' Farewell Circus at London's Olympia. I know, it should have been CHIPperfield's Circus and the 'plaice' BATTERsea, but there you are!

My first guide was published in 1966 to celebrate the centenary of the 'marriage' of the saucy, sizzling chipped potato (she really is the French Fried, you know, because that's where we courted her) to our marvellous and magnificent fried fish of Olde England (and Scotland, Wales and Ireland, of course!). But more of that later . . .

Now, more than twenty years on, I have completely revised and updated the guide for another generation of fried fish fanatics and cheerful chippers.

Sadly, Bertram Mills' Circus and many others are no more. But I am still travelling the country, entertaining children of all ages, with my famous cars, including a 1924 'Laurel and Hardy' type Model T Ford comedy car and that most celebrated of film cars, Chitty Chitty Bang Bang.

I still meet dozens of travelling showmen and other artistes at carnivals, fêtes and galas, and they often recommend their latest 'fry finds'. So, don't be surprised if you see someone juggling, swallowing swords, etc. in the queue at your local chippy – he's not impatient, or over-hungry, just practising his art and 'clocking the shop'.

We have had a lot of help from presenters and listeners of many national, and local, radio stations. To every one of you who has contributed, I say a big thank you.

We've tried to give as much information, and to be as accurate, as we can with entries. Obviously if there have been changes, in price, fare or ownership, I hope they have been for the better. I'm sure you will write and let us know about any changes on one of the forms at the back of the book.

At the time of my first guide, 'fast food' still meant a slip on a banana skin. There were few alternatives to the Great British Fish and Chip Shop. Twenty or so years on, fish and chips are still our nation's favourite, for a reasonably-priced and nutritionally good meal. The main change has been in the size of the competition that has entered the take-away food trade. From Peking to Chicago, Madras to Milan, Hamburg to Hawaii, Mexico to Athens, they have all come trying to sell Britain their national dishes. But the essential joy of the traditional chippy has not changed. Where fast foods boast uniformity in Birmingham, be it Alabama or West Midlands, fish and chips have their own personality. In a world dominated by accountants, computers and marketing men, de-humanized and designer-organized shop fronts, the friendly local chip shop is a comforting haven and link with a less pressurized world that is essentially British.

Put another way, fish and chips don't just have character, they have heart. They are a part of Britain's heritage. A way of life for generations of royalty and roadmen, politicians and plumbers, medics and merchants, celebrities and shop girls. Whoever you are, wherever you are in Britain, you know you are never far from a good chippy. This book hopes to make the search that much easier, and perhaps more interesting. No doubt we've missed out some, which you will tell me about for next time.

In searching for my 'Scrumptious Selection' I've not tried to set one fryer against another – but rather to indicate some who try to set, and keep, their own high standards. Sometimes they may also present their product, premises or themselves in a way that sets them out from the crowd.

In the last few years we've had the lunatic fringe of food and health faddists trying to claim all sorts of unpleasant things about Britain's favourite fare, most of which I disprove in the pages that follow. Personally, I stand by the doctrine of 'a little of what you fancy does you good'! After all, one in six of us eat fish-shop-fry at least once a week – and it's my guess the other five are still in the queue!

So, sally forth with me on this verbal voyage. I do hope there's something within to tickle the palates of your mind, before, like me, you trot off down to the chip shop to savour the flavour.

PIERRE PICTON
1990

'PREFACE'

'PRESERVE FISH AND CHIP ESTABLISHMENTS'
A personal view of the state of frying today

Fish and Chips are to fast food what 'Real Ale' is to beer. Less than a generation ago Britain looked like losing the heritage and identity of many traditional brews. Then a small group of caring beer-drinkers formed CAMRA, the Campaign for Real Ale. They spearheaded what became the most successful consumer rebellion ever.

Now is the time for fish and chip lovers everywhere to take a sip from CAMRA's glass, and mount their own attack. Not against chippies, suppliers or the trade in this case, but against those who would foist every other nation's convenience grub upon us, rather than our own. None are as nutritious, none as digestible, none as healthy and certainly none as reasonably priced as fish and chips.

Moreover, none are as traditional as the nation's original, fine fast food – Fish and Chips, the Great British Eating Institution.

Let's call our appeal PREFACE – Preserve Fish and Chip Establishments.

I believe the British public – and millions of tourists – want to preserve the individuality and variety that only chippies can supply. Most of the UK's 10,000-plus outlets are owner-run. Each one is an individual artist of the range – some more talented than others.

Of course, a chippy's art is out on its own. Give any two fryers the same fine raw ingredients and I'll guarantee the meals will turn out equally good, yet totally different. Even the same fryer can produce different results from day to day, mood to mood, although part of the art is to make these changes less distinguishable. But just like the pint pulled from different parts of a barrel of traditional ale, so too the slightest change in a multitude of possible alternatives in the frying procedure can vary the results.

ix

This is not so with the stereotyped nature of the hamburger-to-chicken-to-pizza brigade. They aim to drain every ounce of originality from the product, premises and personnel. If it is unique it is out, to be replaced by the easily marketed, cloned, synthetic approach – guaranteed to be reproducible any time, anywhere, by almost anyone. However, it is also the highly professional marketing, packaging, advertising and presentation of the franchise groups that has often made fryers appear to have webbed feet. Moreover, as the well-financed multiple continues to forge further into every high street, so spiralling property prices and overheads have forced many, many humble chippies into back alleys, suburbs, or even total oblivion.

In the beginning there were fish and chip shops everywhere, or so it would seem. By 1914 over 25,000 chippies were scattered throughout the land. So it would remain through two world wars, when even governments ensured fryers had an ample supply of ingredients and frying media to supply the nation's needs.

But since 1945, until a few years ago, outlets have decreased dramatically in number, to less than half the total at their peak. However, in many instances, the size and turnover of the 10,000 or so remaining shops have increased, and with a bigger population gross sales have increased.

Each year the country's fryers batter more than 60,000 tonnes of fish, representing a goodly portion of all the white fish eaten in Britain. Then there's about six million tons of potatoes – plus 30,000 tons of oil and fat, which helps them retain their premier position in the £650 million fast food market.

I do not mean to suggest that all the fryers who have gone out of business did not deserve their fat or fate. Or that among those remaining there are not some whom the label 'greasy chippy' is the correct description. We all know of at least one: those who use inferior products; don't change their fat or oil regularly; overload the frier so that the temperature drops from the required 390 degrees farenheit with soggy results; cook everything from sausages to chicken and pancake rolls in the fish and chip oil or fat, and many, many other side-line sins.

But I do feel the trade has been singularly let down by official bodies, who are reluctant to show their support to this £400 million-a year industry.

Where are the Tourist Boards, government and council commercial depart-
ments hailing and helping fish and chips as Britain's world-beating take-
away convenience food? Do they want fish and chips to fade from the taste
buds of our country folk, to be replaced by a mixture of other nations' fare?
Do they want franchised fast food outlets to make Shepperton appear like
Chicago, Manchester turn out like Milan, Kenilworth seem like Kentucky or
Mexborough be mistaken for Mexico?

I'm not suggesting there's not room for competition, or even that some
fast food alternatives don't make a good change. I just don't want to see our
own national dish pushed to one side for the want of improving its image.

So, let's make a start. Start with the children. Make fish and chips more
fun, more exciting, more an eating experience, an eagerly sought-after
event. This applies to parents as much as fryers.

Of course, it should go without saying that culinary standards, and
hygiene must continue to improve and be maintained at all times. But if it
takes a few paper hats and red noses to compete with the multiples, then I'll
look in the bottom of my big trunk!

Until recently the community chippy – those nearer to homes than to the
high street – had avoided much of the competition. True, he'd had to learn
to live with various ethnic take-aways, but neither had had to employ
promotional techniques to out-do the other. But now some of the fast food
franchises – particularly pizza parlours – have begun eating into the
take-home domain of the neighbourhood fry-house. Their phone delivery
services are bound to affect fish and chip sales.

Make no bones about it, the battle for the customer is on. It's often said that
competition is healthy, and the consumer is the winner. But this is not
always true. If breweries had done away with traditional ale, the drinker
would have suffered. How 'plastic' the British pub would soon have become.
The same would happen if foreign fare were to dominate the ready-cooked
meal market.

Fish and chips are still the nation's Number One choice of all fast foods.
But fryers and devotees alike can no longer afford the luxury of com-
placency, even armed with the best ammunition of all – the most nutritious,
tasty, reasonably priced fast food of all. Fish and chips is the original,
traditional, Great British Eating Institution. Make sure it stays that way.

A FISHY TALE

The History Behind a National Institution

FRIED FISH . . .

. . . was available, particularly in the poorer parts of London and other cities, long before it met up with chips and they became the inseparable couple, adored, admired and devoured by millions.

Charles Dickens mentions the fore-runner to fish and chip shops, fried fish warehouses, in *Oliver Twist*, first published around 1838. To merit this inclusion they would have to have been well established. At the time bread, as much as a quarter of a pound, was the partner to fish – or occasionally-baked potatoes. Most fish sellers were street vendors, who carried their wares on trays slung around their necks. The fish was sold cold at around a penny a portion.

The fish had been fried, not to supply a cooked meal at reasonable cost, but to kill the smell and bacteria of an inferior and often stale product, and preserve it a few days longer. Better fish was either shipped live in flooded chests or, later, kept fresh with winter ice, harvested from fields flooded for the purpose, and stored in ice houses. These relatively costly methods put fresh fish beyond the means of all but the reasonably wealthy.

Henry Mayhew, in his book *London Labour and the London Poor*, published in 1861, claims there were around 300 fish-sellers in the capital at the time. One whom he interviewed said he had been in the trade seventeen years, having previously been a 'gentleman's servant'.

'I've lived in good families,' he told Mayhew, 'where there was first rate men-cooks, and I know what good cooking means. I bought a dozen plaice; I forget what I gave for them, but they were dearer than now. For all that I took between eleven and twelve shillings (around 60p) the first night – it was Saturday – that I started; and I stuck to it, and took from seven shillings to ten shillings every night, with more, of course, on Saturday, and it was half of it profit then. I cleared a good mechanic's earnings at that time – thirty shillings (£1.50) a week and more.'

According to Mayhew's information, it took 'ten bob' (50p) to start up in the trade – two shillings (10p) for a pan, half a crown (12.5p) for a tray, sixpence (2.5p) for a saltbox and five shillings (25p) for the fish.

In another of his interviews he tells of a boy thief who specialized in stealing fish from Billingsgate market. 'Some boys have made two shillings (10p) in a morning when fish is dear . . . plenty of costermongers are there who will buy it, rather than off the salesmen.'

Plaice and cod were the most freely available fish, as they are today, along with the tasty haddock.

CHIPPED POTATOES . . .

The recorded history of the chip goes back even further than fried fish. There are records of 'chippers' back in 1780. It is reasonably certain the idea came from France, where '*pommes frittes*' were a popular line during the Revolution (perhaps the guillotine was an early form of chip-chopper!).

Following their introduction to this country, the trade grew fastest in the north of England – from where the name 'chips' is said to originate. In the south the trade tended to be for the 'hot potato seller' with his jacket potatoes. These were baked by the local baker, and kept warm with a kind of water-boiler over a charcoal fire. They were sold with butter and salt.

Whether it was Sir Walter Raleigh, Sir Francis Drake or his cousin, Sir John Hawkins, who introduced the potato to Britain from Spain, where it had been imported from Peru, matters not a lot to our story. Whoever it was, they were first sampled on our shores around 1585.

The good burghers of Offenburg Baden in Germany favoured Drake, and erected a statue to him in the town. The Nazis took the statue down – but did not replace it with one of a Hamburger! Germany is still one of the biggest potato consuming nations in the world.

Potato growing met with considerable initial resistance in Britain. In Ireland, however, the need for a cheap main vegetable to feed the masses broke down even the strongest prejudices.

In fact, the Irish became so dependent on the humble 'praties' – as they were to call them – that millions died of starvation during various crop failures between 1728 and 1851, particularly those of 1845 and 1846. Others fled to Britain – mostly to the industrial towns of the north – in search of work and food. They took with them their love of potatoes.

British farmers, aware of the misfortunes of the Irish over-dependence on the potato crop, were still reluctant to put their faith in the vegetable. Only the possibility of blockade from foreign grain supplies during the Napoleonic and American wars brought government and farmers to recognize its potential as a home-produced staple food.

But the potato still had one drawback – in those early days the crop was seasonal, available only for six months of the year. Improved storage methods overcame this problem in time, and the nation in turn overcame its prejudices and adopted the potato as their premier vegetable. As we enter the 1990s every man, woman and child in the country eats an average 2 lb each every three days.

Its usefulness as a wartime basic foodstuff was not lost on successive governments. The crop was almost doubled in size between 1916 and 1918, and was given a similar boost in 1939.

THE HAPPY MARRIAGE . . .

I wish I could give a precise day and time and place when the nuptials of fish and chips took place. I know the groom wore a fine coat of light, crisp batter and the bride, blushing in the heat, emerged from the ceremony lightly tanned. Salt was thrown as confetti and, before being surrounded by newspapers, the couple drank a toast in – vinegar!

THE DATE: From mentions in numerous registers of the time, we can be fairly certain it was around 1865 that the couple first formalized their union on a regular basis. My first guide was published in 1966 in celebration of the centennial anniversary. Since then the trade and its numerous associations and affiliates have considered this date as the 100-year milestone.

THE PLACE: Some say the family fish and chip shop was spawned in the northern mill towns of Lancashire and Yorkshire, where, to this day, there is still a far greater density of chippies than anywhere else in the land.

Conditions, certainly, were right. These towns had the workshops and foundries to make ranges and had caught the potato-eating habit from the Irish immigrants. There was also a plentiful supply of fish available from the Irish and North seas. Then there was the ready-made market of industrial shift workers, including working women with little time to prepare hot meals.

Others believe the Happy Couple were introduced to one another on the streets of London. Some say the 'marriage' was arranged by Baroness Angela Burdett-Coutts, a great philanthropist and the grand-daughter and heir of the founder of the famous bank. It is claimed she came across an Italian (not French?) custom of frying potato slices and brought this idea together with the fish that had been sold on the streets for decades. There were other sightings of shops in London that sold 'fish and unpeeled spuds' in the late 19th century, but nothing to pin-point an exact date.

Up and down the country many claim to have been in at the start of our national eating institution. I will not attempt to confirm or disprove any of these assumptions. It is enough to say that, by 1914, there were 25,000 chippies in the United Kingdom. This must mean that a large number of outlets are at least celebrating three-quarters of a century of trading!

Steam trawlers, improved refrigeration and the intricate railway system across the United Kingdom all played their part in both spreading the trade and improving standards. However, many of those who claim direct lineage back to those early days might not crow so loudly if they did but realize how unpopular fryers were in many areas. Deodorized oil did not come into its own until the early years of this century. Before this mutton fat or beef dripping was used, or alternatively cotton seed oil. But each carried a far from pleasant, hanging odour for those living in the vicinity of a chippy. Dr Ballard, a London Health Inspector in 1876, while referring to fish-frying as 'a pretty trade', emphasized its nuisance to neighbours.

'There is, I believe, scarcely a Health Officer in London who has not been called . . . to advise as to an appropriate remedy for this nuisance [the smell]'.

By 1911 fish and chip shops were officially labelled an 'Offensive Trade', a title that was to stick until 1940. Ironically, about the same time fryers became officially recognized as an organized unit and trade by the government.

To turn the whole thing on its head, it is no idle boast of the trade itself that fish and chip shops kept the country going during the slump of the 1920s and '30s. This was a recognized fact, particularly in the industrialized areas of the North and Midlands. Having fought against all odds to earn a place in the hearts, as well as the stomachs, of the population, fish and chips were at last to be given official status. During the Second World War, Frederick Lord Woolton, Minister of Food, declared fish and chips were the only take-away food not to be rationed. Mobile fry-vans even carried our famous fare to evacuees around the country – so beginning another chapter in the history of the Great British take-away.

A recent survey by the Sea Fish Industry Authority confirmed that 70 per cent of the British population visits a chippy at least once every three months. This compares with 38 per cent visiting a burger-bar or a mere 20 per cent taking a trip to the pizza parlour. A mere 1 per cent eat pizzas weekly, only 3 per cent chew on a burger every seven days, but a massive 20 per cent of the Great British Public (some 11 million individuals) enjoy fish and chips at least once a week.

Unlike most take-away competitors, fish and chips are regarded as a 'proper meal' rather than a snack by 70 per cent of consumers and is eaten at home by 80 per cent of those buying.

Why does the humble chippy remain supreme? Quite simply because it is the best, most tasty, reasonably-priced and nutritious ready-cooked meal available.

THE ACCESSORIES . . .

Fish and chips are almost unthinkable unless accompanied by salt and vinegar, or lemon (dieticians say a squeeze of lemon is better than vinegar, as it provides Vitamin C).

SALT: Vital to the body's health; we each consume around 10 lb annually. Two Edinburgh doctors once tried to discover the effect of excluding salt from their diet completely for two weeks. At the end they had almost lost their memories, their speech and movements were clumsy, their breathing short and their weight had dropped seriously. Salt is, of course, used in the cooking of fish and chips as well as the shake and sprinkle applied after they're cooked.

VINEGAR: Fundamentally a national drink that has turned sour. As our national drinks are beer and whisky, our vinegar is malt vinegar. On the continent, where the national drink tends to be wine, they use wine vinegar. The vinegar supplied to fish and chip shops begins life the same way as beer; but the liquor obtained from the malt is encouraged to produce acids instead of guarded against them. It takes five days for the liquor to turn sour. After that it is left in enormous vats for between nine and twelve months.

PONDERINGS ON PEAS: mushy or marrowfat. V.A. Whitley & Co Ltd sell over 50,000 tonnes each year, with the greatest number of customers in the north-west. However, in recent years, the nation has been catching on fast to this natural complement to fish and chips. Dried peas should not be steeped for longer than eight hours, particularly when the weather is warm, to avoid organic change in the peas. There are many different ways of preparing, cooking and serving this dish, and no 'perfect' method. Some fryers use sugar in their peas, others – a few – get away without any official steeping at all. Many more don't wash the peas after steeping, but simply transfer them to a pan of clean water for cooking, after straining off the steeping. But most agree they taste delicious when eaten with malt vinegar and pepper – together, of course, with fish and chips. Prior to the mid-1960s the Dutch Jumbo was the favourite pea for making big, green, even-sized, mushy peas. Fast overtaking the Progreta of late is a mixture of Maro and Carop, known as Super Green Marrowfat. Ask your chippy which he uses.

NEWSPAPER WRAPPING: The traditional take-home jacket for fish and chips, originally wrapped directly around the product. But this was brought to an end in the name of hygiene, and the law now insists that the direct wrapping must be unprinted paper. However, many good chippies put an outer layer of newspaper round the take-home fare, thus satisfying every-one. After all, there was much to be said for newsprint, which not only soaks up excess vinegar, but also gives you something on which to wipe your fingers *and* gives the fish-fryer, and the buyer, something to read! These days the general trend is towards paper bags, polystyrene trays and finger sticks – with yet another Olde English custom being sacrificed in the name of progress. In times past the National Federation of Fish Fryers used to send a telegram each year to the National Union of Journalists, proclaiming: 'Our trade is wrapped up in yours!' There's no record of the Press boys and girls replying: 'But yours is often more easily digested!'

FISHY FRIDAYS

Is the tradition of eating fish on Fridays of Catholic or Protestant origin? Let's fish out some facts . . .

The Fish Day, or Fysche Day ('*jour maigre*' in French) is said to be a day in the Roman Catholic Church when meat could not be eaten without ecclesiastical permission. However the saying 'He eats no fish' – now accepted as a description of an honest man, one to be trusted – was originally meant to define a person other than a papist. In the reign of Elizabeth I, papists were opposed to the government. Protestants, to show their loyalty, REFUSED to eat fish on Fridays, to identify themselves as NOT being papists. Shakespeare wrote in *King Lear*: 'I do profess . . . to serve him truly . . . and to eat no fish.'

In another saying we have fish being the best food eaten by monks. 'Neither fish (food for the monk), flesh (food for the people generally), nor yet red herring (food for paupers).' It means, of course, that something is fit for neither one thing nor another. But the fact that fish comes first on the list emphasizes how, in the Middle Ages, the clergy took precedence over the laity.

Mrs Lynn Linton writes: 'She would be a betwixt-and-between . . . neither fish nor fowl.'

So, there you have it, or you don't. You pay your penn'orth and take your choice. Whatever the reason, Fishy Fridays have proven a worthwhile tradition to the fryers and fishmongers of Britain over the years . . .

A LITTLE OF WHAT YOU FANCY DOES YOU GOOD

Despite fad diets and scare stories about what is and what isn't good for you these days, there really is no such thing as unhealthy food – only unhealthy eating!

The doctrine of 'a little of what you fancy does you good' applies equally to succulent fish, tasty chips and crunchy pickled onions as it does to other activities and pastimes! Science has shown a healthy appetite is often the best guide to what you should eat. The first essential of good food is to stimulate your appetite and make your mouth water. This outpouring of the digestive juices prepares the way for the rapid and easy assimilation of the meal.

What could be more appetizing than the sight, sound and smell of sizzling fish and chips, provided it is fresh and cooked in spotlessly clean surroundings? The hot oil or fat seals in the natural juices and adds to the wholesome flavour of the food.

But, just how nourishing *is* fish and chips?

Your body is constantly using up energy. Energy can only be replaced by the food we eat, which is expressed as calories. Mr Average needs about 2,500 calories a day, Mrs Average around 500 fewer. However, someone doing really hard, physical work could need around 4,500 calories each day. The precise figure varies from person to person.

The size of your portion of fish and chips will vary from county to county, town to town, shop to shop. But it will probably be between 3 and 6 oz (85 to 170 g) of fish and 4 to 6 oz (113 to 170 g) of chips.

For the aFISHionados and weight CHIPpers, 4 oz of cod or skate in dry, crispy batter gives just 199 calories, plaice 279 or haddock 307. There are four and a half times more calories in lamb or pork than in either cod or haddock. In beef the multiple is three and a half, with chicken weighing in with three times the calories of white fish.

Of course, it is not just calories that concern us, but also the proportion of protein, carbohydrate and fat contained in food. Fish is full of protein, which is body-building. It is needed for growth and the repair of tissue, like muscle, that is constantly being broken down in the course of our daily activities. An average 6 oz portion of haddock will give about half the total protein needed by the body to carry out a clerical job. There is further protein in chips. Cod or haddock contain as much protein as beef and more than either lamb or pork.

Carbohydrates in sugary and starchy foods are also an important source of energy. Unfortunately, if we eat more than we need, the excess is turned into fat and we put on weight. White fish contains little carbohydrate, but potatoes are rich in it. Depending on their thickness, chips weigh in at between 40 and 85 calories per ounce (28 g). The thicker the chip the lower the fat content.

White fish contains as little as 1.2 per cent fat. Cod fried in batter has as little as 10 per cent fat content, compared with 17 per cent in beefburgers, 25 per cent in sausages or 45 per cent in fried streaky bacon. In fact, the fat content in lamb is 43 times, pork 41 times, beef 35 times and chicken 25 times greater than in either cod or haddock.

But food is not just a matter of protein, carbohydrate, fat and calories. It must also supply us with adequate vitamins which, in minute traces, are necessary for good health.

Vitamin C, for instance, is a proven health additive. Although potatoes are not rich in it, like green vegetables and citrus fruit are, because we eat so many of them they can give us a fair amount of the Vitamin C we need. In the ordinary way, a large portion of Vitamin C is lost in cooking. But when chips are fried at high temperatures, the vitamin is 'locked in' and retained in the chips.

Frying fat also contains Vitamins A and D. Vitamin A is necessary for growth in children, for the health of the skin and other surface linings, such as the air passage. Vitamin D promotes healthy teeth and bones, particularly in children. Both Vitamins A and D are found in plenty in halibut, salmon, mackerel and herring.

Further, there's only half as much nicotinic acid in beef, lamb or pork as in either cod or haddock.

A good, balanced diet also contains an adequate supply of minerals. Fish minerals are calcium, phosphorus and iodine. Calcium, for instance, is needed for forming bones; iron is needed for the formation of red blood cells. Cod and haddock contain twice the calcium of beef, lamb or pork. Shellfish – cockles, for instance – are rich in iron.

Confused? No need to be. You are safe in the knowledge that fish and chips cooked well are not only the tastiest, and most reasonably priced ready-cooked meal available, but also the most nutritious.

Abbreviations

T/A	Take-away
R	Restaurant
L	Licensed to sell alcohol, for consumption on or off the premises
P	Parking
T	Toilets
Wheelchair access:	outlets with easy access for wheelchairs
Wheelchair friendly:	outlets where the staff are happy to help with wheelchair access which could otherwise be a little difficult

Note: While every effort has been taken to ensure that entries are accurate at the time of going to print, some change in services and prices are inevitable from time to time. Please let us know of any changes you come across by writing to: *The Gourmet's Guide to Fish and Chips*, Alan Sutton Publishing Limited, Phoenix Mill, Far Thrupp, Stroud, Gloucestershire, GL5 2BU, or by returning the questionnaire at the back of this book.

The Gourmet's Guide to
FISH & CHIPS

ENGLAND

AVON

Bath

EVANS' FAMOUS FISH AND CHIPS, Abbey Gate Street. Tel: 0225 463981

Open: Mon – Sat 11.30 a.m. – 6.00 p.m. (June – Sept
till 9.00 p.m.) for take-away and self-service restaurant;
11.30 a.m. – 2.30 p.m. waitress dining rooms.

Facilities: T/A; R (L); T; wheelchair access.

Fish-finds: Cod, Dover and lemon sole, fish cakes, fish fingers,
haddock, huss, scampi and skate. Fish and chips to take-
and-taste from around £1.50, sit-and-savour with tea and
bread & butter from around £3.30.

Fry: Groundnut and palm oil.

Side-lines: Mushy peas, pickled onions. Other foods.

Wrapping: Self-seal, double-lined bags with carriers if requested.

*Though dating back to 1910, this large, traditional fish and chip café,
belongs more to the Lyons Corner House era and donkey-rides by the sea.
Les Dawson and other celebrities from the theatre are known visitors. Nice
children's special – cone of chips and a bottle of pop for around 60p.*

*Like anywhere in this beautiful city, Evans' is best approached on foot.
Directions are no guarantee of finding it easily. Either head for Marks and
Spencer in Stall Street, with Evans' near the rear entrance, or take the
scenic route – from Grand Parade near the Fernley Hotel promenade past*

Sally Lunn's House (the oldest property in historic Bath), down into Abbeygreen Square with its Crystal Palace pub, and you'll find it through the archway in the southernmost corner. Well worth walking up an appetite! Incidentally, it takes nearly every sort of plastic money.

SEAFOOD, Kingsmead Street. Tel: 0225 465190

Open:	Mon – Sat 11.30 a.m. – 3.00 p.m.; Mon – Thu 5.30 p.m. – 11.30 p.m.; Fri 6.00 p.m. – midnight; Sat 5.00 p.m. – midnight; Sun 6.00 p.m. – 11.00 p.m.
Facilities:	T/A & R; P (road); T; wheelchair access.
Fish finds:	Cod, Dover and lemon sole, fish cakes, haddock, plaice, scampi, shark. Fish and chips to take-and-taste from around £1.45; sit-and-savour around £2.15.
Fry:	Fat, palm oil.
Side-lines:	Mushy peas, pickled gherkins, pickled onions. Other foods.
Wrapping:	White paper, polystyrene trays; chip cones.

Nestling in the shadow of the huge plane tree in Kingsmead Square, this outlet is well patronized by locals – always a pointer to quality, particularly in a tourist magnet town like Bath. Mr H.S. Barnes bought the shop eight years ago, though he's been in the trade a good few more. A cockney by birth, he's obviously learnt not only how to fry but how to keep his staff happy – so they, in turn, are pleasant and courteous with their customers. Seating for fifty-eight diners in the restaurant.

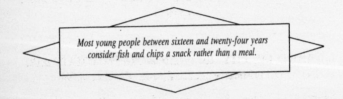

Most young people between sixteen and twenty-four years consider fish and chips a snack rather than a meal.

Bristol

MULLIGAN'S, College Green. Tel: 0272 226440

Open:	Mon–Sat midday – 2.15 p.m.; 6.30 p.m. – 10.45 p.m. (last orders). Sun midday – 2.30 p.m.; 6.30 p.m. – 10.00 p.m.
Facilities:	R (L); P near; T
Fish finds:	Cod, haddock, hake, plaice, skate. Sit-and-savour from around £5.00.
Speciality:	Lobsters caught from their own pool within the restaurant.
Fry:	Vegetable fat. (Fish also grilled or poached with sauces.)
Side-lines:	Mushy peas, pickled gherkins.

Beppe and Chris Vella opened their first Mulligan's on a bleak moorland road in South Wales a few years ago. Though highly experienced caterers, the cynics stacked the odds against them. How wrong they were – it is now one of the most successful eating establishments in the principality, and they then sold it to Whitbread. The Bristol outlet has a large bar area rather like an American 'singles bar', where even those not eating may drink. It is built on the site of the former Villa Bianca and the adjoining building, in one of the most prestigious positions in Bristol. Quite a fish experience with seating for no less than two hundred diners. Everything about this place, from bare-board, church pew, mock-marble and abundance of brass interior, to the freshness of the fish, keenness of the prices and the pride of Porsches parked about, spells Success with a capital 'S'.

PLAWECKI'S CITY FRIED FISH & CHIPPED POTATO BAR, 17 Christmas Steps, St Michaels. Tel: 0272 273580

Open:	Mon – Sat midday – 2.00 p.m.; 7.30 p.m. – 11.30 p.m.

Facilities: T/A & R; T; wheelchair access.

Fish finds: Cod, haddock, hake, plaice. Fish and chips to take-and-taste from around £1.55; sit-and-savour a few pence more.

Fry: Mixture of dripping and oil – 'it gives a different flavour.'

Side-lines: Other foods.

Wrapping: Trays and white wrap plus carriers; newspaper wrap on request!

The argument rumbles on as to which is the oldest chippy in Britain – though there's photographic evidence to prove they were frying here at the turn of the century at least. However, it's doubtful anyone would challenge the title of oldest building for a chippy – circa 1380 – although if someone opened next door they'd hold the record – that building was erected in 1264! In days of yore, there were no fewer than twenty ale houses within a few yards of Christmas Steps, but the Three Sugar Loaves (once called the Gaiety) has always been just a couple of chip lengths across the flag-stoned alley. Neither establishment minds you taking your pint to the chippy – as long as you return the glasses. Singled out by TV AM as tops in England and second in the UK, as a traditional chippy it certainly takes some beating. Mind your head on the beams!

When Bristol's most famous ex-patriot, Cary Grant, re-visited this magnificently traditional shop nestling at the foot of Christmas Steps a few years ago, he remarked how unchanged it seemed from his childhood memories. Robert Plawecki has been frying deliciously crisp batter around fresh fish from either Whitby or Aberdeen. Robert insists he can squeeze twenty sit-and-savours up the stairs to the rear, and will open a side door to accommodate wheelchairs. He even says he gets regular coach bookings – but I think he means to take-and-taste. A regular endorsement comes from visits by super-chef of TV Keith Floyd.

BEDFORDSHIRE
Kempston

YE BUNYAN FISH SHOPPE, 14 Bunyan Road. Tel: 0234 853022

Open:	Tue – Thu midday – 2.00 p.m.; 5.00 p.m. – 10.00 p.m.; Fri 11.30 a.m. – 2.00 p.m.; 4.30 p.m. – 10.00 p.m.; Sat 11.30 a.m. – 2.00 p.m.; 4.30 p.m. – 10.00 p.m.
Facilities:	T/A; P near.
Fish finds:	Cod, haddock, huss, plaice, skate. Fish and chips to take-and-taste from around £1.35.
Fry:	Own recipe.
Side-lines:	Mushy peas. Other foods.
Wrapping:	White paper.

When I was first introduced to this chippy I thought of various 'corny' lines about flat feet and flat fish. Then I remembered that The Pilgrims Progress *author John Bunyan was born on the other side of Bedford, a few miles away. He was imprisoned in the town for unauthorised preaching for twelve years in 1660. Now there are innumerable memorials to him around the area – so why not a fine chippy in the Saxon shopping centre? Anyway, what's in a name when the fare is crisp and tasty? The queues that form can vouch for the answer. Run by manager and chief fryer Sidney McReady himself.*

> *The fat content of cheese is three to five times greater than that of cod fried in batter.*

BERKSHIRE
Ascot

ASCOT FISH BAR, 6 Royal Hunt House, Fernbank Road.
Tel: 0344 883842

Open:	Mon – Sat 11.30 a.m. – 2.00 p.m.; 5.00 p.m. – 10.00 p.m.
Facilities:	T/A; P; T.
Fish finds:	Cod, haddock, huss, plaice, skate. Fish and chips to take-and-taste from around £2.20.
Fry:	Groundnut oil.
Side-line:	Battered mushrooms.
Wrapping:	White paper, trays.

The first Ascot race meeting took place in July 1711. The area has had nearly three hundred years, therefore, to develop a social reputation for all things fine. Mr Puckey's chippy is no exception. From 1986 onwards, his efforts were rewarded with an award for the high standard of hygiene and staff presentation attained and maintained in his establishment. It's nice to see that the colour of the award matches that of the crisp golden batter covering the large, scrumptious fish portions.

Reading

TERRY'S FISH BAR, 166 Oxford Road. Tel: 0734 573834

Open:	Mon – Sat 11.30 a.m. – 10.30 p.m.
Facilities:	T/A; P near; wheelchair friendly.
Fish finds:	Cod, haddock, scampi. Fish and chips to take-and-taste from around £1.30.
Fry:	Vegetable oil.
Side-lines:	Pickled onions. Other foods.
Wrapping:	Trays, paper, greaseproof, bags, cartons.

This is a family run traditional chippy, no fads or finery. They cook a nice piece of plaice with jumbo sized portions of chips. Pop into the Rose and Thistle pub for a quick wash down, and if you are Reading Football Club supporters, say the word!

Wokingham

**MUSKY'S QUALITY FISH AND CHIPS, 26 Peach Street.
Tel: 0734 780192**

Open:	Mon – Sat 11.45 a.m. – 11.00 p.m. (Fri & Sat till midnight); Sun 5.30 p.m. – 11.00 p.m.

Facilities:	T/A.
Fish finds:	Cod, haddock, plaice, rock. Fish and chips to take-and-taste from around £1.50.
Fry:	Vegetable oil.
Wrapping:	White news.

When on your way to Royal Ascot in your chauffeur-driven limo, resplendent in topper and tails, you might stop and get James to pop into Musky's for cod and chips for your and your guests, accompanied by a magnum of bubbly.

BUCKINGHAMSHIRE
Bourne End

SUPER PLAICE, 46 The Parade. Tel: 06285 21968

Open:	Mon – Sat 11.30 a.m. – 2.00 p.m.; 4.30 p.m. – 10.30 p.m.
Facilities:	T/A; P near.
Fish finds:	Cod, fish cakes, haddock, plaice, rock, skate. Fish and chips to take-and-taste from around £2.00.
Fry:	Vegetable oil.
Side-lines:	Mushy peas, pickled gherkins, pickled onions. Other foods.
Wrapping:	Bags or trays; outer white paper.

Alan Jones is the kind of fryer who really sets out to please your needs. He'll cut extra large fish to order, or, for the diet-conscious, fry the fish without batter. As a result he has built up quite a trade, not only from regular patrons, but for party orders of almost any size. The business has been trading in the main shopping parade next door to National Westminster Bank for around ten years.

Stop Press: sit-and-savour coming soon – May or June 1990.

> Some say huss and rock salmon are one and the same – and most refer to them as such. Others say rock has a bone and is a catfish, whereas huss has a jelly-type spine and is otherwise a dogfish.

New Bradwell (Nr Milton Keynes)

NAPOLI FISH BAR, 175 Newport Road. Tel: 0908 313193
and
30 St James Street. Tel: 0908 317038

Open:	Mon – Sat 11.30 a.m. – 2.00 p.m.; 4.30 p.m. – 11.00 p.m. (Fri & Sat till 11.30 p.m.).
Facilities:	T/A; P.
Fish finds:	Cod, haddock, plaice, rock, skate, all delivered fresh daily. Fish and chips to take-and-taste from around £1.50.
Fry:	Oil.
Side-lines:	Mushy peas, pickled gherkins, pickled onions. Other foods.
Wrapping:	Double wrap of white off-cuts.

Both outlets are family-run by the Pillas (Maria and Giovanni) – quite naturally with an Italian flavour. However, after a decade of frying in this red-brick town on the main Wolverton to Newport Pagnell Road, the fish take first place. Outlet number two (in fact the main premises) is opposite the Community Centre. The outside is stone clad, with green tiled floor and white and green tiled walls inside. Eileen Glover from Leicester (a long way to come for a bite) drew our attention to the clean appearance of the Newport Road outlet and the friendly, warm welcome given by owners and staff alike. The presentation and standard of meals served is very high.

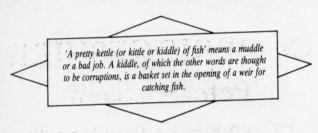

'A pretty kettle (or kittle or kiddle) of fish' means a muddle or a bad job. A kiddle, of which the other words are thought to be corruptions, is a basket set in the opening of a weir for catching fish.

Woburn Sands

HAZELL'S FISH BAR, 47 Station Road. Tel: 0908 583144

Open:	Tue – Fri midday – 2.00 p.m.; 5.00 p.m. – 10.00 p.m.; Sat midday – 8.00 p.m.
Facilities:	T/A; P (front); T; wheelchair access possible.
Fish finds:	Cod (three sizes), fish cakes, haddock, plaice, rock, roe, scampi, skate. Fish and chips to take-and-taste from around £1.50.
Fry:	Oil.
Side-lines:	Mushy peas, pickled gherkins, pickled onions, small vegetarian menu. Other foods.
Wrapping:	Fibre trays or news off-cuts.

Opened twenty years ago – almost before Milton Keynes existed! In fact, the chippy is in the countryside on the Beds/Bucks border. It's the nearest chippy to Woburn Abbey. Whether the Marquis of Tavistock is partial to plaice I don't know – he certainly wasn't in the queue when we called in. You'll find Hazell's opposite Neville's Antiques, near the Junction with Weathercock Lane – in which you'll find the Weathercock pub. The fish bar looks clean and fresh with a white-walled exterior and pine panels within. For the wider selection of fish go early. M.J. Watts manages the outlet for Numitor (Ross) Ltd.

CAMBRIDGESHIRE
Peterborough

ONE 'N' ONE, 102 New Road, Woodston. Tel: 0733 61044

Open:	Mon 4.30 p.m. – 7.30 p.m.; Tue – Sat 11.30 a.m. – 1.45 p.m.; 4.30 p.m. – 11.00 p.m.
Facilities:	T/A; P.
Fish finds:	Cod, haddock, plaice, rock, skate. Fish and chips to take-and-taste from around £1.40.
Fry:	Beef dripping.
Side-lines:	Mushy peas, pickled onions. Other foods.
Wrapping:	Polystyrene trays, white news and printed bags.

John Venters is locally known as the Boss Man, so don't answer back, have the right money ready, no talking in the queue and if you don't fancy queueing, the Boss runs a mean delivery service with generous portions. Listed among his other foods are battered onions rings, so be nice!

SKIPPERS FISH & CHIPS, 314–316 Lincoln Road. Tel: 0733 46672

Open: Mon – Sat 11.30 a.m. – 11.00 p.m. (Fri & Sat till 11.30 p.m.).

Facilities: T/A & R (L); T (R); wheelchair access (help available).

Fish finds: Cod, haddock, plaice. Fish and chips to take-and-taste from around £1.50; sit-and-savour around £2.60.

Fry: Groundnut oil.

Side-lines: Mushy peas.

Wrapping: White news.

Steve Goodacre and Martin Bunning have only owned this 70-year-old outlet a little over a year; though they've been in the trade thirty years between them. The premises were stripped and completely refurbished in the spring of 1989 – with Buster Merryfield ('Uncle' from Only Fools and Horses*) performing the re-opening ceremony. The new decor has a distinctly nautical air – with the exterior painted in sea blue and the name written in 'rope' lettering. Their extensive efforts have already been rewarded by being declared an area winner in the 'Fish and Chip Shop of the Year' contest, and the pair of them won a separate award in 1987 as 'Fish Traders of the Year' (for their services to the Industry). By the way, Steve's the one (apart from Buster) with the beard, and Martin sports a nifty line in striped shirt, bow tie and dark tabard – but then, so does Steve!*

CHESHIRE
Crewe

LES'S FISH BAR, Victoria Road. Tel: 0270 257581

Open:	Mon & Tue 11.00 a.m. – 5.30 p.m.; Wed 11.00 a.m. – 2.00 p.m.; Thu & Fri 11.00 a.m. – 7.00 p.m.; Sat 11.00 a.m. – 5.00 p.m.
Facilities:	T/A & R; P; T.
Fish finds:	Cod, fish cakes, haddock, plaice, scampi. Fish and chips to take-and-taste from around £1.75.
Speciality:	Potato fritters.
Fry:	Vegetable oil.
Side-lines:	Beans, mushy peas.
Wrapping:	Boxes, white news, trays.

This is the sister shop (or should I say brother, Les!) to Mr and Mrs Manning's first shop in Winsford. It's been open since the late 1980s in this, the home of what were the largest railway construction workshops in the world – they'd made 4,000 engines in the sixty years before the turn of this century. They boast a pretty good school of art and also, now, a pretty good chippy!

Knutsford

MR. CHIPS, 5 Toft Road. Tel: 0565 3460

Open:	Mon – Sat 11.30 a.m. – 1.30 p.m.; 5.00 p.m. – 11.30 p.m. (midnight Fri & Sat).

Facilities:	T/A & café; P; T.
Fish finds:	Cod, king size haddock on request. Fish and chips to take-and-taste from around £1.45.
Fry:	DryFry Gold oil.
Side-lines:	Mushy peas.
Wrapping:	Polystyrene boxes with flip-over lids, then bags.

When Elizabeth Gaskell based her book Cranford *on her childhood experiences in Knutsford, it was just a small village in early 19th-century England. They almost certainly didn't have a chippy, though this one has been in existence for over sixty years. Proprietor Alan Mahon acknowledges that the interior, which was modernized a decade ago, probably needs re-doing for the 1990s. But many of his famous regulars don't look at the decor when they know the fish has been delivered fresh daily from Aberdeen (that's why he keeps the menu short). Bobby Charlton, Dennis Taylor, 'Ken Barlow' and 'Rita Fairclough', from the 'Street' all pass through the mock-Tudor exterior to sample the fare. Nearest pub is the King's in Princess Street, with an Oddbins in King Street for off-sales.*

Stop Press: Refit and refurbishment expected by the summer of 1990.

Macclesfield

MARSHALL'S FISH & CHIPS, 95/97 Chestergate. Tel: 0625 614804

Open:	T/A: Mon – Sat 11.30 a.m. – 2.00 p.m.; Mon – Fri 4.30 p.m. – 11.00 p.m.; R: Mon – Fri 10.00 a.m. – 11.00 p.m.; Sat 10.00 a.m. – 2.00 p.m.
Facilities:	T/A & R; P near.
Fish finds:	Cod, haddock, plaice, prawns, scampi. Fish and chips to take-and-taste from around £1.25.

Fry:	Vegetable oil.
Side-lines:	Mushy peas, pickled onions, saveloys. Other foods.
Wrapping:	White news, plastic carrier bags.

Macclesfield stands on the river Bollin and was once famous for its silk industry. The first mill opened around 1750 – which was even a bit before this, the oldest chippy in the town. Although it has been totally refurbished from cellar to roof, it was first opened over fifty years ago. It also claims the crown as the shop with the oldest single ownership in the town. Find it via the A537 Knutsford to Chelford road towards the town centre through Chestergate. Well worth seeking out the friendly proprietors, Dave Smith and Chris Roberts.

Northwich

SEAFARER RESTAURANT & TAKE-AWAY, 7 Chester Way.
Tel: 0606 43169/46266

Open:	Mon – Sat 11.00 a.m. – 11.00 p.m.; Sun 5.30 p.m. – 11.00 p.m.
Facilities:	T/A & R; P; T.
Fish finds:	Cod, haddock, plaice (breaded or battered), scampi. Fish and chips to take-and-taste from around £1.50. Sit-and-savour slightly more.
Fry:	Palm oil.
Side-lines:	Mushy peas and other foods.
Wrapping:	Trays and white news, plus paper bags.

Neil Stevenson has been frying in this market town on the junction of the rivers Dane and Weaver for nearly eighteen years. If you like salt with your meal you should have no problem here – for Northwich became known as the centre of Britain's salt industry! This town centre outlet has a busy take-away counter and 60-seater restaurant decorated on a nautical theme with ships' wheels and plants around. Banquette seating in orange with green carpeting. Only fresh fish is used.

Poynton

STRAWBERRY PIG, 57 Park Lane. Tel: 0625 875923

Open:	Mon – Sat 11.30 a.m. – 2.00 p.m.; 4.30 p.m. – midnight; Sun 5.30 p.m. – midnight.
Facilities:	T/A; P near; wheelchair access.
Fish finds:	Cod, plaice, scampi. Fish and chips to take-and-taste from around £1.80.
Fry:	Vegetable oil.
Side-lines:	Mushy peas and other foods.
Wrapping:	Trays, white paper.

John and Rachel Manion have run this outlet since 1989 – though they've been in the trade for a long time. After a day out on one of the dozen or so golf courses within reach or at the National Trust's Lyme Park nearby, what better than a hearty meal of fish and chips? And where better than the Strawberry Pig. If you think the name is a bit strange, all is explained in an interesting poem displayed on the wall, along with piggy pics.

Stockport

THE MILL CHIPPY, 59 Church Road, Newmills. Tel: 0663 46891

Open:	Mon – Sat 11.30 a.m. – 1.30 p.m.; Tue, Wed & Sat 4.30 p.m. – 6.30 p.m.; Thu & Fri 4.30 p.m. – 10.30 p.m.

Facilities:	T/A; P near; wheelchair friendly.
Fish finds:	Cod, haddock, whiting. Fish and chips to take-and-taste from around £1.60.
Fry:	Vegetable fat.
Side-lines:	Mushy peas. Other foods.
Wrapping:	Polystyrene boxes.

If you can batter and deep fry cod, haddock and whiting to the satisfaction of all your many customers, and a team of high frying experts, then you have got to be good. The management and staff of the Mill Chippy fished their way to become Enterprise Award Winners in the Sea Fish Industry Authority's 'Fish and Chip Shop of the Year' in 1989.

The name potato comes from the Spanish word 'patata'.

Wallasey

PAUL'S CONTINENTAL, 25 Poulton Road, Seacombe. Tel: 051 638 8696

Open:	Mon – Sat 11.30 a.m. – 1.45 p.m.; 4.30 p.m. – 11.30 p.m.; (Tue – Thu eves 7.00 p.m. – 8.30 p.m.).
Facilities:	T/A; P near.
Fish finds:	Cod, haddock, plaice. Fish and chips to take-and-taste from around £1.35.
Fry:	Vegetable fat.
Side-lines:	Mushy peas. Other foods.
Wrapping:	Wet-wrap and newsheet.

A lot of thought obviously went into the design of this outlet opposite the Dale pub. From the repro Victoriana to the clean neon image, it is obvious that the proprietors do not intend stopping at one outlet. If the standard of fresh fare and the cleanliness of the premises can be reproduced in other areas, I can see a lot more than the ferry crossing to Liverpool! Mind you, chip shop proprietors are notorious for change.

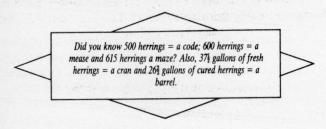

Did you know 500 herrings = a code; 600 herrings = a mease and 615 herrings a maze? Also, $37\frac{1}{2}$ gallons of fresh herrings = a cran and $26\frac{2}{3}$ gallons of cured herrings = a barrel.

Wilmslow

JACKSON'S SUPPER BAR, 24 Church Street. Tel: 0625 528661

Open:	Mon – Sat 11.00 a.m. – 2.00 p.m.; 5.00 p.m. – midnight; Sun 7.00 p.m. – midnight.
Facilities:	T/A; P; T.
Fish finds:	Cod, fish cakes, haddock, plaice (breadcrumbs or battered), scampi. Fish and chips to take-and-taste from around £1.50.
Fry:	Vegetable oil.
Side-lines:	Mushy peas. Other foods.
Wrapping:	Bags or trays plus white news.

There's been a chippy on this site for more than fifty years, and until twelve years ago it was run by the same family. For the last quarter of a century Harry Jackson's family, who took over Pimlotts, a local wet fish concern, continued to supply the fish to the premises. When the previous family gave up, the Jacksons took on the traditional fry-house. Standards have been kept high, and you're always assured of the pick of fresh fish, of course. The colour scheme is varying shades of beige and orange. The fair sex among the staff are donned in yellow overalls with the humble males in more sombre beige. Mr Jackson's other outlet, in Station Road, Urmston, has probably the best name for a chippy I've heard for a long time: The Seaking. Incidentally, their wet fish outlet nearby recently won the Sea Fish Quality Award for Excellence.

Merryweathers, 31 Water Lane. Tel: 0625 539618

Open:	Mon – Sat 11.00 a.m. – 11.00 p.m.
Facilities:	T/A & R; P (opposite); T; wheelchair friendly.
Fry:	Groundnut oil.
Side-lines:	Mushy peas. Other foods.
Wrapping:	White paper, trays.

The very congenial Mr Smith is a Merryweathers-franchised fryer at this completely refurbished fish and chip shop, with its hygienically fresh sorbet-and-sage decor and seating for twenty-six in the delightful diner. When you sit-and-savour the super fry on offer don't forget to leave room for a little Alabama Fudge Cake with real ice-cream. Do you think Lewis Carroll's mythical Cheshire Cat knows of this cheerful chippy?

> All is fish that comes to my net (Auri bonus est odor ex re qualibet) – I'll deal in anything from which I can profit and turn everything to some use. (Origin: The Steele Glas, by G. Gascoigne – died 1577).

Winsford

FOODCRAFT, 232 High Street. Tel: 0606 592444

Open: Mon – Sat 10.00 a.m. – 2.30 p.m.; 4.00 p.m. – 10.15 p.m.

Facilities: T/A; P.

Fish finds: Cod. Fish and chips to take-and-taste from around £1.65.

Fry: Whitley's Dri Fri oil.

Side-lines: Mushy peas. Other foods.

Wrapping: Hot boxes and bags or white news.

Proprietor John Finney has been frying in this town centre shop for nearly twenty-five years. He only sells one fish because a lot of his time is taken baking both sweet and savoury pastry goods. But that doesn't make the batter any less crisp, the fish any less fresh or the chips any less scrumptious.

LES'S FISH BAR, 15 Dingle Walk. Tel: 0606 556425

Open:	Mon & Tue 10.30 a.m. – 5.30 p.m.; Wed 10.30 a.m. – 2.00 p.m.; Thu & Fri 10.30 a.m. – 7.00 p.m.; Sat 10.30 a.m. – 4.00 p.m.
Facilities:	T/A; P near.
Fish finds:	Cod, fish cakes, haddock, plaice. Fish and chips to take-and-taste from around £1.00.
Fry:	Vegetable oil.
Side-lines:	Mushy peas. Other foods.
Speciality:	Potato fritters.
Wrapping:	Boxes, trays and white news.

Now moved to larger premises in Dingle Walk, with a 68-seater restaurant, this is the Mannings' second outlet. Les and his wife have been frying for a dozen years, but in Winsford for only five. The decor is bright and cheerful in red and white, with the staff decked out similarly in red dresses with red and white tabards. Only fresh fish is used, cooked well and served with a smile.

CLEVELAND
Billingham

BARNACLES, 146 Queensway, 1st Floor. Tel: 0642 532069

Open:	Mon – Sat 11.00 a.m. – 8.00 p.m.
Facilities:	T/A & R (L); P near; T.
Fish finds:	Cod, haddock, lemon sole, plaice, rock, skate. Fish and

chips to take-and-taste from around £1.20; sit-and-savour around £2.45.

Fry: Jennings FatMix.

Side-lines: Mushy peas. Other foods.

Wrapping: Trays, white paper.

There's no barnacles on these fish and chips. Brand new for 1990, clean and tidy, quick service and a very plush sit-and-savour area. It might even win an award like its sister shop in Stockton-on-Tees. This outlet is run by Mr Irvine, leader of the pack with years of frying experience.

Guisborough

LAMBERT'S, 24 Bow Street. Tel: 0287 34227

Open: Tue – Thu 11.30 a.m. – 1.30 p.m.; Fri – Sun 7.30 p.m. – 11.00 p.m.

Facilities: T/A; P near; T; wheelchair friendly.

Fish finds: Cod and chips to take-and-taste from around £1.25.

Fry: Oil.

Side-lines: Mushy peas. Other foods.

Wrapping: Trays, paper, greaseproof, bags.

Guisborough Priory is worth a visit after or before you taste Lambert's super fish and chips. It's a 'one fish' and chip shop – specializing in delectable cod with mountains of chips for around £1.25.

Hartlepool

FISH SHOP, 72 Oxford Road. Tel: 0429 274278

Open: Mon 7.45 p.m. – 11.00 p.m.; Tue Wed 11.00 a.m. –
1.10 p.m.; 7.45 p.m. – 11.00 p.m.; Thu 11.00 a.m. –
1.10 p.m.; 4.00 p.m. – 10.30 p.m.; Fri & Sat
11.00 a.m. – 1.10 p.m.; 4.00 p.m. – 11.00 p.m.

Facilities: T/A & R (L); P near; T; wheelchair friendly.

Fish finds: Cod. Fish and chips to take-and-taste from around £1.30.

Fry: Jennings FatMix.

Side-lines: Mushy peas. Other foods.

Wrapping: Trays, paper, greaseproof, bags.

*Every connoisseur of fish and chips knows all about the Fish Shop near the
centre of Hartlepool, retailing only one type of fish, which is none other
than commendable cod, battered and fried with super chips, for £1.30.*

Take away food; take home litter.

Middlesborough

ROONEY'S, 23 Newport Road. Tel: 0642 223923

Open: Mon – Wed 11.30 a.m. – 8.30 p.m.; Thu – Sat
11.30 a.m. – 10.30 p.m.

Facilities: R (L); P near; T; wheelchair friendly.

Fish finds:	Cod, haddock, plaice, scampi, skate. Fish and chips to sit-and-savour around £2.50.
Fry:	Fat.
Side-lines:	Mushy peas, pickled cabbage, pickled onions. Other foods.
Wrapping:	Cardboard containers.

This fine, unusual fishery is opposite the bus station and adjacent to the Hill Street Centre. You won't get any Hill Street Blues visiting Rooney's, it's licenced for those who wish to sit-and-savour, and you can have aperitifs in the bar before going upstairs to the diner. The outlet was opened nine years ago and has built up a good reputation for freshly cooked food. Children are welcomed with their own special menu.

Redcar

COATHAM'S, 113 Queen's Street. Tel: 0642 472422

Open:	Mon 4.30 p.m. – 11.15 p.m.; Tue – Sat 11.30 a.m. – 1.30 p.m.; 4.30 p.m. – 11.15 p.m.
Facilities:	T/A; P near; wheelchair friendly.
Fish finds:	Cod, haddock, halibut, huss, plaice, rock, scampi, shark, skate. Fish and chips to take-and-taste from around £1.20.
Fry:	Vegetable oil.
Side-lines:	Mushy peas, pickled onions. Other foods.
Wrapping:	Trays, white paper, greaseproof, bags, cartons.

Yet another super traditional fish and chip shop. If you have never tasted shark, you don't know what you're missing. Make sure you eat it before it eats you. Chips with everything here.

WEST DYKE FISHERIES, 69a West Dyke Road. Tel: 0642 473266

Open:	Mon – Sat 11.30 a.m. – 2.00 p.m.; 7.30 p.m. – midnight.
Facilities:	T/A; P.
Fish finds:	Cod, haddock, skate. Fish and chips to take-and-taste from around £1.15.
Fry:	Superior frying fat.
Side-lines:	Mushy peas. Other foods.
Wrapping:	White news.

The probable reason why H.F. Bulmer doesn't sell either plaice or sole is the number of corny lines about people making 'plaice bets' on the way to, or 'sole searching' over what to tell the wife after, a day at the races. After fifty years of trading, anyway, I'm sure he knows exactly what his customers like in the way of fresh fish – want to bet on it, Bruce?

Stockton-on-Tees

BARNACLES, 15 Dovecote Street. Tel: 0642 602000

Open:	Mon – Sat 11.00 a.m. – 8.00 p.m.
Facilities:	T/A & R (L); P; T.
Fish finds:	Cod, haddock, lemon sole, smoked mackerel, plaice, prawns, salmon, scampi. Fish and chips to take-and-taste from around £1.20; sit-and-savour around £2.45.
Fry:	Jennings FatMix.
Side-lines:	Mushy peas. Other foods.
Wrapping:	Trays, white paper.

Mrs Smith oversees this wonderful fishy emporium in the centre of town. It has a marvellous restaurant, seating seventy in the diner, and if you're there between 3.30 p.m. and 6.30 p.m., try the Shoppers' Special: fish and chips, tea, bread and butter, brought to your table by one of the many smart waitresses. Barnacles won the North East Fish and Chip Shop of the Year Award, organized by the Sea Fish Industry Authority.

**DURHAM LANE FISH BAR, 8 Durham Lane, Eaglescliffe.
Tel: 0642 786992.
Also at Glebe Fish Bar, Norton.**

Open:	Mon – Sat 11.30 a.m. – 1.30 p.m.; 4.30 p.m. – 9.00 p.m.
Facilities:	T/A; P.
Fish finds:	Cod, haddock, plaice, scampi. Fish and chips to take-and-taste from around £1.35.
Fry:	Fat.
Side-lines:	Fish cakes, mushy peas. Other foods.
Wrapping:	Greaseproof and white paper.

Neil Pearson has run this outlet only since mid-1988. You'll find it sandwiched between an ironmonger's and a butcher's in a parade of shops. The food is well cooked in fat, the way most Northerners prefer it – sorry, Mrs Currie.

CORNWALL
Bodmin

GOLDEN FRY, 46 Higher Bore Street. Tel: 0208 73191

Open:	Mon – Sat 9.30 a.m. – 10.30 p.m.
Facilities:	T/A & R; P; T.

Fish finds: Cod, haddock, lemon sole, plaice. Fish and chips to take-and-taste around £1.55; sit-and-savour from £2.20.

Fry: Bibby's P100 vegetable fat.

Side-lines: Cornish pasties, fish cakes, mushy peas, pickled onions.

Wrapping: Paper bags, white paper.

A few months ago W.H. May celebrated twenty years at the helm of this fine, traditional chippy in Bodmin on the river Camel. The town has a large Gothic church and some of the earliest radio transmissions took place from a station on Bodmin Moor. But that's history, and the Golden Fry is about fish. Good fish, well cooked and served with a smile in spotless surroundings.

Falmouth

PENMERE FISH & CHIPS, 2 Penmere Hill. Tel: 0326 314598

Open: Mon 4.30 p.m. – 7.00 p.m.; Wed 11.45 a.m. – 1.30 p.m.; 4.30 p.m. – 7.00 p.m.; Thur – Sat 11.45 a.m. – 1.30 p.m.; 4.30 p.m. – 10.00 p.m. (July & Aug: Mon – Sat 11.45 a.m. – 1.30 p.m.; 4.30 p.m. – 10.00 p.m.).

Facilities: T/A & R (L); P near; T.

Fish finds: Cod, haddock, plaice, scampi. Fish and chips to take-and-taste from around £1.50; sit-and-savour around £2.50.

Fry: North Devon pure beef dripping.

Side-lines: Mushy peas, pickled onions. Other foods.

Wrapping: White wrap then newspaper.

This outlet has been trading for a quarter of a century, though David

Perrin only took over in the mid-1980s. The 30-seater restaurant is tastefully decorated with stained, pine clad walls, carpeted floor and attractively artexed ceiling. You'll find it, like the tourists do in summer, at the top of Penmere Hill behind the Fal Recreation Ground. If you fancy a drink on the way, there's the Clipper Way pub in Boslowick Road.

Helston

THURLEY'S FISH RESTAURANT, 9 Meneage Street. Tel: 0326 572991

Open: Mon – Sat 11.30 a.m. – 1.30 p.m.; 4.30 p.m. – 11.30 p.m.

Facilities: T/A & R; P near; T.

Fish finds: Cod, cod's roe, haddock, plaice, scampi. Fish and chips to take-and-taste from around £1.60; sit-and-savour around £2.10.

Fry: Groundnut oil.

Side-lines: Mushy peas, pickled onions. Other foods, including Cornish pasties as a speciality.

Wrapping: Traditional white wrap.

You'll find the chippy at the bottom end of the street between the National Provincial and Cheltenham and Gloucester building societies. Mind, the chippy was sure to have been there first. This family establishment has been trading for over forty years. P.J. Ashworth is in charge, and as with most outlets in this part of the world, he emphasizes that they also sell Cornish pasties as a speciality. The nearest pubs are the Red Lion and the Bee Hive Inn, about 50 yd away. The off-licence is a similar distance from the chippy. If you happen to be around on 8 May and your name isn't T. Wogan, don't forget the annual celebration of the Furry (to rhyme with 'hurry'!) or Floral Dance, and afterwards have a nice fish and chip supper in the Superdiner.

Penzance

WHARFHOUSE RESTAURANT & MIKE'S TAKEAWAY, Wharf Road.
Tel: 0736 66888

Open:	Daily midday – 1.30 p.m.; 5.00 p.m. – 7.30 p.m. (Fri & Sat till 8.30 p.m.) Easter to end October.
Facilities:	T/A & R (L); P; T.
Fish finds:	Cod, haddock, plaice, scampi, sole. Fish and chips to take-and-taste from around £1.50; sit-and-savour around £2.00.
Fry:	Palm oil, hard vegetable fat.
Side-lines:	Mushy peas, pickled onions. Other foods, including Cornish pasties as a speciality.
Wrapping:	White news.

Mr O'Neill runs this popular summer outlet. The restaurant, which seats ninety, has a huge picture window overlooking St Michael's Mount, and is tastefully decorated in shades of blue with a fitted carpet. Children are catered for – leave your buckets and spades outside – with high chairs available, and their parents can have a drink at the bar while they wait for their meal. Jacket potatoes and side salads are served as an alternative to chips. All their delicious sweets are home-made. No wonder a number of officers and staff from Penwith District Council recommend this establishment. Find it opposite the harbour car park and near the railway station. If you fancy either walking off your meal or working up an appetite, Penzance is a mere 8 miles from Land's End!

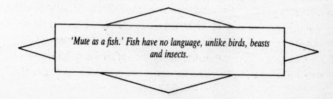

'Mute as a fish.' Fish have no language, unlike birds, beasts and insects.

Polperro

CAPTAIN'S CABIN, Lansallos Street. Tel: 0503 72292

Open:	Sun – Fri midday – 2.30 p.m.; Mon – Thu & Sun 7.00 p.m. – 9.30 p.m. (Fri & Sat till 11.00 p.m.).
Facilities:	R (L); P near; T; wheelchair access possible.
Fish finds:	Conger eel, crab, goujons of sole, haddock, hake, halibut, John Dory, lobster, monkfish, mussels, oysters, prawns, salmon, skate, turbot, whiting. Sit-and-savour from about £4.00 (lunch), £5.00 (evening). Gourmet Sea Food Platter £25.00 (per person, for two or more).
Fry:	Own fry.
Side-lines:	Salads. Other foods.

Due to the over-fishing of pilchards in Cornwall in the 1920s, only the tinned variety are landed in Polperro these days. As this fine outlet serves only fresh fish, the menu is 'limited' to the magnificent selection above. There is, however, a special children's menu available. The Gourmet Platter includes nine varieties of fish or shellfish, freshly cooked to order. Lesley Jacobs – who's been in the business a quarter of a century – has owned this quaint 40-year-old quayside premises, with its low beams and flowers on each table, for four years.

St Austell

FRYDAYS EATING HOUSE, 4 Victoria Place. Tel: 0726 65710

Open:	Mon – Sat 10.00 a.m. – 6.00 p.m. (summer 9.00 a.m. – 6.00 p.m.).
Facilities:	T/A & R.
Fish finds:	Cod, cod's roe, fish cakes, haddock, smoked mackerel, plaice, scampi. Fish and chips to take-and-taste from around £1.45; sit-and-savour £2.25.
Fry:	Palm oil.
Side-lines:	Mushy peas, pickled onions.
Wrapping:	Polystyrene trays or boxes and paper.

A real Cornish chippy, decorated in the restaurant to a very high standard. It's in the centre of the town near the Holy Trinity Church, parts of which date back to the 13th century. You can always tell the quality of a chippy – unless it has a very slow fryer – by the length of the take-away queue. Be prepared to wait at this one.

Truro

GINGHAM FISH BAR, Malabar Road, Highertown. Tel: 0872 73555

Open:	Tue – Sat 11.45 a.m. – 1.00 p.m.; Tue – Thu 4.45 p.m. – 7.30 p.m. (Fri till 9.00 p.m.; Sat till 9.30 p.m.).
Facilities:	T/A; P near.
Fish finds:	Cod, haddock, plaice, rock. Fish and chips to take-and-taste from around £1.50.
Fry:	Dripping.

Side-lines:	Mushy peas, pickled gherkins, pickled onions. Other foods including freshly baked pizza and Cornish pasties.
Wrapping:	Polystyrene-type boxes.

Brian Hobbs, who for some reason is know to all as Jim, took over this fine friendly chippy nearly three years ago. A glance or two at his list of side-lines, of which I only show a selection, is indication enough that he really tries to give his customers what they want. He always ensures the standard of cooking and quality of service is of the highest. To find the Gingham, take the A390 ring road out of Truro, turn right at the Esso garage at Highertown into Malabar Road. Don't take the wrong turning or you might end up in Truro, Nova Scotia!

LETHERBARROW'S FISH & CHIP CAFE, 16 River Street.
Tel: 0872 73261

Open:	Mon – Sat 11.30 a.m. – 2.30 p.m.; 4.30 p.m. – 10.00 p.m.
Facilities:	T/A & R; P (street).
Fish finds:	Cod, fish cakes, haddock, plaice. Fish and chips to take-and-taste from around £1.50; sit-and-savour around £1.90.
Fry:	Fat.
Side-lines:	Mushy peas, pickled eggs, pickled onions.
Wrapping:	Bags, greaseproof and white off-cuts or trays.

These's seating for thirty-two in D.B. Letherbarrow's establishment, where he's been frying since 1983. The floors are green and the walls decorated with wood-panelling and green glass tiles. It's opposite the County Museum and just a block or so from the Cathedral that took over thirty years to complete, starting in 1880. My researcher tells me they cook the batter to perfection and the chips are always crisp, golden and hot. There are compliments for the staff as well: quick and pleasant. Overall, the outlet is excellent value. Recommended by, among others, Mrs M. Wynne, who hailed from the 'afishionado' territory of Lancashire, until she retired to Cornwall. Mr Letherbarrow has been frying for over forty years; the premises have been a chippy, however, for more than thirty years.

SOLE PLAICE, 20 Pydar Street. Tel: 0872 71629

Open:	Mon – Sat 11.30 a.m. – 9.30 p.m.
Facilities:	T/A & R; P near; T.
Fish finds:	Cod, haddock, lemon sole, plaice. Fish and chips to take-and-taste from around £1.70.
Fry:	Fat.
Side-lines:	Mushy peas, pickled onions. Other foods.
Wrapping:	Greaseproof bags and white off-cuts.

Tony Allen has been frying in this listed building in the centre of Truro – near Boots, Dixons, Marks & Spencer, and opposite C & A and Courts – for over nine years. There's always a queue at the take-away, but the wait is worth it. Quite excellent quality with good service and generous portions. The interior of the shop has fawn, hessian-effect, patterned wallboards topped with mirror tiles. The counter is in orange teak. Woodgrain wallboard covers the passage to the restaurant that seats seventy-eight. The walls here are green leaf-patterned wallpaper with a huge sunset mural along one side. Spotless throughout. He recently carried out his own printed survey among customers and locals – and received a resounding thumbs up with comments like 'best in the west', 'everything is great', 'as visitors from Old Windsor we make a point of stopping here every year' and many, many more compliments. Tony's outlet recently won a special award for enterprise in the Sea Fish 'Fish and Chip Shop of the Year' competition.

COUNTY DURHAM
Birtley

BIRTLEY BIMBIS. Tel: 091 4102056

Open:	Daily 9.30 a.m. – 11.30 p.m.
Facilities:	T/A & R; P; T.
Fish finds:	Cod, haddock, plaice. Fish and chips to take-and-taste from £1.70; sit-and-savour around £2.50.
Fry:	Oil, some fat.
Side-lines:	Mushy peas, pickled gherkins, pickled onions. Other foods.
Wrapping:	Cartons.

During the First World War an armaments factory was built in Birtley. They also established a colony, known as Elizabethville, for about 6,000 Belgian exiles. Their offspring are obviously as keen on good fish and chips as the home-grown population, judging by the queues that regularly form at this branch of the well-run Bimbi chain of fry-houses. L. Bimbi and Sons have been frying for thirty years in the Eorth-East. Their head office is in Durham City.

Burnopfield

DENE FISHERIES, 40 Front Street. Tel: 0207 70110

Open:	Mon, Wed – Sat 11.00 a.m. – 1.30 p.m.; Wed & Thu 6.00 p.m. – 11.30 p.m.; Fri 5.30 p.m. – midnight; Sat 6.30 p.m. – midnight.
Facilities:	T/A; P.

Fish finds: Cod, haddock. Fish and chips to take-and-taste from around £1.45.

Fry: Fat.

Side-lines: Fish cakes, mushy peas, pickled onions. Other foods.

Specialities: Black pudding, haggis, rissoles.

Wrapping: Polystyrene trays, bags, white paper.

One of those places where, as a town, although they are officially in Durham, they have a closer association with Gateshead and Newcastle-upon-Tyne since they are only just over the border. Joseph Brown (but not the cockney singer who chants about jellied eels!) has been running this fine chippy for more than twenty years. He's known as Joe Jovey. It is a traditional outlet that has gained attention in the past from the local media for its fine fries and pleasant service. You'll find it adjoining the Burnopfield Social Club.

COUNTY DURHAM

Darlington

BIMBIS, High Row. Tel: 0325 482755
Also at Tubwell Row. Tel: 0325 283770

Open:	Daily 9.30 a.m. – 11.30 p.m.
Facilities:	T/A & R; P; T.
Fish finds:	Cod, haddock, plaice. Fish and chips to take-and-taste from around £1.70; sit-and-savour around £2.50.
Fry:	Oil with some fat.
Side-lines:	Mushy peas, pickled gherkins, pickled onions. Other foods.
Wrapping:	Cartons.

The Bimbi family concern is based in Durham City. They've been frying from one outlet or another in the north-east – they currently own ten – for over thirty years. Over the years they've collected numerous awards for the quality of their fare and cleanliness of their outlets. The increase in trade indicates they consistently keep to the standards they set.

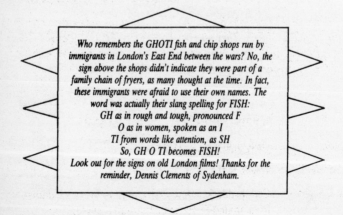

Who remembers the GHOTI fish and chip shops run by immigrants in London's East End between the wars? No, the sign above the shops didn't indicate they were part of a family chain of fryers, as many thought at the time. In fact, these immigrants were afraid to use their own names. The word was actually their slang spelling for FISH:
GH as in rough and tough, pronounced F
O as in women, spoken as an I
TI from words like attention, as SH
So, GH O TI becomes FISH!
Look out for the signs on old London films! Thanks for the reminder, Dennis Clements of Sydenham.

Durham City

BIMBIS, 27 Neville Street. Tel: 091 384 6470

Open:	Daily 9.30 a.m. – 11.30 p.m.
Facilities:	T/A & R (L); P; T.
Fish finds:	Cod, haddock, plaice. Fish and chips to take-and-taste from around £1.70; sit-and-savour around £2.50.
Fry:	Fat and oil.
Side-lines:	Mushy peas, pickled gherkins, pickled onions. Other foods.
Wrapping:	Cartons.

One of the specialities of this outlet is ready-cooked and frozen fish and chips for the freezer/convenience market. Roger Whittaker is not the only one who longs to go back to this county town and city, with its 11th-century cathedral and university castle. Tony Smith, studying law at Reading University, not only sings the praises of this establishment but waxes on about how 'unspeakably awful' he has found those near his present abode. For legal reasons, perhaps, he declines to name them!

L. Bimbi & Sons have the head office of their ever-expanding fish and chip empire at this address. They now have four other outlets in Durham, one in Birtley and four in Newcastle-upon-Tyne. All have similar high standards, opening times, fish range and prices.

BIMBIS, Market Place. Tel: 091 384 8974

Open:	Daily 9.30 a.m. – 11.30 p.m.
Facilities:	T/A & R (L); P; T.
Fish finds:	Cod, haddock, plaice. Fish and chips to take-and-taste from around £1.70; sit-and-savour around £2.50.

COUNTY DURHAM

Fry: Fat and oil.

Side-lines: Mushy peas, pickled gherkins, pickled onions. Other foods.

Wrapping: Cartons.

Another L. Bimbi & Sons outlet. This was the 1988 Northern England and Wales area champion in the Sea Fish Industry's 'Fish and Chip Shop of the Year' contest. Whenever I hear Roger Whittaker sing about leaving Durham Town, I want to jump up and say: 'But it's a city!' Though, of course, technically it is also the county town of the area, and the Town Hall, which dates back to the 16th century, is very close to this outlet. The Bimbi family started in the trade over thirty years ago. They have gained an increasing following for their fine fare and spotless premises dotted around the area. Knowing what a gourmet Mr Whittaker is, I wonder if he deemed it worthwhile to sample these tasty fries!

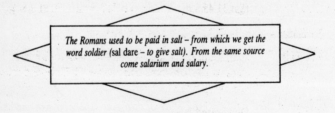

The Romans used to be paid in salt – from which we get the word soldier (sal dare – to give salt). From the same source come salarium and salary.

Shildon

CLEMS, 7 Albert Street. Tel: 0388 773400

Open: Mon – Thu 11.00 a.m. – 1.30 p.m.; 4.00 p.m. – 11.30 p.m.; Fri 11.00 a.m. – 1.30 p.m.; 4.00 p.m. – 11.45 p.m.; Sat 11.00 a.m. – 1.30 p.m.; 7.00 p.m. – 11.45 p.m.

Facilities: T/A & R; P; T; wheelchair access.

Fish finds: Cod, haddock, halibut, lemon sole, plaice. Fish and chips to take-and-taste from around £1.25; sit-and-savour £1.50.

Fry: Jennings Mix.

Side-lines: Mushy peas, pickled onions. Other foods.

Wrapping: Greaseproof, pink paper.

Another family-run trade fish and chip shop, no airs and graces, but sleeves up and kick the traces. Very clean and good value for money. Get in early and avoid the queues.

Spennymoor

CLEM'S FISH RESTAURANT, 16 Clyde Terrace. Tel: 0388 815451

Open: Daily 11.00 a.m. – 1.45 p.m.; 4.00 p.m. – 11.30 p.m. (Sat 11.45 a.m. – 2.00 p.m.; 5.00 p.m. – 11.30 p.m.).

Facilities: T/A & R; P; T; wheelchair access.

Fish finds: Cod, haddock, halibut, lemon sole, plaice. Fish and chips to take-and-taste from around £1.25; sit-and-savour around £1.50.

Fry: Deodorized fat.

Side-lines: Mushy peas. Other foods.

Wrapping: Greaseproof, pink paper.

'Clem' (Mr Oliver Oxenham), first arrived in this industrialized area in 1955, and opened his shop three years later. Now one of his sons runs this shop, with the other running a second outlet at 7 Albert Street, Shildon – opposite the King William pub. The nearest pub to the Spennymoor shop is the Gilbert across the road. Both outlets keep up the fine standard set by Mr Oxenham Snr. The Spennymoor premises are pine-panelled with ample red seating and green and yellow tiled floors. A similar colour scheme is a feature of the Shildon shop.

CUMBRIA
Ambleside

WALNUT FISH BAR, Old Post Office Buildings, Compston Road.
Tel: 05394 32521

Open: Mon – Sat 11.45 a.m. – 1.30 p.m.; 5.00 p.m. – 10.30 p.m.

Facilities: T/A & R; P near.

Fish finds: Haddock, scampi. Fresh haddock and chips both to take-and-taste and sit-and-savour from around £1.50.

Fry: Palm oil.

Side-lines: Mushy peas, pickled onions.

Wrapping: Trays and white news.

'I wandered lonely as a cloud
With thoughts on where for chip and gill?
When all at once I saw a crowd,
At last, some golden haddock fils.'

With apologies to William Wordsworth, to whom there is a memorial window in the church of St Mary in Ambleside. The church was designed by Sir G.G. Scott, but the fries are cooked at the Walnut by Mr and Mrs D. Crook, who've been here since the mid-1980s. A true value-for-money chip shop and totally refurbished in style, well frequented by locals and in summer, by visitors, many of whom return year after year to verify the quality of the fare. Mrs Helen Knowles from Tring in Hertfordshire is one such visitor who recommends it.

Kirkby Lonsdale

STAN'S PLAICE, 4 Jinglin Lane, The Square.
Tel: 0468 71032

Open:	Tue – Sat 11.30 a.m. – 1.30 p.m.; 4.30 p.m. – 8.00 p.m. (restaurant till 7.30 p.m.).
Facilities:	T/A & R; P; T.
Fish finds:	Cod. Fish and chips to take-and-taste from around £1.40; sit-and-savour about £1.50.
Fry:	Vegetable oil.
Side-lines:	Mushy peas.
Speciality:	Cumberland sausage.
Wrapping:	Greaseproof, white news, trays.

J. 'Stan' Deacon only took over this range a couple of years ago – though he's been frying for eighteen years. Celebrities like Jim Bowen and Mike Harding have already been known to frequent his shop on the corner of the square, next to the TSB. Pale green walls and ceiling top a pine dado in the take-out, with the small dining room clad throughout in pine. The sit-in section really is homely, with table-cloths on the tables, plus flower arrangements, and a carpeted floor. Add good, fresh fish and friendly service, and what more could you want? If the answer's a drink, then there's the Royal Hotel also in the Square.

> The Worshipful Company of Fishmongers, one of the twelve Great Livery Companies of the City of London, is also among the most ancient, with an unbroken existence going back over 700 years.

Kirkby Stephen

HORSESHOE FISH RESTAURANT, 52 Market Street. Tel: 07683 71415

Open:	Mon – Sat 11.30 a.m. – 1.30 p.m.; 5.30 p.m. – 8.30 p.m. (closed Tue); Sun 5.30 p.m. – 8.30 p.m. (Summer: open till 9.30 p.m.).
Facilities:	T/A & R; P near; T; wheelchair friendly.
Fish finds:	Cod, haddock. Fish and chips to take-and-taste from around £1.50; sit-and-savour around £2.20.
Fry:	Jennings FatMix.
Side-lines:	Mushy peas. Other foods.
Wrapping:	White paper, greaseproof.

You will find this delightful fish and chip restaurant handy for the energetic fell walker, and not too far from the Lakes. There's ample room to rest your weary bones in the 60-seater diner and tuck into a super Hiker's Fishy Special, which is cod or haddock, tea, bread and butter for around £2.20; mushy peas extra.

Penrith

LITTLE CHIPPY, 23 Corn Market. Tel: 0768 64508

Open:	Mon – Sat 11.30 a.m. – 1.30 p.m.; 4.30 p.m. – 11.30 p.m. (Sat 11.00 p.m.).
Facilities:	T/A; P near.
Fish finds:	Fish cakes, haddock, scampi. Fish and chips to take-and-taste from around £1.50.
Fry:	Vegetable oil.

Side-lines: Mushy peas, pickled onions. Other foods.

Wrapping: Trays, white paper, greaseproof, plastic bags.

What about fish and chips before taking a long walk around the Lake District? Call in at the Little Chippy, a small traditional take-away, which has been run by Mr & Mrs Gilford for the last six years. Tourists from all over the world pop in before taking to the hills.

TOWN HEAD FISH SHOP, 46 Strickland Gate. Tel: 0768 64508

Open: Mon – Sat 11.30 a.m. – 1.30 p.m.; 4.00 p.m. – 10.00 p.m.; Sat 4.00 p.m. – 8.00 p.m.

Facilities: T/A; P near; T.

Fish finds: Cod, haddock, scampi. Fish and chips to take-and-taste from around £1.40.

Fry: Vegetable oil.

Side-lines: Mushy peas, pickled onions. Other foods.

Wrapping: Polystyrene trays, white paper, greaseproof.

Another little take-and-taste traditional chippy, serving the community and visitors alike in every way. Sited alongside the old A6, it is the truckers' favourite. Parking outside. Ivy and Morris Patrickson run the outlet, giving cheerful personal service. Cod and chips please!

Fisher of souls – the Devil ('the chief baits with which the great Fisher of Souls conceals his hooks, are the causes of your declining the career to which I would incite you.' Sir Walter Scott: The Monastery, chapter XI).

DERBYSHIRE
Buxton

THOMPSON'S CAFE, 9 High Street. Tel: 0298 22596

Open:	Mon – Thu 11.30 a.m. – 1.45 p.m.; 8.00 p.m. – midnight; Fri 11.30 a.m. – 1.45 p.m.; 5.00 p.m. – midnight; Sat 11.00 a.m. – 2.00 p.m.; 5.00 p.m. – midnight.
Facilities:	T/A & R; P near; T; wheelchair access to shop.
Fish finds:	Cod, haddock, plaice. Fish and chips to take-and-taste from around £1.25; sit-and-savour around £1.50.
Fry:	Vegetable oil.
Side-lines:	Mushy peas, pickled onions. Other foods.
Wrapping:	Trays and white news.

Paddy and Bev Manson run this well-liked establishment that has been open for frying for around thirty years. It's opposite the Halifax Building Society in the Market Place. Buxton was once famous as a health resort with its mineral springs producing a spa water, good for the treatment of rheumatism – so they say – gout, sciatica and other such ills. No doubt this chippy would be recommended to cure starvation: many swear by its nourishing and health-giving properties, because a little of what you fancy does you good! Eat and be merry in this 50-seater diner. Pass the water please!

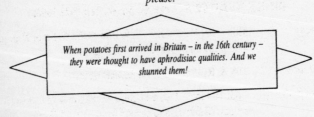

When potatoes first arrived in Britain – in the 16th century – they were thought to have aphrodisiac qualities. And we shunned them!

Ilkeston

MR BRIGGS, 7 Nottingham Road. Tel: 0602 324782

Open:	Tue – Fri 11.30 a.m. – 1.30 p.m.; Fri – 5.00 p.m. – 10.00 p.m.; Sat 11.30 a.m. – 1.30 p.m.
Facilities:	T/A; P near.
Fish finds:	Cod, fish cakes (home-made), haddock, plaice. Fish and chips to take-and-taste from around £1.20.
Fry:	Vegetable fat.
Side-lines:	Mushy peas.
Wrapping:	Greaseproof, trays, white news.

Already run by the third generation of the Briggs family, brothers three – John, Stuart and Gordon – with young Caroline quite obviously waiting in the wings to start up the next era. Opened originally around 1915 by the brothers' maternal grandmother, the outlet has a wet fish shop adjoining through a sliding door. Usual shop hours, but I am sure the boys will oblige with a wet kipper after hours for Sunday breakfast. Terrazzo-tiled flooring, white-tiled walls with blue trim to set off the spotless image, in the wet-fish outlet, but gold trim to match the range in the chippy. Sited on the corner of White Lion Square, the quality of their fare is heralded for miles around.

DENNIS WEBSTER'S, 3 Pelham Street. Tel: 0602 309801

Open:	Mon – Fri 11.30 a.m. – 1.30 p.m.; Thu & Fri 5.00 p.m. – 9.30 p.m.; Sat 11.00 a.m. – 2.00 p.m.
Facilities:	T/A & R; P near; T; wheelchair access.
Fish finds:	Cod, haddock. Fish and chips to take-and-taste from around £1.30; sit-and-savour from around £1.50.

Fry:	Vegetable oil.
Side-lines:	Mushy peas.
Wrapping:	White news.

There's been fish frying in this little side-road off the main shopping street for about seventy years; Dennis Webster took over the establishment more than thirteen years ago – lucky for some. A typical old-style chippy watching the world go by while continuing to give excellent service and quality of food. Just to remind Dennis there is a world outside, his customers have brought him souvenir tea-towels from all points of the compass. He's built up quite a collection. He has an excellent 24-seater diner (mainly lunch). Recommended by Mrs J. Tenchill.

DEVON
Torquay

BABBACOMBE FISH & CHIP SHOP, 24 Princes Street.
Tel: 0803 329928

Open:	Mon – Sat 11.45 a.m. – 1.30 p.m.; 5.00 p.m. – 11.00 p.m.
Facilities:	T/A; P near; wheelchair friendly (but with a step up).
Fish finds:	Cod, haddock, huss, lemon sole, plaice, skate. Fish and chips to take-and-taste from around £1.85.
Fry:	Groundnut oil.
Side-lines:	Mushy peas, pickled gherkins, pickled onions. Other foods.
Wrappings:	Trays, paper.

46

The Hanbury family are frying high at the moment with accolades from all quarters with two recent awards, a close second in the Sea Fish Industry 'Fish and Chip Shop of the Year' contest, and first in the Daloon Foods competition. Brill when you think there's 10,000 chippies dotted around Great Britain. So whatever you choose to take-and-taste it's got to be good. I'm exhausted . . . I think I'll nip into the George Inn close by for a glass of celebratory champers!

Bovey Tracey

BOVEY FISH BAR, 77 Fore Street. Tel: 0626 833386

Open: Tue – Sat midday – 2.00 p.m.; 5.30 p.m. – 10.00 p.m.

Facilities: T/A & R; P near; T.

Fish finds: Cod, fish cakes, haddock, plaice, rock, scampi, skate. Fish and chips to take-and-taste from around £1.50; sit-and-savour around £2.00.

Fry: Vegetable oil.

Side-lines: Mushy peas, pickled gherkins, pickled onions. Other foods.

Wrapping: Bags wrapped with plain paper, carrier bags.

Melvin Hutchinson has only owned this 20-year-old outlet for a couple of years, though he's had others for nearer ten. Refurbished completely in brown and white, with co-ordinating vinyl floor, carpets, tables and curtains. The restaurant is in two sections, seating thirty comfortably. The King of Prussia pub in a 400-year-old listed building is just a few doors away. While eating or supping you may spare a thought for the town's Church of Thomas Beckett that was built by Sir William de Tracey as a penance for the murder of the archbishop.

Braunton

SQUIRE'S FISH RESTAURANT, Exeter Road. Tel: 0271 815533

Open:	Mon – Sat 12.45 p.m. – 2.30 p.m.; 5.00 p.m. – 10.45 p.m.
Facilities:	T/A & R (L); P near; T; wheelchair access.
Fish finds:	Cod, haddock, plaice. Fish and chips to take-and-taste from around £1.75; sit-and-savour around £2.85.
Fry:	Own recipe.
Side-lines:	Other foods.
Wrapping:	White wrap.

Mike and June Squire have owned this delightful outlet just off the Taw estuary for over fifteen years. It has the advantage of being set in one of the most beautiful parts of the country, on the edge of the Braunton Burrows with its excellent golf course. Not that the Squires have that much time to rest on their laurels – they're too busy keeping the business ahead of the rest. I say ahead, because they were selected by Sea Fish as 1989 area winners for South Wales and the West in their 'Fish and Chip Shop of the Year' contest. The restaurant has seating for ninety.

Exeter

CHIP INN, 56 Alpington Road. Tel: 0392 74715

Open:	Mon – Thu midday – 2.00 p.m.; 5.00 p.m. – 11.00 p.m.; Fri & Sat 11.45 a.m. – 2.00 p.m.; 5.00 p.m. – 11.00 p.m.
Facilities:	T/A; P near; T (on request).
Fish finds:	Cod, fish burgers, fish cakes, plaice. Fish and chips to take-and-taste from around £1.45.

Fry: Groundnut oil.

Side-lines: Mushy peas, pickled gherkins, pickled onions. Other foods.

Wrapping: Paper off-cuts.

The spotless decor is matched by the clean overalls of the staff. There's a television in the shop so that customers won't miss any part of their favourite programme while waiting for their fare. If you want to speed up your take-away even more, telephone your order in advance. Coach parties are welcome at this friendly shop, where they are keen to satisfy the health-conscious. It's in the group of shops opposite the Crawford Inn and next door to Wood's Garage.

Exmouth

BRIXINGTON FISH & CHIP SHOP, Brixington Parade, Churchill Road. Tel: 0395 266000

Open: Tue – Sat midday – 1.30 p.m.; Mon – Sat 5.30 p.m. – 10.30 p.m.

Facilities: T/A; P; wheelchair access.

Fish finds: Cod, haddock, hake, lemon sole, plaice, pollack, rock, skate, Torbay sole. Fish and chips to take-and-taste from around £1.40.

Fry: Vegetable oil.

Side-lines: Mushy peas, pickled gherkins, pickled onions. Other foods.

Wrapping: White paper.

The range of fish is perhaps not surprising when it is known that the proprietor, Gerald Statham, is one of the largest wet fish wholesalers in East Devon. The all-white shop reflects the cleanliness of the outlet and the freshness of the fare. It's in a precinct of eight shops on a housing estate, with the Farmhouse Inn just 30 yd away. Mrs E.M. Bacon recommends. If you have time, you could always buy fresh fish from Mr Statham and cook it yourself.

North Tawton

COWLEY HOUSE CAFE, The Square. Tel: 0837 82392

Open:	Tue & Thu midday – 1.30 p.m.; 5.00 p.m. – 7.30 p.m.; Wed midday – 1.30 p.m.; 8.00 p.m. – 10.30 p.m.; Fri & Sat midday – 1.30 p.m.; 5.00 p.m. – 10.30 p.m.
Facilities:	T/A & R; P; T.
Fish finds:	Cod, plaice. Fish and chips to take-and-taste from around £1.30; sit-and-savour around £1.95.
Fry:	Vegetable fat.
Side-lines:	Fish cakes, mushy peas, pickled onions. Other foods.
Wrapping:	Trays and white paper.

This nine-year-old outlet was recently taken over by Ken and Chris Hinkley. North Tawton, apart from having many historical sites, is also home to the largest cheese factory in Europe. You'll find the chippy in the centre of the town facing the clock tower. The decor is both pleasant and homely, including an aquarium with a fountain to entertain children and adults! When a doctor not only recommends the establishment for its cleanliness and quality of chips ('I can't make better at home') but drives twenty miles from Exeter to enjoy them, you know the place must be special. Naturally, I can't read the doctor's signature on the letter – only that he hails from Winchester Avenue.

Plymouth

PERILLA'S, 34 Mayflower Street. Tel: 0752 667843

Open:	Mon – Sat 11.30 a.m. – 2.30 p.m.; 5.00 p.m. – 11.30 p.m.
Facilities:	T/A & R (L); P near; T.
Fish finds:	Cod, haddock, lemon sole, plaice, scampi. Fish and chips to take-and-taste from around £1.75; sit-and-savour around £2.50.
Fry:	Vegetable oil.
Side-lines:	Mushy peas, pickled onions. Other foods.
Wrapping:	Cartons plus white wrap (to change shortly).

This outlet has the Frying Perillas at the helm, and has been established for many years. The family have been in the fish and chip trade for almost half a century, so no wonder so many customers speak so highly of them. The decor is clean and bright and they go out of their way to cater for the whole family's sit-and-savour, with high chairs and special children's meals. Plymouth has recently celebrated its diamond jubilee as a city – but there are many who are saving the celebrating for the golden fare from Perilla's. Plenty of room in the 120-seater diner with shandy or champagne.

PERILLA'S, 33–35 Market Avenue. Tel: 0752 661307

Open:	Mon – Sat 11.30 a.m. – 2.30 p.m.; 5.00 p.m. – 11.30 p.m.
Facilities:	T/A & R; P (street); T.
Fish finds:	Cod, haddock, lemon sole, plaice, scampi. Fish and chips to take-and-taste from around £1.75; sit-and-savour around £2.50.

Fry: Vegetable oil.

Side-lines: Mushy peas, pickled onions. Other foods.

Wrapping: Cartons and white paper.

The enterprising Perilla family oversee this outlet too; it is right next door to the Mall Public House and diagonally opposite Plymouth's covered market, so it's a must for shoppers and tourists alike. There are seats for 100 people, so take the weight off your feet and enjoy super fish and chips.

DORSET

Bournemouth

ALMA FISH BAR, 82 Alma Road, Winton. Tel: 0202 520330

Open: Mon – Sat 11.30 a.m. – 2.00 p.m.; 4.30 p.m. – 11.00 p.m.; Sun 5.00 p.m. – 11.00 p.m.

Facilities: T/A; P near.

Fish finds: Cod, haddock, plaice, rock (in summer), scampi. Fish and chips to take-and-taste from around £1.45.

Fry: Vegetable fat.

Side-lines: Mushy peas, pickled gherkins, pickled onions. Other foods, including vegetarian.

Wrapping: Polystyrene trays and paper, greaseproof.

Though the outlet is relatively new, with the latest shop design and presentation, the proprietor, Mr Low, is well versed in the art of frying. Bournemouth has become known as a health resort, so it is natural this outlet should be noted for its clean, fresh approach to the trade. All cod is both skinned and boned on the premises before frying. You'll find the shop on the continuation of the clearly marked A3049 Boscombe road.

CHEZ FRED, 10 Seamoor Road, Westbourne. Tel: 0202 761023

Open: Mon – Sat 11.30 a.m. – 2.00 p.m.; 5.00 p.m. –
10.00 p.m. (restaurant closes half-hour earlier).

Facilities: T/A & R; P near; T; wheelchair friendly.

Fish finds: Cod, haddock, halibut, lemon sole, plaice, rock, skate.
Fish and chips to take-and-taste from around £1.60;
sit-and-savour around £2.95.

Fry: Vegetable oil.

Side-lines: Pea fritters, pickled gherkins, pickled onions. Other
foods.

Wrapping: Greaseproof, lined bags.

*Chez Fred by name, run by the capable Capel family, was Daloon Foods'
choice for 4th place in the 'Fish and Chip Shop of the Year Award 1989'.
Fish par excellence in or out – a nice little 50-seater diner. Have a bottle of
pop or a glass of wine. Nice one, mon ami . . .*

53 *DORSET*

HALFWAY FISH BAR, 112 Bournemouth Road, Parkstone.
Tel: 0202 741778

Open:	Mon – Sun 11.30 a.m. – 2.00 p.m.; 5.00 p.m. – 10.00 p.m.
Facilities:	T/A; P near; wheelchair friendly.
Fish finds:	Cod, haddock, plaice, rock, skate. Fish and chips to take-and-taste from around £1.50.
Fry:	Vegetable oil.
Side-lines:	Mushy peas, other foods.
Wrapping:	Greaseproof, paper.

Another chippy with a winning way. It must be the way they cook them, otherwise why would the customer and holiday-maker keep coming back for more? Well it's the super milky white cod, real chips – and I'll let you into their secret, the Halfway came tops in a Daloon Foods' 'Fish and Chip Shop of the Year Award'!

MERRYWEATHERS, 530 Christchurch Road, Boscombe.
Tel: 0202 36221

Open:	Mon – Sat 11.30 a.m. – 2.30 p.m.; 4.30 p.m. – 10.30 p.m. (Sat close 9.30 p.m.); open Sun in summer.
Facilities:	T/A; P; wheelchair access.
Fish finds:	Cod, haddock, huss, plaice, scampi, skate. Fish and chips to take-and-taste from around £1.70.
Fry:	Groundnut oil.
Side-lines:	Mushy peas, pickled onions. Other foods.
Wrapping:	Cartons, paper bags.

I make no excuses for including in this volume each of the Merryweather

54

chain, for the standard Mr Richardson and his colleagues set, and attain, for their outlets is worthy in each case. This outlet is managed by Martin Eldridge who has been frying for eight years. It was added to the Merryweather group at the end of last year. Boscombe was swallowed up and became part of Bournemouth in 1931. They both used, historically, to be referred to as 'watering holes'. But man needs sustenance as well – and where better (or is it batter) to find it than at Merryweathers?

SUPERFISH, 186 Seabourne Road, Southbourne. Tel: 0202 426158

Open:	Mon – Thu 11.30 a.m. – 2.00 p.m.; 5.30 p.m. – 11.00 p.m.; Fri 11.30 a.m. – 2.00 p.m.; 5.00 p.m. – 11.30 p.m.; Sat 11.30 a.m. – 2.30 p.m.; 5.00 p.m. – 11.30 p.m. (restaurant closes half-hour earlier).
Facilities:	T/A & R (L); P near; T; wheelchair friendly.
Fish finds:	Cod, haddock, halibut, huss, lemon sole, plaice, skate and more. Fish and chips to take-and-taste from around £1.85; sit-and-savour around £2.70.
Fry:	Beef dripping.
Side-lines:	Pickled gherkins, pickled onions. Other foods.
Wrapping:	Trays, greaseproof, white paper.

Excuse me, where can I get good fish and chips from? I don't know, but I know a man who does. Fresh and tasty, reasonably priced, great place, super diner. What else can I say? Try it!

> *In the first quarter of the last century supplies to Billingsgate fish market multiplied by five, to over 12,000 tonnes per year, following improved distribution and fishing techniques.*

Bridport

LONG'S, 23 West Street. Tel: 0308 23199

Open:	Mon – Sat 11.30 a.m. – 2.15 p.m.; 5.00 p.m. – 11.30 p.m. (Fri 4.30 p.m. – 11.30 p.m.).
Facilities:	T/A & R; T.
Fish finds:	Cod, haddock, plaice, rock salmon, scampi. Fish and chips to take-and-taste from around £1.50; sit-and-savour around £2.20.
Fry:	Vegetable fat.
Side-lines:	Mushy peas, pickled onions. Other foods.
Wrapping:	Trays, greaseproof bags, white paper.

David Long heads this family-run business. They have owned this market-town outlet for over sixty years, though the building has quite a history. It started life as a basket and sheep hurdle shop, when the forecourt was rented to farmers coming to market, for sheep sales. Tables and chairs now stand where the lambs once waited to come under the hammer to partner mint sauce. In another life the building was also The White Horse Inn, though the Tiger is now the nearest watering hole. Coming up to the present, much of this local history can be gleaned from the silk screen pictures on the walls of the take-out. The pinewood panelled restaurant is served by a dumb waiter lift. Among the mouth-watering specials is a ¾lb boneless and skinless cod and chips for around £3.00. Graham Davies and Phillip Harris are the fryers.

Broadstone

LONG'S, 179 Blandford Road. Tel: 0202 694798

Open:	Mon – Sat 11.30 a.m. – 2.15 p.m.; 5.00 p.m. – 11.30 pm.

Facilities:	T/A & R; P near.
Fish finds:	Cod, haddock, plaice, scampi. Fish and chips to take-and-taste from around £1.45; sit-and-savour around £2.20.
Fry:	Vegetable oil.
Side-lines:	Pea fritters, pickled gherkins, pickled onions. Other foods.
Speciality:	Home-made fish cakes.
Wrapping:	White paper.

Long established, always super succulent fresh fish with good portions and great chips. Now the secret with a take-and-taste is to eat fish and chips straight away, while they're still crisp – plenty of salt and vinegar on mine, please! If you need a drink the Dorset Soldier pub is nearby. Cheers! If you need sanctuary pop down to the Priest's house at Wimbourne.

Corfemullen

LONG'S, 159 Wareham Road. Tel: 0202 602524

Open:	Mon – Sat 11.30 a.m. – 2.15 p.m.; 5.00 p.m. – 11.30 p.m. (Fri & Sat 4.30 p.m. – 11.30 p.m.).
Facilities:	T/A; P near.
Fish finds:	Cod, haddock, plaice, rock. Fish and chips to take-and-taste from around £1.45.
Fry:	Vegetable oil.
Side-lines:	Pea fritters. Other foods.
Speciality:	Home-made fish cakes.
Wrapping:	White paper.

What is Corfemullen famous for? Fish and chips of course. The bright and light decor reflects the freshness of the products. Ask anybody the way to Long's – see you there . . .

Creek Moor

LONG'S, 43 Benmoor Road. Tel: 0202 604214

Open:	Mon – Sat 11.30 a.m. – 2.15 p.m.; 5.00 p.m. – 11.30 p.m. (Fri & Sat 4.30 p.m. – 11.30 p.m.).
Facilities:	T/A; off-licence; P near.
Fish finds:	Cod, haddock, plaice, rock, scampi. Fish and chips to take-and-taste from around £1.40.
Fry:	Vegetable oil.
Side-lines:	Pea fritters. Other foods.
Speciality:	Home-made fish cakes.
Wrapping:	White paper.

Another traditional chippy serving fresh, chunky fish in golden crunchy batter – add a pea fritter and you're laughing! The staff are so friendly in this spotless shop. People come from miles around for a chip and a chat and a bottle of stout to take home – or they relax in the Acorn pub nearby.

Dorchester

HAPPY SOLE, 35 High West Street. Tel: 0305 263441

Open:	Daily: 11.45 a.m. – 2.00 p.m.; 5.00 p.m. – 11.00 p.m. (Fri & Sat till 11.30 p.m.).

Facilities:	T/A & R; P; T; wheelchair access.
Fish finds:	Cod, haddock, plaice, scampi. Fish and chips to take-and-taste from around £1.50; sit-and-savour around £2.40.
Fry:	Groundnut oil.
Side-lines:	Mushy peas, pickled onions. Other foods.
Wrapping:	Greaseproof lined and insulated bags.

Tony and Jeanette Plummer took over the range here two years ago and insist all meals for the restaurant are cooked to order. There's also a children's menu and coach parties are catered for. Special take-aways for pensioners. The outlet was first established over fifty years ago, with the original bay window in the take-away still in place. There's a piano in the restaurant, the ivories of which have been tickled by many a talented customer. There's room for over fifty in the sit-and-savour section.

QUALITY FISH & CHIPS, 14 Fordington Green. Tel: 0305 69615

Open:	Tue – Sat midday – 2.00 p.m.; 5.00 p.m. – 11.00 p.m.
Facilities:	T/A; P near.
Fish finds:	Cod, haddock, plaice. Fish and chips to take-and-taste from around £1.50.
Fry:	Oil.
Side-lines:	Mushy peas, pickled onions. Other foods.
Wrapping:	White paper with greaseproof.

'Good, but not religious-good' wrote Thomas Hardy who is often associated with this market town on the Frome river. He could have been talking about the delicious fare dished up at this outlet – the succulence of which makes one feel sure it must be a sin to eat! Mr C.J. Inett is the proprietor of this traditional chippy near the Bull pub. They have been 'Frying Tonight' at this premises for over half a century. It's another place

where B.J. Matthews likes to buy take-outs to 'eat with my fingers from paper, sitting in my car with a good view and peace all round. What more could anyone want?'

Poole

LONG'S OAKDALE FISHERIES, Dorchester Road. Tel: 0202 674017

Open:	Mon – Sat 11.30 a.m. – 2.30 p.m.; 5.00 p.m. – 11.30 p.m. (Fri & Sat 4.30 p.m. – 11.30 p.m.).
Facilities:	T/A & R (L); P near; T.
Fish finds:	Cod, haddock, huss, plaice in breadcrumbs, scampi, skate, trout. Fish and chips to take-and-taste from around £1.50; sit-and-savour £2.20.
Fry:	Dripping.
Side-lines:	Pickled gherkins, pickled onions. Other foods.
Wrapping:	Fibre trays, white greaseproof bags and white paper.

With a wet fish outlet on the premises it is natural they are able to offer this magnificent selection of fish at any time. They also have their own off-licence and ice-cream parlour and restaurant within the same building. Not quite competing with the Poole Guildhall that was built in 1761, nevertheless they've been frying here for fifty-eight years – and under the same ownership for forty-five. It's situated 300 yd along the Dorchester Road, past the Oakdale School traffic lights. The fryers are Lance Glover and Andrew de Freville.

The original British fast-food: fish and chips.

Portland

THE CHIPPER, 37 Chiswell. Tel: 0305 821 565

Open:	Daily 11.45 a.m. – 2.15 p.m.; 5.00 p.m. – 11.30 p.m.
Facilities:	T/A & R (L).
Fish finds:	Cod, haddock, huss, plaice, skate. Fish and chips to take-and-taste from around £1.60.
Fry:	Vegetable oil.
Side-lines:	Pickled gherkins, pickled onions.
Wrapping:	Paper and trays.

Brian Avis has been frying here for six years. He has recently enlarged the restaurant seating to cater for fifty. Try a glass of wine with your fish, and coke for the kids. You'll find the outlet as you arrive in Victoria Square, 100 yd from Portland Naval Base, on the road clearly marked to Chiswell. Well worth taking the trip over the Chesil Bank.

RAY'S FISH SHOP, 35 Straits, Easton. Tel: 0305 821822

Open:	Mon, Tue, Fri & Sat 9.00 a.m. – 11.15 p.m.; Wed & Thu 9.00 a.m. – 11.30 p.m.; Sun 5.00 p.m. – 11.00 p.m.
Facilities:	T/A; off-licence; P.
Fish finds:	Cod, haddock, huss, smoked mackerel, plaice, poached fish, shark, skate, swordfish. Fish and chips to take-and-taste from around £1.20.
Fry:	Fat.
Side-lines:	Mushy peas, pickled onions. Other foods.
Wrapping:	Trays and white off-cuts.

Ray Stone has been running this outlet for going on fifteen years. You'll find it opposite the library and near the Corner House pub. The decor is French beige tiling on the walls and quarry-tiled floors – appropriate in an area noted for its stone quarries. Seafood pancakes are among the specialities and praise has been high from Mr and Mrs P. Butcher and Beverley, and also from Mrs Bunty May. They remind me that Ray always offers children a 'chip-on-a-stick' while they are waiting.

Southbourne

LONG'S, 179 Tuckton Road. Tel: 0202 429818

Open:	Mon – Sat 11.30 a.m. – 2.15 p.m.; 5.00 p.m. – 11.30 p.m. (Fri & Sat 4.30 p.m. – 11.30 p.m.).
Facilities:	T/A & R; P near; T.
Fish finds:	Cod, haddock, plaice, rock salmon, scampi. Fish and chips to take-and-taste from around £1.40; sit-and-savour around £2.10.
Fry:	Vegetable oil.
Side-lines:	Pea fritters. Other foods.
Speciality:	Home-made fish cakes.
Wrapping:	White paper.

This is a fish and chip experience King Neptune recommends: fresher than fresh. Superb decor – as it should be after a £125,000 refit. In the 35-seater luxury diner I'll have a large rock salmon and a bottle of your best wine, and a fanta for little Fiona. No, the wife doesn't drink – she's driving.

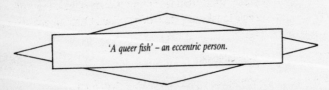

'A queer fish' – an eccentric person.

Swanage

JUST THE PLAICE, 355 High Street. Tel: 0929 423578

Open:	Mon – Sat midday – 2.00 p.m.; Mon – Sun 5.00 p.m. – 10.00 p.m. (till 11.00 p.m. in summer).
Facilities:	T/A & small R; P; T.
Fish finds:	Cod, haddock, plaice, skate. Local fish when available. Fish and chips to take-and-taste from around £1.85.
Fry:	Oil.
Side-lines:	Pickled onions. Other foods.
Wrapping:	Trays and in bags.

Proprietor F. Hay has been here only a few years, but has already refurbished the premises to a very high standard, in a very striking green that can't be missed. It is at Herston Cross, just before you get into Swanage. He sells skate when he can get a locally-caught fresh supply and cooks only to order. The Globe Inn is nearby. The outlet comes with the blessing of Canon and Mrs W.A.M. Langdon.

PARADE FISH RESTAURANT, 1 The Parade. Tel: 0929 422362

Open:	Daily Mar – Oct 11.00 a.m. – 11.00 p.m.
Facilities:	T/A & R; T; wheelchair access.
Fish finds:	Bass, cod, conger, dover & lemon sole, haddock, hake, plaice, rock, whiting and over twenty others. Fish and chips to take-and-taste from around £1.50; sit-and-savour £2.25.
Fry:	Vegetable oil.
Side-lines:	Mushy peas, pickled onions. Other foods.

Specialities: Grilled local fish. Shark steaks.

Wrapping: Polystyrene trays and paper.

Dave Kerley's famous chippy would need to be in a boat to be nearer the sea – it's only 8 yd away! It's been a fry-house for nearly fifty years – though during the last World War was known as a house of ill repute, satisfying the three 'overs' of the US First Armoured Division stationed nearby. A far more savoury reputation has developed more recently – one of the finest quality fish restaurants in the south-west. The turn-over of 12 tonnes of fish and sea food in eight months speaks for itself. Mrs Mary Lees recommends.

Weymouth

MARLBORO RESTAURANT, 46 St Thomas Street. Tel: 0305 785700

Open: Daily July – Sept 11.45 a.m. – 11.00 p.m.; Oct – June 11.45 a.m. – 2.00 p.m.; 4.45 p.m. – 11.00 p.m. (restaurant till 9.00 p.m.).

Facilities:	T/A & R (L); P near; T.
Fish finds:	Cod, fish cakes (home-made), haddock, plaice, scampi. Fish and chips to take-and-taste from around £1.50; sit-and-savour around £2.40.
Fry:	Vegetable fat.
Side-lines:	Pickled gherkins, pickled onions. Other foods.
Wrapping:	Trays, paper, bags. Extra in winter.

Michael and Vincent Johnson's chippy has been established in this Grade III Listed Building for around fifteen years. Sited on a corner plot, the windows are of Georgian style – appropriate as the town's popularity dates from the time of George III. The chippy is fully tiled throughout the take-away, and the back wall of the restaurant has been returned to its original stone facing. There's room for forty to sit-and-savour. Find it near the town bridge.

SEAGULL, Harbourside, 10 Trinity Street. Tel: 0305 784782

Open:	Summer, daily; winter Tue – Sat midday – 2.00 p.m.; 5.30 p.m. – 11.00 p.m.
Facilities:	T/A & R; P; T near; wheelchair access.
Fish finds:	Cod, haddock, plaice, rock salmon, scampi, skate. Fish and chips to take-and-taste from around £1.35; sit-and-savour £2.00.
Fry:	Own mixture of fat and oil for taste.
Side-lines:	Mushy peas, pickled eggs, pickled onions. Other foods.
Wrapping:	Paper.

Mrs Jeanette Ashley's shop overlooks the outer harbour. There's been frying going on here since 1948. The premises are painted black and white outside with a traditional green, cream and white interior. The restaurant, spotlessly clean, has formica-topped tables to seat twenty-four, with padded chairs. Waitress service is very efficient, with staff geared out in green check overalls. The impression, with terrazzo floor throughout, pot plants and a large picture of seagulls, is one of cleanliness, friendliness and efficiency. The Old Rooms Inn opposite is the place to quench your thirst, though there's Tesco's take-away drinks department for those wishing to drink elsewhere. I received several recommendations amongst others from Mr and Mrs B. Shaw of Somerset and T. Maclachlan who lives in Weymouth.

Wimborne

LONG'S, 73A Leigh Road. Tel: 0202 883119

Open:	Mon – Sat 11.30 a.m. – 2.30 p.m.; 5.00 p.m. – 11.30 p.m.
Facilities:	T/A; P; T.
Fish finds:	Cod, haddock, hake, plaice, rock, scampi, shark, skate, squid. Fish and chips to take-and-taste from around £1.45.
Fry:	Fat.
Side-lines:	Pea fritters, pickled onions. Other foods.
Wrapping:	White bags, paper, trays, carrier bags.

The town has a famous collegiate church founded by Edward the Confessor; and this outlet is near the King's School of English. This means that during the summer, hundreds of foreign students from all over the world descend on the area – and take home the memory of wonderful English fish and chips, supplied by Long's. To help them pick up our ways, the outlet has the menu printed in six different languages. With its mahogany front and blue-tiled interior, you'll find it close by the Coach and Horses pub.

ESSEX
Billericay

MERRYWEATHERS, 60 High Street. Tel: 0277 652539

Open:	Mon – Sat 11.30 a.m. – 2.30 p.m. 3.30 p.m. – 10.30 p.m.
Facilities:	T/A & R; P near.
Fish finds:	Cod, haddock, plaice, rock, roe, scampi. Fish and chips to take-and-taste from around £2.20; sit-and-savour £3.00.
Fry:	Groundnut oil.
Side-lines:	Pickled eggs, pickled gherkins, pickled onions. Other foods.
Wrapping:	Stay-hot food containers wrapped in greaseproof.

The church tower in this Essex town is considered one of the finest examples of brick architecture. This outlet is one of those taken over from Associated Fisheries by the highly successful Merryweather group. Most staff are trained to fry to their exacting standards and the fare served here, half-way down the High Street next to Boots, is not only pleasing to the eye, but highly satisfying to the palate. Just consistently good!

Brentwood

MERRYWEATHERS, 84 High Street. Tel: 0277 225184

Open:	Daily 11.30 a.m. – 10.30 p.m.
Facilities:	T/A & R (L); T; P; wheelchair access.
Fish finds:	Cod, haddock, huss, plaice, skate. Fish and chips to

take-and-taste from about £1.80; sit-and-savour from around £2.95.

Fry: Groundnut oil.

Side-lines: Pickled eggs, pickled gherkins, pickled onions. Other foods.

Wrapping: Stay-hot food containers wrapped in greaseproof.

Mrs Lynn Stothard as manager of this smart outlet, keeps up the exacting, high standards set by the Merryweather group, acquired by Carol and her band less than two years ago. Perhaps known more for its associations with the car industry, this urban district, eighteen miles from London, does boast a fine secondary school, founded in 1557, and the even earlier White Hart Inn (didn't they write a musical about it?). No, that's the White Horse Inn, which dates from 1480. But the fish and chips are fresh and up to date.

Brightlingsea (Nr Colchester)

**PISCES FISH BAR, 5 Manor Shopping Parade, Off Park Drive.
Tel: 0206 303049**

Open: Tue – Thu midday – 2.00 p.m.; 5.00 p.m. – 11.00 p.m.; Fri & Sat 11.45 a.m. – 2.00 p.m.; 4.30 p.m. – 11.00 p.m.

Facilities: T/A & R; P; T; wheelchair access.

Fish finds: Cod, huss, plaice, scampi, skate. Fish and chips to take-and-taste from around £2.00; sit-and-savour around £3.75.

Fry: Fat.

Side-lines: Pickled gherkins, pickled onions. Other foods.

Wrapping:	Polystyrene dishes, greaseproof bags with white newsheet.

The local council have regularly awarded the Pisces their hygiene award. We found this spotless chippy, on the Manor housing estate opposite Colne High School, well deserving of the citation. On Tuesdays and Wednesdays they do a special, economic lunch for senior citizens. They also do special party rates for local clubs and organizations. Brightlingsea is a well-known sailing centre south-east of Colchester. And if you are stuck for the readies, Des – he's the boss – will accept luncheon vouchers.

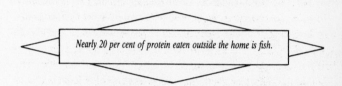

Nearly 20 per cent of protein eaten outside the home is fish.

WINKIES FISH AND CHIP TAKE-AWAY & RESTAURANT,
7 New Street. Tel: 020630 4208

Open:	Tue & Wed midday – 1.30 p.m.; 5.00 p.m. – 9.00p.m; Fri & Sat 11.45 a.m. – 2.00 p.m.; 4.30 p.m. – 10.00 p.m.
Facilities:	T/A & R (L); P; T; wheelchair access.
Fish finds:	Cod, haddock, plaice, rock eel, skate. Fish and chips to take-and-taste from around £1.80.
Fry:	Fat.
Side-lines:	Mushy peas, pickled gherkins, pickled onions. Other foods.
Wrapping:	Greaseproof, bags, white wrap.

Terry Austin took over this 60-year-old outlet in the mid-1980s, though he's been frying for the last decade. They have been busy refurbishing and rebuilding throughout, plus adding a smart licensed restaurant. You'll find them opposite the library in this well-known sailing centre at the mouth of the Colne.

Clacton-on-Sea

REG'S FISHERIES, 21 St John's Road, Great Clacton. Tel: 0255 421487

Open: Mon – Fri 11.45 a.m. – 2.00 p.m.; Mon – Thur 4.45 p.m.
               – 11.00 p.m.; Fri 4.30 p.m. – midnight; Sat 11.30 a.m. –
               midnight.

Facilities: T/A & R (L); P; T (inc disabled); wheelchair access.

Fish finds: Cod, haddock, Dover and lemon sole (when available),
               plaice, rock eel, scampi, skate. Fish and chips to take-
               and-taste from around £1.55; sit-and-savour from £2.25.

Fry: Nut oil.

Side-lines: Pickled gherkins, pickled onions. Other foods.

Wrapping: Paper plus polystyrene containers.

*The partnership of Stephen Skinner and Philip Hinderwell, with several
other Skinners, has run this outlet very successfully for over a decade. The
restaurant has been extended to cater for up to ninety covers. The work
included complete refurbishment of kitchen and other facilities. We
followed up on the recommendation of T.J. Brownsmith; the food is well
prepared with large helpings, pleasantly served. The premises are opposite
the Queen's Head pub. They also do a good trade in outside catering for
large functions. Ask for details.*

Colchester

HICKS, 120 High Street. Tel: 0206 574948

Open: Mon – Thu 11.00 a.m. – 11.00 p.m.; Fri & Sat
               11.00 a.m. – 3.00 a.m.

Facilities: T/A & R (L); T; wheelchair access.

Fish finds:	Cod, haddock, Mediterranean prawns, peeled prawns, plaice, rock, smoked salmon, scampi, skate. Fish and chips to take-and-taste from around £2.10; sit-and-savour around £3.85; child's portion £1.75.
Fry:	Vegetable oil.
Side-lines:	Pickled gherkins, pickled onions. Other foods.
Wrapping:	Specially made, printed bags.

Jane and Terry Hicks had this outlet completely refurbished when they took over a few years ago; they've been in the trade over eleven years. You'll find it opposite the Red Lion Walk shopping precinct in this, reputedly the oldest town in England. The town has the largest Norman castle in Britain, which was purchased by the town council for £8,000 in 1920, with money provided by Lord Cowdray. A few doors away from the George pub, the restaurant here seats forty-eight. Nice to see a proprietor identifying for customers' edification just where around our coast each type of fish is landed – though I can find no mention of Colchester oysters!

Grays

R. MUMFORD & SON, 8 Cromwell Road. Tel: 0375 374153

Open:	Daily 11.30 a.m. – 2.00 p.m.; Mon 5.30 p.m. – 9.00 p.m.; Tue – Fri 5.30 p.m. – 10.00 p.m.; Sat 5.00 p.m. – 11.00 p.m.
Facilities:	T/A & R (L); P; T; wheelchair access.
Fish finds:	Cod, Dover and lemon sole, haddock, rock eel, skate. Fish and chips to take-and-taste from around £2.10; sit-and-savour around £4.75.
Fry:	Groundnut oil.
Side-lines:	Pickled gherkins, pickled onions. Other foods.

Wrapping: White trays with either paper bags or carrier.

Mr Mumford has headed this family-run business for thirty years. It's opposite the Thameside Library complex and public car park. The shop was recently thoroughly modernized throughout. It now boasts full air conditioning and a cold air system. The colour scheme is predominantly green, with white tablecloths in the restaurant, which seats sixty-eight. You may easily find yourself sharing the queue with, or dining alongside, Fatima Whitbread, George Chisolm, David Essex or other stars who pop in from the theatre opposite. Over the years this outlet has been recommended by numerous guides for its no-messing English fish and chips approach to a good hearty meal. Why should we be any different? We heartily agree.

Typical British village: a collection of homesteads, a church, a pub and at least one fish and chip shop.

Halstead

MARTIN'S FISH BAR, 1 Martin's Road. Tel: 0787 472324

Open: Tue – Sat 11.00 a.m. – 1.30 p.m.; 4.30 p.m. – 10.00 p.m. (till 10.30 p.m. Fri).

Facilities: T/A; P.

Fish finds: Cod, haddock, plaice, rock eel, scampi, skate. Fish and chips to take-and-taste from around £1.60.

Fry: Vegetable oil.

Side-lines: Pickled gherkins, pickled onions. Other foods.

Wrapping: Greaseproof paper (at least triple-wrapped). Plastic bags if necessary.

Mr C.K. Dai, a kindly, well-mannered gentleman, has been serving the populace of this small market town for a few years, and frying for over a decade. The friendly service, appealing portions and fresh cooking was brought to our attention by Miss A.R. Brazier of Chelmsford. We assure you, Mr Dai, the courtesy you and your staff show is much appreciated by your many friends who are also customers.

Harlow

MR LUIGI'S, 108 The Stow Shopping Parade. Tel: 0279 25086

Open:	Daily 11.30 a.m. – 9.00 p.m.
Facilities:	T/A.
Fish finds:	Cod, plaice, rock, skate. Fish and chips to take-and-taste from around £1.95.
Fry:	Vegetable fat.
Side-lines:	Pickled gherkins, pickled onions. Other foods.
Wrapping:	Trays and paper bags.

Luigi is the new owner of this long-established shop in the sprawl of urbanization called Harlow. It's funny to think that only a little over half a century ago this was a village with a population of less than three thousand. I suppose there were even less people when the Romans settled here.

Some chippies use margarine on their bread, with the claim their batter is 'so rich' that to serve butter on bread would be unfair to their customers' cholesterol level!

Harwich

HA'PENNY PIER, The Pier at Harwich, The Quay. Tel: 0255 241212

Open:	Sun – Fri midday – 2.00 p.m.; 6.00 p.m. – 9.30 p.m.; Sat midday – 9.30 p.m.
Facilities:	R (L); P near; music; wheelchair access.
Fish finds:	Cod, fish pie, haddock, mackerel, plaice, scampi, whitebait. Fish and chips to sit-and-savour from around £4.00.
Fry:	Vegetable oil.
Side-lines:	Pickled gherkins, pickled onions. Other foods.

The Ha'penny Pier Restaurant and Hotel are easy to find on the quayside. They are in a magnificent Victorian building with the fish and chip diner on the ground floor, immaculate fish restaurant on the first floor (Lobster and all that). If you want to stay the night before boarding your ferry to the Hook of Holland, the en suite rooms are a floor above. Nothing but fresh fish is served, as you might expect from a portside location. If you don't want haddock, skate or plaice, do try the Ha'penny Pier delicious Cod Pie, and if you have the children with you, junior can tuck into the kids' menu.

Hatfield Heath

SKIPPER'S DELIGHT, The Chestnuts. Tel: 0279 730174

Open:	Tue – Sat midday – 2.00 p.m.; 5.00 p.m. – 10.00 p.m.
Facilities:	T/A; P near; wheelchair access.
Fish finds:	Cod, haddock, plaice, rock, scampi, skate. Fish and chips to take-and-taste from around £1.95.

Fry: Vegetable oil.

Side-lines: Pickled gherkins, pickled onions. Other foods.

The Taylor family are high fryers where fish and chips are concerned: for the last three years they have been frying away like mad, building up a very good reputation for serving fresh and wholesome food at reasonable prices, in hygienically clean surroundings. Take exit 8 off the M11 (the same exit as that for Stansted Airport and Mount Fitchet Castle).

Loughton

ALEXANDER'S CHARIOT BRASSERIE, 202 High Road.
Tel: 081 508 2436
and
16–18 South Walk, Basildon. Tel: 0268 522470

Open: Daily 11.30 a.m. – 11.00 p.m. (restaurant Sat till 12.30 a.m.).

Facilities:	T/A & R (L); P; T.
Fish finds:	Cod, haddock, halibut, plaice, rock, salmon, scampi, sole. Fish and chips to take-and-taste from around £2.00; sit-and-savour from around £3.20.
Fry:	Oil.
Side-lines:	Pickled gherkins, pickled onions. Other foods.
Wrapping:	Specially made lined greaseproof bags.

Alec Smith claims his establishments – modern and smart in appearance with keen, young staff – are among the busiest and most popular in Essex. He opened in Loughton over twenty years ago, in the middle of the High Street in this bustling urban district on the edge of Epping Forest. The restaurant seats 120. The fresh fish and pleasant service were first brought to our attention by M.R. Clements of Barkingside. The selection is first class, tastefully served in a variety of ways.

Maldon

WHEELER'S, 13 High Street. Tel: 0621 853647

Open:	T/A: Tue – Sat 11.00 a.m. – 2.00 p.m.; 4.00 p.m. – 11.00 p.m.; R: Tue – Sat 11.45 a.m. – 1.45 p.m.; 6.00 p.m. – 9.30 p.m.
Facilities:	T/A & R (L); P near; T (inc. disabled); wheelchair access (1 step).
Fish finds:	Cod, haddock, huss, plaice, scampi, skate. Fish and chips to take-and-taste from around £1.50; sit-and-savour around £2.70.
Fry:	Groundnut oil.
Side-lines:	Pickled gherkins, pickled onions. Other foods.
Wrapping:	White bags and white wrap.

Ross Wheeler's family have been frying at this renowned establishment for over eighty years. Not to be mistaken for the other well-known restaurant concern by the same name which is currently being franchised around the country, this Wheeler's was nevertheless selected as the best fried fish restaurant in the country a few years ago by a consumer organization. The fish is all bought fresh. Find it next to an estate agent – who, no doubt, would love the chance to market his neighbour's building with its 16th-century oak beams etc . . .

Rayleigh

MERRYWEATHERS, 70 High Street. Tel: 0268 771757

Open: Mon – Sat 11.30 a.m. – 2.30 p.m.; 5.00 p.m. – 10.30 p.m.

Facilities: T/A & R (L); P near; T.

Fish finds: Cod, haddock, halibut, plaice, rock, scampi, skate. Fish and chips to take-and-taste from around £2.20; sit-and-savour from around £3.00.

Fry: Fat.

Side-lines: Mushy peas, pickled gherkins, pickled onions. Other foods.

Wrapping: Food containers and greaseproof.

If you want something to do while your fish is frying, why not go and have a look at the famous Rayleigh Windmill close by? This outlet is another of the Merryweather chain; it was bought from Associated Fisheries who had been frying here for over a generation. Cod and chips was the most popular dish when this shop opened, and it still is today. The chips are firm and the fish is crisply battered.

Romford

MARCUS FISH BAR, 71 High Street. Tel: 0708 41554

Open: Mon – Sat 11.00 a.m. – 10.00 p.m.

Facilities: T/A & R; P near; wheelchair friendly.

Fish finds: Cod, haddock, plaice, rock, skate. Fish and chips to take-and-taste from around £1.95; sit-and-savour around £2.20.

Fry: Groundnut oil.

Side-lines: Pickled gherkins, pickled onions. Other foods.

Speciality: Chocolate and jam gateaux.

Wrapping: Trays, white paper, bags.

The Marcus family have been successfully frying here for the last twenty-five years, pleasing everybody from far and wide with generous helpings of fresh fish and chips, whether served in the spotless 28-seater diner or at the take and taste counter. You will find this super chippy courting the London Road roundabout at the end of the High Street.

Southend-on-Sea

FISHERMAN'S WHARF, Western Esplanade. Tel: 0702 346773

Open: Daily 11.30 a.m. – 10.30 p.m.

Facilities: R (L); T.

Fish finds: Huge menu of fish and shellfish from cod to caviar plus live oysters and fresh lobsters. Dover sole and two vegetables £11.95.

Fry:	Oil.
Side-lines:	Pickled gherkins, pickled onions.
Speciality:	Whole Dover sole stuffed with spiced prawns.

Four years ago they created Fisherman's Wharf – though it looks as though it has been there at least as long, if not longer than, its famous brothers in San Francisco and New York. The fish tastes as fresh as in either of these: maybe that's because they have their own wet fish outlet, at the rear of 120 Hemlet Court Road, Westcliff-on-Sea. Mr S.R. Sale is the manager. He asks me to highlight their house speciality: whole Dover sole stuffed with spiced prawns. They also serve whole or half lobsters in five different ways.

South Woodham Ferrers

MERRYWEATHERS, Reeves Way. Tel: 0245 320294

Open:	Mon – Sat 11.30 a.m. – 2.30 p.m.; 4.30 p.m. – 9.30 p.m.
Facilities:	T/A & R (L); P near; T.
Fish finds:	Cod, haddock, halibut, plaice, rock, roe, scampi, skate. Fish and chips to take-and-taste from around £1.75; sit-and-savour around £2.50.
Fry:	Fat.
Side-lines:	Pickled gherkins, pickled onions. Other foods.
Wrapping:	White paper and greaseproof into bags.

Now owned by the highly successful Merryweather group, this outlet has been open just over six years. You'll find it next to the Post Office, near the Oakland Hotel. When Southend gets too busy, or after a visit to the beautiful gardens at Hyde Hall or Hanningfield Water, it's well worth searching out this establishment on the north side of the River Crouch.

Stansted

CHINA GARDEN, Station Road. Tel: 0279 812941

Open: Mon 5.00 p.m. – 9.30 p.m.; Tue 11.00 a.m. – 2.00 p.m.;
5.00 p.m. – 10.00 p.m.; Wed – Sat midday – 2.00 p.m.;
5.00 p.m. – 10.00 p.m.

Facilities: T/A; P near; wheelchair friendly.

Fish finds: Cod, fish cakes, haddock, plaice, rock, scampi, skate.
Fish and chips to take-and-taste from around £2.20.

Fry: Vegetable fat.

Side-lines: Pickled onions. Other foods.

Wrapping: Trays and white paper.

*The China Garden fish and chip shop is right next door to the China
Garden Chinese take-away, and is under the same management. The
chippy is patronized and favoured by the Stansted-to-London train
commuters because of its convenience to the station, and its super succulent
fish and chips. If you have time, why not pop in to see one of the most
famous Norman strongholds in Britain, Mount Fitchet Castle which is open
daily from March to October. The children will love it.*

GLOUCESTERSHIRE
Chipping Campden

G.H. & M.L. KEITLEY, The Chippy, Sheep Street. Tel: 0386 840388

Open: Wed & Thu midday – 1.30 p.m.; 5.45 p.m. – 9.00 p.m.;
Fri 11.45 a.m. – 1.30 p.m.; 5.45 p.m. – 9.00 p.m.;
Sat 11.45 a.m. – 1.30 p.m.; 5.00 p.m. – 9.00 p.m.

Facilities:	T/A; L (off-licence); P near.
Fish finds:	Cod, haddock, plaice. Take-and-taste fish and chips from around £1.20.
Fry:	Oil.
Side-lines:	Mushy peas, pickled onions. Other foods.
Wrapping:	Greaseproof and white paper.

A truly family business run by Mum and Dad (Gordon and Mary), son and daughter! The family have been in the trade for nearly thirty years in this market town that was once the centre of the wool trade. You'll find them in the centre of Sheep Street, opposite the Citroen Garage. If they're not there, rather than 'Gone Fishin' the sign will read 'Gone Golfin', for Dad or 'Gone Sketchin' for son. We won't talk about Dad's handicap, but son is a highly respected local artist. The fish and chips are good too!

Gloucester

D.A. DYKE, 23 Sydenham Terrace (off Stroud Road). Tel: 0452 22106

Open:	Tue – Sat 11.00 a.m. – 2.30 p.m.
Facilities:	T/A; P.
Fish finds:	Cod, haddock, plaice. Fish and chips to take-and-taste from around £1.20.
Fry:	Pure groundnut oil.
Side-lines:	Pickled onions. Other foods.
Wrapping:	Trays, white news.

This really is a traditional chippy, where a fryer of nearing forty years' experience is still in charge of the range. Danny Dyke's is a good example of how often the most reasonably priced outlets, far from cutting corners, have some of the tastiest fare to be found. You'll find the shop on the corner of Stanley Road near the Stroud Road Post Office. Mr Roche's Wine Vat off-licence is 100 yd further along Stanley Road. Although Keith Allen of Surbiton has now moved from Gloucester, he savours the flavour of Danny's frys.

YE OLDE FISH SHOPPE & RESTAURANT, 8 Hare Lane.
Tel: 0452 22502

Open:	Mon 11.30 a.m. – 2.15 p.m.; Tue – Fri 11.30 a.m. – 2.15 p.m.; 4.30 p.m. – 8.30 p.m.; Sat 11.15 a.m. – 6.30 p.m.
Facilities:	T/A & R (L); P; T; wheechair access.
Fish finds:	Cod, haddock, plaice, scampi. (Also hake and lemon sole when available.) Fish and chips to take-and-taste from around £1.50; sit-and-savour from £2.00.
Fry:	Both lard and oil.
Side-lines:	Mushy peas, pickled onions. Other foods.
Wrapping:	Paper, polystyrene trays or boxes.

Edward II was enshrined in the Benedictine monastery here following his murder at Berkeley Castle in 1327. The building in which this chippy is housed was built in 1450, almost a hundred years before the monastery became Gloucester Cathedral, and this town on the left bank of the Severn became a city. Quite naturally it is listed as a building of special architectural interest, being a fine example of a timber-framed dwelling. It was originally outside the north gate of the city, but now has a beautiful view of the cathedral. The restaurant can seat seventy-five and has waitress service. The decor, in keeping with the building, is beams and plaster – and the floors really do slope. A nice touch is a wishing-well feature, which has produced over £2,000 for charity. Terry Green has been frying for going on forty-five years in this 60-year-old outlet. The fare is well endorsed by Ted and Dorothy Beddis of Cinderford.

Stroud

KINGFISHER, 2 High Street. Tel: 0453 750777

Open: Mon 11.30 a.m. – 2.00 p.m.; Tue – Fri 11.30 a.m. –
2.00 p.m.; 5.00 p.m. – 9.30 p.m.; Sat 11.30 a.m. –
9.00 p.m.

Facilities: T/A; P near.

Fish finds:	Cod, haddock, plaice. Fish and chips to take-and-taste from around £1.55. Special senior citizens price £1.15.
Fry:	Vegetable oil.
Side-lines:	Mushy peas, pickled eggs, pickled gherkins, pickled onions, milk shakes. Other foods, including vegetarian pasties.
Wrapping:	Polystyrene trays, white news.

You'll always get a cheery welcome at this spotlessly clean outlet on Stroud's main shopping street. There has been a chippy on this site for at least the past decade, and this one is run by the brother of the Mr Pardale who runs the Kingfisher in Stratford-upon-Avon. George and Tsambika opened up here on 1 June 1987: 'A very memorable day: exactly a month after our wedding', which was in their native Rhodes. Now they run it with the assistance of baby Sevasti! Lunchtimes and Saturdays are their busiest periods, but even when there isn't a long queue be prepared to wait a few minutes: everything is freshly fried on order. 'Service with a smile' is the motto here – 'this at least is free of charge!' jokes Tsambika.

GREATER LONDON
Archway N19

ICELAND FISH BAR, 11 Archway Road. Tel: 071 272 6606

Open:	Mon 5.00 p.m. – 11.30 p.m.; Tue – Sat 11.30 a.m. – 2.00 p.m.; 5.00 p.m. – 11.30 p.m.
Facilities:	T/A; P near.
Fish finds:	Cod, Dover and lemon sole, haddock, halibut, plaice, rock, scampi, skate. Fish and chips to take-and-taste from around £2.10.

Fry:	Oil.
Side-lines:	Pickled gherkins, pickled onions. Other foods.
Wrapping:	Greaseproof bags, white paper.

Antonios Kantretti's fine shop has been hanging out the 'Frying Today' sign for going towards a quarter of a century. You'll find it easily on the corner of the High Street, all decked out in blue and white tiles with an illuminated, suspended ceiling and ceramic tile floor. An indication of the quality of the fare is given by the large number of lorry drivers who stop off before heading north up the A1. The Dog pub is nearby.

Battersea SW11

FRANKIE'S FISH BAR, 170A Lavender Hill. Tel: 071 228 0806

Open:	Mon – Sat 11.45 a.m. – 3.00 p.m.; 4.45 p.m. – 11.30 p.m.
Facilities:	T/A.
Fish finds:	Cod, haddock, plaice, rock, skate. Fish and chips to take-and-taste from around £1.75.
Fry:	Palm oil.
Side-lines:	Pickled gherkins, pickled onions. Other foods.
Wrapping:	White paper, paper bags.

Frank Le Lau has been running this cheerful chippy for more than ten years. It's just a few yards from Battersea Arts Centre, which gives a pretty good idea of the majority of his customers, and art students are pretty good judges of quality when it comes to food. Frankie's obviously passes the test.

Belsize Park NW3

MAXWELLS OF EALING, 177 Haverstock Hill. Tel: 071 586 9277

Open:	Mon – Sat midday – 2.30 p.m.; 5.00 p.m. – 11.00 p.m (Sat till 10.30 p.m.).
Facilities:	T/A & R; P; T.
Fish finds:	Cod, Dover and lemon sole, haddock, halibut, plaice, rock, scampi, skate, trout. Fish and chips to take-and-taste from around £2.75; sit-and-savour around £2.95.
Fry:	Palm oil.
Side-lines:	Mushy peas, pickled gherkins, pickled onions. Other foods.
Wrapping:	Bags, paper, polystyrene trays.

Paul Lambert oversees this fine establishment, and his team must be doing something right for they have been featured in newspapers as far away as Dallas and Denmark. Stars like Meryl Streep, Boy George, Sting, Judith Chalmers and Brian Murphy have all popped in for their excellent fare. It's product and service that mere mortals queue for – and this shop certainly tries its best. We had a written recommendation from J. Flanagan, a satisfied customer. Don't dash in and out, sit-and-savour.

Chelsea SW10

JOHNNIE'S FISH BAR, 494 Kings Road. Tel: 071 352 3876

Open:	Daily 11.00 a.m. – 11.45 p.m.
Facilities:	T/A & R; T.
Fish finds:	Cod, haddock, scampi. Fish and chips to take-and-taste from around £2.30; sit-and-savour around £3.10.

Fry: Dripping.

Side-lines: Pickled gherkins, pickled onions. Other foods.

Wrapping: Double wrap, greaseproof, paper.

The world really would come to an end for many Chelsea pensioners, and others, if Burt stopped frying regularly, as he has done since 1976. He's down opposite the famous World's End pub in what, until a few years ago, used to be called 'the unfashionable end' of Chelsea. That meant where real Chelsea residents could afford to live and eat, and tourists seldom ventured. Now even the local chippy describes itself as being situated in 'a beautiful area on the side of a piazza dotted with trees and seats, with low walls enclosing flower beds.' Never mind, Whistler's Reach and the River Thames are still just a fisherman's pitch away. The restaurant, by the way, seats twenty. The outlet comes recommended by C. Lloyd-Jones, who lives along the river at Cheyne Walk.

Colindale NW9

LOUIS & ANDREAS FISH BAR, 203 Edgeware Road. Tel: 081 200 6771

Open: Tue – Thu 11.30 a.m. – 10.00 p.m.; Fri & Sat 11.30 a.m. – midnight.

Facilities: T/A; P.

Fish finds: Cod, haddock, plaice, rock, skate. Fish and chips to take-and-taste from around £2.20.

Fry: Groundnut oil.

Side-lines: Pickled gherkins, pickled onions. Other foods.

Speciality: Home-made fish cakes.

Wrapping: Bags, white paper.

Photis Zographou and his wife have been overseeing this outlet for over a

87   *GREATER LONDON*

decade. They buy only fresh fish and fillet it all before frying. The standard is good and the service pleasant. They are just past the Colindale VW dealer, opposite F.W. Woolworth. Do try the fish cakes made from 100 per cent cod, made on the premises.

Ealing W5

CRISPINS, 40 The Broadway. Tel: 081 567 0559

Open:	Mon – Sat 10.00 a.m. – 1.30 a.m.; Sun 5.00 p.m. – midnight.
Facilities:	T/A & R; P near; T; wheelchair friendly.
Fish finds:	Cod, haddock, halibut, plaice, rock, skate. Fish and chips to take-and-taste from around £2.30; sit-and-savour around £2.60.
Fry:	Palm oil.
Side-lines:	Pickled gherkins, pickled onions. Other foods.
Wrapping:	White paper, greaseproof, bags.

Crispins has been serving good fish and chips for a very long time. The staff are friendly, and prices are reasonable. Just £2.30 for haddock and chips to take-and-taste, a little more if you're going to sit in the 70-seater diner.

MAXWELLS, 5–6 The Green, High Street. Tel: 081 840 2307

Open:	Mon – Thu 11.30 a.m. – 2.00 p.m.; 5.00 p.m. – 11.00 p.m.; Fri & Sat 11.30 a.m. – 2.30 p.m.; 5.00 p.m. – 10.30 p.m.
Facilities:	T/A & R (L); P; T.
Fish finds:	Cod, haddock, halibut steaks, lemon sole, plaice fillets,

plaice on the bone, rock salmon, scampi, skate, swordfish. Fish and chips to take-and-taste from around £2.05; sit-and-savour around £2.95.

Fry:	Palm oil.
Side-lines:	Pickled gherkins, pickled onions. Other foods.
Wrapping:	Trays and paper.

This smart chippy has been in the same ownership for a number of years, with Roy and Carol in charge. The reproduction olde-worlde frontage leads into a spotless, chequered-floored take-away. The restaurant has a mock-Tudor style with honey beige walls setting off dark wood beams. Copies of Tate Gallery pictures hang around the room, and there are Windsor chairs and individually adjustable lamps over each table. Available for private hire on Sundays. Three Pigeons and Queen Victoria pubs close by, also near Ealing Green and the underground station opposite.

Earls Court SW5

HI-TIDE RESTAURANT, 7 Kenway Road, Earls Court. Tel: 071 373 9170

Open:	Mon – Sat midday – midnight; Sun 5.00 p.m. – 11.00 p.m.
Facilities:	T/A & R (L); P near; T.
Fish finds:	Cockles (sometimes), cod, cod's roe, haddock, mussels, plaice, rock, scampi, swordfish. Fish and chips to take-and-taste from around £2.20; sit-and-savour around £3.00.
Fry:	Oil.
Side-lines:	Pickled gherkins, pickled onions. Other foods.
Wrapping:	Greaseproof bags, paper.

If Australians ever learn to fry British fish and chips it will be no small thanks to Mr Lovick and family, who run this patriotically British chippy outpost in the middle of Kangaroo Valley. There's been a fry-house on this site – just down the side street opposite the Earl's Court Road entrance to the underground station – for over sixty years. The restaurant seats fifty, split between the ground floor and basement. In an area with an ever-changing populace, it would be easy for an outlet to let its standards drop. Not so the Lovicks, who take pride in their presentation and fare. It's worth fellow Brits remembering they are there and visiting them now and again. I promise you, I'll give all the XXXXs in Earls Court, it's worth it!

Eltham SE9

ELTHAM GRILL HOUSE & FISH BAR, 2–3 Chequers Parade.
Tel: 081 859 0807

Open:	Mon – Sat 11.30 a.m. – 9.00 p.m. (Mon till 3.00 p.m.).
Facilities:	T/A & R (L); T.
Fish finds:	Cod, cod's roe, haddock, plaice, rock, scampi, skate.
Fry:	Groundnut oil.
Side-lines:	Pickled gherkins, pickled onions. Other foods.
Wrapping:	Greaseproof paper.

This tidy outlet has been in the ownership of Kypros Panayl for more than fifteen years, though he's been frying for over thirty years. He serves only fresh fish and names cod as his customers' number one choice. You'll find this fry-house next to Boots the Chemist, in this London suburb 7 miles south-east of London Bridge. If you need to work up an appetite try either Eltham Park or Avery Hill, or visit Eltham Palace with its 15th-century moat bridge and banqueting hall. Mind, they don't serve fish and chips at the Palace 'like wot they does at Eltham Grill'.

Finchley Central N3

CORAL BAY, 1 Station Road. Tel: 081 346 9493

Open: Mon – Sat 11.30 a.m. – 10.30 p.m.

Facilities: T/A & R (L); T; wheelchair access.

Fish finds: Cod, cod's roe, Dover and lemon sole, haddock, halibut, plaice, rock eel, salmon, scampi, skate. Fish and chips to take-and-taste from around £2.30; sit-and-savour around £3.95.

Fry: Groundnut oil.

Side-lines: Pickled gherkins, pickled onions.

Wrapping: Bags, carriers, cones, paper, trays.

Lakis Vryonides heads this family-run operation, established in Finchley a few years ago. It's right on the spot – the underground station, across the road, was put into the history books of every child of the '60s with The Kinks pop group's hit record 'Finchley Central (On the Northern Line)'.
The shop was officially opened by the lovable, late, dear Diana Dors (herself a lover of everything a bit 'naughty and nice' – like fish and chips cooked by Lakis). Enterprising alternative on the menu: fish fried in egg and matzos meal for a few pence extra. Also grilled or poached. The outlet is always sparklingly clean and bright – right down to the plastic-sealed menu cards!

Golders Green NW11

REDFORDS, 126 Golders Green Road. Tel: 081 455 2789

Open: Daily 12.30 a.m. – 2.30 p.m. (till 3.00 p.m. Sun); 5.30 p.m. – 10.00 p.m. (closed Jewish holidays).

Facilities: T/A & R (L, wines & beers); P near; T; wheelchair access.

Fish finds: Cod (fillet and cutlet), Dover and lemon sole, gefielta fish, haddock (fillet and cutlet), halibut, plaice (on and off bone). Fish and chips to take-and-taste from around £3.50; sit-and-savour from about £6.35.

Fry: Pure nut oil.

Side-lines: House specialities, pickled gherkins, pickled onions. Other foods.

Wrapping: Greaseproof, personalized boxes.

I know it doesn't sound too fishy, but you must start with the beetroot soup, followed by plaice, cod or haddock, especially cooked in egg and matzos meal. Find it half a mile from the underground station, in the main shopping area.

Hackney E8

FAULKNER'S, 424 Kingland Road. Tel: 071 254 6152

Open: Mon – Thu midday – 2.00 p.m.; 4.00 p.m. – 10.00 p.m.; Fri & Sat midday – 11.30 p.m.

Facilities: T/A & R (L); P; T; wheelchair friendly.

Fish finds: Cod, Dover and lemon sole, fish cakes (home-made), haddock, plaice (on the bone or fillet), rock salmon, salmon, skate. Fish and chips to take-and-taste from around £2.30; sit-and-savour about £4.80.

Fry: Groundnut oil.

Side-lines: Pickled gherkins, pickled onions. Other foods.

Wrapping: Flat boxes, cartons, white paper, greaseproof bags.

*There are motor cars and then there are Rolls Royces; there are fryers of
food and then there is John Faulkner and his fryer Michael (Mick)
Webber. When he sold his world-famed Sea-Shell in Lisson Grove,
Marylebone, John re-named this sister outlet with his own moniker – and
why not? On first thoughts I had my doubts that the Rollers, Mercedes and
Porsches would follow him to this East End location, but then I realized
not only its closeness to the City of London, but also the extent of the
Docklands developments. He certainly couldn't have got much closer to
Billingsgate before they moved the fish market! But the freshest fish is what
you will always get at an establishment with this name above the door –
with craftsmen fryers making sure it reaches you in the finest way possible.*

Holborn WC1

FRYER'S DELIGHT, 19 Theobalds Road, Tel: 071 405 4114

Open: Mon – Sat midday – 11.00 p.m. (restaurant till
10.00 p.m.).

Facilities: T/A & R.

Fish finds: Cod, cod's roe, haddock, plaice, rock, skate. Fish and
chips to take-and-taste from about £2.00; sit-and-savour
around £2.50.

Fry: Fat.

Side-lines: Pickled gherkins, pickled onions. Other foods.

Wrapping: Greaseproof bags, paper.

*Giovanni Ferdenzi has run this proud chippy in Holborn for well over
twenty years. It sits opposite Holborn Police Station with a Victoria Wine
off-licence next door. The Queen's Head, Dolphin and Entterprise pubs
are also close at hand. He's got seating at five tables of six, each with red
formica tops. The seats are green leatherette covered and the floor black
and white chequered. Wood panels, grey and blue formica and a huge*

mirror make up the wall covering. His press credits vary from London dining publications to the New York Times! If an American tourist wants to sample the original fast food take-away meal, what better place to start than this near-West End traditional outlet? A recent Daily Express article with photographs of Giovanni and his two sons, who work with him, was followed by one son being interviewed about the shop on LBC Radio.

Islington N1

UPPER STREET FISH SHOP, 324 Upper Street. Tel: 071 359 1401

Open:	Mon 5.30 p.m. – 10.00 p.m.; Tue – Sat midday – 2.00 p.m. (Sat till 3.00 p.m.).
Facilities:	T/A & R; T; wheelchair access.
Fish finds:	Cod, Dover sole, haddock, halibut, monkfish, skate (wing and middle). Fish and chips to take-and-taste from around £2.50; sit-and-savour around £5.00. Daily dishes include halibut poached in fresh herb sauce, sea-bass, salmon or lemon sole, and oysters all year.
Fry:	Pure groundnut oil.
Side-lines:	Mushy peas, gherkins, pickled onions. Other foods.
Wrapping:	White paper.

With Olga Conway out front and husband Alan riding the range, there's no getting away from either the quality of the fare or the atmosphere of bustling excitement that permeates at all times. This is something more than a traditional fish café; somehow one would expect bouillabaisse to come as easily as cod or plaice. Home-made desserts like pear and almond tart, jam roly-poly and the scrumptious and beautifully messy treacle tarts make up for it not being licensed: they are their own high! However, if you want to drink you can bring your own bottle, and they don't charge corkage. Seats forty-eight adults, and special children's portions are available.

Marylebone NW1

SEA-SHELL, 49–51 Lisson Grove. Tel: 071 723 8703

Open:	Mon – Fri midday – 2.00 p.m.; 5.00 p.m. – 10.30 p.m.; Sat all day.
Facilities:	T/A & R (L); T.
Fish finds:	Cod, Dover and lemon sole, haddock, halibut, plaice, Cornish rock salmon, salmon cutlets. Fish and chips to take-and-taste from around £2.75; sit-and-savour around £5.70.
Fry:	Groundnut oil.
Side-lines:	Pickled onions. Other foods.
Wrapping:	Flat boxes, cartons, double greaseproof bags, white wrap.

Mecca Leisure now own this famous chippy which was founded by John Faulkner. The standard is good. You're not just paying for London's smartest chippy outlet, the quality of fresh fish and the pleasant and efficient service, but also to rub shoulders with celebrities and royalty who often appear in the queue. At the moment it is still to the nation's chip shops what Mark Birley's Annabel's is to clubland.

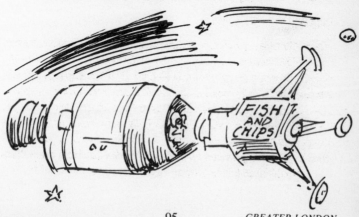

Mill Hill NW7

LA CARPA D'ORO, 40 The Broadway, Mill Hill.
Tel: 081 906 3494/ 081 959 3924

Open:	Tue – Sat 11.30 a.m. – 2.30 p.m.; 5.30 p.m. – 11.00 p.m.
Facilities:	T/A & R; P (street); T; wheelchair access.
Fish finds:	Cod, Dover and lemon sole, haddock, hake, halibut, king prawns, plaice, rock salmon, scampi, trout. Fish and chips to take-and-taste from around £2.90; sit-and-savour about £6.50.
Fry:	Groundnut oil.
Side-lines:	Pickled gherkins, pickled onions. Other foods.
Wrapping:	Polystyrene trays, boxes.

This outlet, with immaculate decor and pleasant service, was set up over six years ago. It's situated about 100 yd from the Mill Hill roundabout on the left-hand side opposite the National Westminster Bank. To satisfy the various ethnic and religious groups resident in the area, they cook to the customers' choice in either matzos meal, batter or on the griddle. This means that only fresh fish is cooked, to order, and the highest standards are maintained. Franca and Luigi 'Pronto!!' Torlini have been in charge of the range from the start.

Muswell Hill N10

TOFF'S OF MUSWELL HILL, 38 Muswell Hill Broadway.
Tel: 081 883 8656

Open:	Tue 10.30 a.m. – 10.30 p.m.; Wed – Sat 11.30 a.m. – 10.30 p.m.

Facilities:	T/A & R (L); T; P; wheelchair access.
Fish finds:	Cod, Dover and lemon sole, haddock, hake, halibut, plaice, rock, salmon, sea bass, skate, trout. Fish and chips to take-and-taste from around £2.90; sit-and-savour around £5.25.
Fry:	Groundnut oil.
Side-lines:	Pickled onions.
Wrapping:	Cartons, paper bags.

You don't need to be a Toff to enter Andreas Toffalli's immaculate north London establishment – but you'll sure as anything feel like a Toff when you've devoured his fine fare! This fine fish emporium only opened its doors in June 1988, but within a few months had attracted the attention of the Sea Fish Industry Authority, who voted it the best fish and chip shop in Great Britain for 1988/89. Not bad going, Sir. Not that Andreas is new to the trade in any way – hardly: he's been frying since he left school in 1955! After thirty-five years he sure has got it right – as the queues of faithful customers demonstrate.

Notting Hill Gate W8

GEALE'S FISH RESTAURANT, 2 Farmer Street. Tel: 071 727 7969

Open:	Tue – Sat midday – 3.00 p.m.; 6.00 p.m. – 11.00 p.m. (Closed Tue after Bank Holidays, 5 days at Easter, 3 weeks in August and 2 weeks at Christmas.)
Facilities:	R (L); T; wheelchair access.
Fish finds:	Cod, Dover and lemon sole, fried clams, haddock, halibut, plaice, rock, skate, shark. Fish and chips from around £5.50; take-away by arrangement only.

Fry: Fish in fat, chips in oil.

Side-lines: Mushy peas, pickled gherkins, pickled onions.

Christopher Geale has now disposed of the Hillgate Street fetch-and-carry listed in my original 1966 guide. The restaurant, with its brown exterior paintwork and tree-shrubs in pots by the door, is found more easily on foot. Take the cut through from the Bayswater Road by the Gate Cinema (formerly the Classic). The place has changed little in the half-century the family have been trading, and has justly built up its reputation as a respectable dining room in which to devour our favourite food. More like an Olde-English-Tea-Shoppe than a fish fryer's establishment, with its lace curtains and primrose-coloured table-cloths. This 'granny' of fish houses is just the place for a lingering meal with an elderly relative. The wine list offers plenty of variety, from inexpensive champagne to beers supplied by the Henley Brewery. The world will be a better place if the next half-century sees Geales remain the same as it has been, and is today.

Peckham SE15

BERT'S PIE & EEL SHOP, 3 Peckham Park Road. Tel: 071 639 4598

Open: Mon 5.00 p.m. – 6.45 p.m.; Tue – Sat 11.30 a.m. – 1.45 p.m.; 5.00 p.m. – 6.45 p.m.

Facilities: T/A & R.

Fish finds: Jellied eels, pie and mash, stewed eels. Pie and mash around 75p; jellied eels 80p.

Wrapping: Insulated cartons, paper bags, white paper.

Any true Londoner – if you can find one – will tell you, there's nothing quite like a plate of jellied eels, or pie and mash with green liquor. And if you're looking for a true Londoner, then you're more likely to find one in the Old Kent Road than most other places, and that's where you'll also find Bert's – opposite North Peckham Civic Centre – on the corner of Peckham Park Road. And in case you're wondering, yes, an eel is as much a fish as any other. As Eastenders' Ma Beale would have said: 'I'm not 'avin' any argument, that's as far as it goes. That's ya lot.' After all, Bert's has been there for fifty years serving costermongers and tourists alike – though the Pearlies are getting thin on the ground! It's run by Mrs L.M. Allard, Mr C.A. Allard and Miss E.A. Allard.

Piccadilly W1

BESHOFF'S, Unit 17, Trocadero Centre.
Tel: 071 287 4863

Open:	Mon – Wed, Sun midday – midnight; Thu – Sat midday – 4.00 a.m.
Facilities:	T/A & R (L); T; wheelchair access.
Fish finds:	Cod, Dover and lemon sole, haddock, plaice, skate, turbot and more. (Fish of your choice can be grilled or deep fried.) Fish and chips to take-and-taste from around £2.30; sit-and-savour around £4.85.
Fry:	Groundnut oil.
Side-lines:	Range of sauces.
Wrapping:	Boxes, double bags.

Beshoff's have a long established outlet in Dublin's fair city and now one in London, 100 yd from Piccadilly, a kipper's throw from Leicester Square. The Grand Opening in January 1990, was performed by the Irish political potentate Charles Haughey. Viscount Linley and others from the caviar and cod set attended. If you can take your eyes off the antiques and the ritzy fittings which simulate an Edwardian oyster bar, get stuck into the fine fish that's on offer. The kids will enjoy it too. Great place for theatre-goers, avant et après.

Putney SW15

ROCK 'N' ROE, 281 Putney Bridge Road. Tel: 081 788 5618

Open: Mon – Fri 11.30 a.m. – 2.30 p.m.; 5.00 p.m. – midnight;
              Sat 11.30 a.m. – midnight.

Facilities: T/A & R (L); P near; T.

Fish finds: Cod, crab sticks, haddock, plaice, rock, scampi, skate.
              Fish and chips to take-and-taste from around £2.05;
              sit-and-savour around £2.30.

Fry: Groundnut oil.

Side-lines: Mushy peas, pickled gherkins, pickled onions. Other
              foods.

Wrapping: Traditional paper and bags.

*The Hinton family have been in the frying business for over thirty years.
Brother Robert, known as Captain Bob to his customers, runs a similarly-
named outlet in New Malden. He is known to burst into serenade while he
fries. No reports of similar waftings from this end of town – though Jan
and Fred Evans sing the praises of the fare loud and clear. The decor is
suitably nautical, with fishing nets, oak beams and brown and white
plaster. There is a 16-seater restaurant, to which you can bring your own
bottle from the nearby Peter Dominic if you wish, and they'll even supply
the glasses. Alternatively, the Castle pub is close at hand.*

Queen's Park NW6

MERRYWEATHERS, 51 Salisbury Road. Tel: 071 624 3555

Open: Mon – Sat 11.30 a.m. – midnight; Sun midday –
              8.00 p.m.

Facilities:	T/A & R (L wine & beer); P; T; wheelchair access.
Fish finds:	Cod, haddock, plaice, rock, skate. Fish and chips to take-and-taste from around £2.10; sit-and-savour around £3.25.
Fry:	Groundnut oil.
Side-lines:	Mushy peas, pickled onions. Other foods.
Wrapping:	Cartons, paper bags.

There are those who eat Britain's favourite take-away from choice, those who eat it as the cheapest, most nourishing cooked meal available, and those who do so for both. Add that extra piece of something special, a decor that is not only spotless but also interesting and pleasing to the eye, and you are getting close to the Merryweathers experience. They bought this outlet from Associated Fisheries several years ago, and put Michael Upton in charge with his wife alongside. It's in the middle of bed-sitter-land, opposite Queen's Park railway station. With plenty of alternative take-away outlets available to the resident and more movable population, it's quality, quantity and cost that draw the queues to this fine outlet.

Soho W1

GRAHAMES, 38 Poland Street. Tel: 071 437 3788/0975

Open:	Mon – Sat midday – 2.45 p.m.; Tue – Sat 5.30 p.m. – 8.30 p.m. (Fri & Sat till 8.30 p.m.).
Facilities:	R (L) (some take-outs allowed, on plates); P near; T.
Fish finds:	Haddock, halibut, plaice, sole. Fish and chips to sit-and-savour around £3.25.
Fry:	Groundnut oil.

Side-lines: Pickled gherkins. Other foods.

Speciality: Gefielta fish.

Every time I visit this very Jewish establishment, now owned by Mecca Leisure, it's as though I am caught in a very pleasant time-warp. For thirty years one of the nicest of Soho fish restaurants has been serving up the best gefielta fish money can buy. Not only to the kosher community prominent in the nearby rag-trade and movie businesses, but to many of the faith, and otherwise, in the theatrical profession – like the stars of the nearby London Palladium. Take my advice, it's as well to book, and enjoy, already!

Victoria SW1

SEAFRESH FISH RESTAURANT, 80–81 Wilton Road. Tel: 071 828 0747

Open: Mon – Sat midday – 10.45 p.m.

Facilities: T/A & R (L); P street; T; wheelchair access.

Fish finds: Cod, haddock, kalamari, king prawn, plaice, rock, scampi, seafood plate, skate, sole. Fish and chips to take-and-taste from around £2.95; sit-and-savour around £4.95 (any fish grilled about £1.00 extra).

Fry: Groundnut oil.

Side-lines: Pickled gherkins, pickled onions. Other foods.

Wrapping: Greaseproof paper, white paper, own bags.

If you want a good meal ask a London cabby to take you to a good chippy and, like as not, he'll bring you here, and charge you – even though he was heading this way for his own dinner! This haunt of taxi-drivers and toffs, schoolboys and housewives, office workers and executives retains its reputation as one of the best in central London, even after nearly a quarter of a century. The restaurant and take-away, fine fish and first rate service make you feel like royalty, (Buckingham Palace is just up the road), and the ample portions are fit for any Royal. If you are struggling to see your plate clear, don't be shy, ask for a 'pet bag', and I'm sure they'll oblige. An ideal spot for the tourist to witness a modern example of what a true chip shop is all about – but don't expect to be treated any differently to the rest of us: take your place in the queue! Seating for eighty in the diner.

West Hampstead NW6

NAUTILUS FISH RESTAURANT, 27–29 Fortune Green Road. Tel: 071 435 2532

Open:	Mon – Sat 11.30 a.m. – 2.30 p.m.; 5.00 p.m. – 10.30 p.m.
Facilities:	T/A & R (L); P near; T.
Fish finds:	Cod, Dover and lemon sole, haddock, halibut, hake, plaice, salmon, skate, trout. Fish and chips to take-and-taste from around £2.50; sit-and-savour around £5.00.
Fry:	Groundnut oil.
Side-lines:	Pickled gherkins, pickled onions. Other foods.
Wrapping:	White paper sheets.

D.A. Peratikou's place must fry kosher, because he assures me most of his customers are 'of the Faith'. One thing's for sure, the place has always been spotless every time I have visited over the nearly fifteen years he has run it. And for another, the fare is always 'just right' with piping hot, fresh chips and really crisp, lightly battered fish. If things had not been so, I'm sure someone from West Hampstead Police Station, right next door, would have noticed! The Prince of Wales pub is quite close and, for take-home fans, an Unwins off-licence is just yards from the Nautilus. As Mrs N. Brooks says so aptly in her recommendation, 'Enjoy! Enjoy!' We have, already, Mrs Brooks!

GREATER MANCHESTER
Altrincham

COSTAS FISH & CHIPS, 35 Hale Road. Tel: 061 928 0400

Open:　　　　Mon – Sat 11.30 a.m. – 2.00 p.m.; 4.30 p.m. – midnight.

Facilities:　　T/A; P; T.

Fish finds:　　Cod, haddock, plaice. Fish and chips to take-and-taste from around £1.30.

Fry:　　　　Fat.

Side-lines:　　Mushy peas, pickled onions. Other foods.

Wrapping:　　Greaseproof, white news and trays.

Costa Shengas has been running this main road outlet since the mid-1970s. The shop is fully tiled in white and beige with the floors in brown terrazzo, offset with palm plants. Looking for a drink? Mag's, also in Hale Road, is the nearest off-licence and the Tatton in Tipping Street is the local pub.

THE DON SUPPER BAR, 3 Church Street. Tel: 061 928 4300

Open:　　　　Mon – Fri 11.30 a.m. – 2.00 p.m.; Mon – Wed 5.00 p.m. – 11.30 p.m.; Sat 11.30 a.m. – 2.00 p.m.; 5.00 p.m. – midnight.

Facilities:　　T/A & R; P near; T.

Fish finds:　　Cod, haddock, plaice. Fish and chips to take-and-taste from around £1.30; sit-and-savour around £1.50.

Fry:　　　　100 per cent vegetable fat.

Side-lines: Mushy peas, pickled onions. Other foods.

Wrapping: Greaseproof, white news and carrier bags.

Mr Harris prides himself in the traditional style of his chippy. It's been there for over sixty years, and the building itself dates back to 1760. The Tudor exterior leads into a modernized take-away section with a tropical fish tank as the focal point. He only uses top quality, fresh produce – hence the 'fish-of-the-week' approach. The restaurant, seating fifty, is carpeted and the decor is kept to the Tudor style. A quiet, friendly place to enjoy top class fish and chips that don't look as though they have seen fat – but have all the succulent taste that assure you they have. Just right. It's to be found on the main Manchester Road, about a quarter of a mile from the Cresta Court Hotel.

Bolton

CHARLIE'S CHIPS, 121 Lee Gate, Harwood. Tel: 0204 55536

Open: Mon – Sat 11.30 a.m. – 2.00 p.m.; Mon – Wed 5.00 p.m.
            – midnight.; Thu – Sat 4.15 p.m. – midnight; Sun
            8.00 p.m. – midnight.

Facilities: T/A; P.

Fish finds: Cod, plaice. Fish and chips to take-and-taste around
            £1.35.

Fry: Vegetable oil.

Side-lines: Mushy peas.

Wrapping: Paper or trays with bags or cones for chips.

*Charles Cummins moved his business to this location only last year, but he
has all the fast food entrepreneurial ideas to go from strength to strength –
right down to his wrapping, which is specially printed: 'Enjoy fish and
chips, the original fast food take-away.' The contents live up to the
promotion, which is more than can be said for most fast foods. You have a
nice day, you hear Charles! The decor of his outlet is red and white,
designed it would appear with the potential to franchise on to other outlets.
He really has worked hard to compete with the big boys – and derserves to
win the Seven Stars. Sorry, that's the name of the nearest pub! But he did
win the Sea Fish Industry 'North West England Fish and Chip Shop of the
Year' award last year, and came second in the Daloon championship 1989
as well. He's making so many waves that even the* Financial Times *wrote
about him recently!*

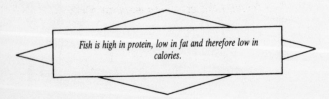

Fish is high in protein, low in fat and therefore low in
calories.

Cheadle Hulme

WHITTAKER'S FISH BAR, 61 Station Road. Tel: 061 485 2206

Open:	Mon & Tue 11.30 a.m. – 2.00 p.m.; 7.30 p.m. – 11.00 p.m.; Wed – Fri 11.30 a.m. – 2.00 p.m.; 4.45 p.m. – 11.00 p.m.; Sat 11.30 a.m. – 2.00 p.m.; 7.00 p.m. – 11.00 p.m.
Facilities:	T/A & R; P near; T – with permission.
Fish finds:	Cod, haddock, plaice, scampi. Fish and chips to take-and-taste from around £1.55; sit-and-savour around £2.10.
Fry:	Vegetable oil.
Side-lines:	Mushy peas, pickled onions. Other foods.
Speciality:	Pineapple fritters.
Wrapping:	White bags, white news.

Certainly a big 'E' for effort for this one – in every department. The shop is spotless, bright and cheerful; the fish is only ever fresh with crispy batter and firm, dry chips as well; and the staff are efficient, bright and pretty in their blue caps and smocks over white tunics. Should the staff forget their purpose, for even one second, proprietor Len Young has a big sign on the wall reminding them: THE CUSTOMER. Nice one, and worthy of all the things Viola Eaton gives as reasons why she travels from Stockport regularly. You'll find them opposite the shopping centre with the Junction Inn close by. You could rub shoulders with show-biz celebrities, the odd jazz player popping in for a trombone and chips – and not forgetting all the American tourists and me. Great plaice!

Manchester

BURNS FISH RESTAURANT, 12 Warburton Street, Didsbury. Tel: 061 434 0538

Open:	Tue – Sun midday – 2.00 p.m.; 5.30 p.m. – 10.30 p.m.
Facilities:	R (L); P in front; T; wheelchair friendly.
Fish finds:	Cod, haddock, silver hake, halibut, lemon sole, lobster and other shellfish, plaice on the bone, scampi. Fish and chips to sit-and-savour from around £5.50.
Fry:	Vegetable oil.
Side-lines:	Mushy peas, pickled gherkins, pickled onions. Other foods.
Children:	Welcome if they are well behaved (early evening only).

For years London has had its Geales and Grahames. A couple of years ago south Wales got Mulligans. I now predict they will be adding Burns to the list of fish restaurants with that extra something. A glance at the decor and you could be mistaken in thinking you were in the revered halls of Simpson's in the Strand, or the like, with its decades of history and sophisticated ambiance. Floor-to-ceiling mahogany panelling and matching fittings, similar tables and powder-blue seated dining chairs with matching napkins. The final touch – candles in 'Wee-Willie-Winkie' style sticks, on each table. Colin Burn and his team obviously put a lot of thought into his highly successful frying operation, right down to the cleverly designed menu. The Management are always on hand to meet you, be you a simple fish like you and me, or a super sole like Bobby Charlton, Sir Matt Busby, Stuart Hall or other celebrities who have sat and savoured here.
Recommended by Roxanne Garnham.

MARIO'S FISH BAR, 2–6 Southway, Eccles Precinct. Tel: 061 789 1602

Open:	Mon – Sat 9.00 a.m. – 6.00 p.m. (café & dining room); 11.00 a.m. – 7.00 p.m. (take-away).

Facilities:	T/A & R; P near; T.
Fish finds:	Cod, plaice. Fish and chips to take-and-taste from around £1.25; sit-and-savour around £1.60.
Fry:	100 per cent vegetable oil.
Side-lines:	Mushy peas. Other foods.
Wrapping:	Greaseproof, trays.

Mario Paphitis has really gone to Town (not the Town Hall pub nearby) with the decor of his triple-unit outlet. The floors are terrazzo-tiled, the walls mahogany-panelled and from the ceiling hang four chandeliers with matching wall lights. Add illuminated signs and background music in the 68-cover, air-conditioned restaurant and it's difficult to imagine what more you could want – with the knowledge that the fare is fine and the service splendid. No wonder he's been trading for twenty years.

Middleton

THOMPSON'S, 31 Manchester New Road. Tel: 061 643 4831

Open:	Mon – Sat 11.00 a.m. – 3.00 p.m.; 4.15 p.m. – midnight (Tue half-day).
Facilities:	T/A & R; P; T.
Fish finds:	Cod, haddock, plaice. Fish and chips to take-and-taste from around £1.20; sit-and-savour around £1.35.
Fry:	Own recipe.
Side-lines:	Mushy peas. Other foods.
Wrapping:	Greaseproof and outer wrap.

In days of yore, Middleton was famous for its silk and cotton factories and calico printing works. These days the yarns are spun by customers waiting in the queue at T.W. Thompson's establishment. In the nearly forty years he's been frying, he's heard many a tale from customers in this town centre establishment. The outlet is fully modernized both with equipment and the latest seating for about eighty, and spotlessly clean.

Oldham

**BUTTERWORTH'S FISH AND CHIPS, 104–106 Union Street.
Tel: 061 624 4402**

Open: Mon – Wed 11.00 a.m. – 2.00 p.m.; Thu 11.00 a.m. – 2.00 p.m.; 4.00 p.m. – 6.30 p.m.; Fri 11.00 a.m. – 2.00 p.m.; 4.00 p.m. – 7.00 p.m.; Sat 11.00 a.m. – 2.00 p.m.; 4.00 p.m. – 6.30 p.m.

Facilities: T/A & café; P; T; wheelchair access.

Fish finds: Cod. Fish and chips to take-and-taste from around £1.50; sit-and-savour from £1.70.

Fry: Vegetable oil.

Side-lines: Mushy peas. Other foods.

Wrapping: Polystyrene containers.

This year Harry and Olga Butterworth's grand establishment on Union Street will celebrate its fortieth anniversary. Many chippies have celebrities visiting them – including, at this one, most members of Oldham Rep, and many Coronation Street cast members – but how many have been featured on television themselves? Stuart Hall made a thorough investigation of the establishment and fare for Granada's 'Look North' programme. The result? Try it yourself, as humourist Mike O'Connor does regularly, and you will be sure not to be disappointed. Bring all your friends – ample seating for 100 people in the friendly diner.

MERRYWEATHERS MOTHER HUBBARD'S, 270 Manchester Street.
Tel: 061 652 0873

Open:	Sun – Thu midday – 10.30 p.m. (Fri & Sat till 11.30 p.m.).
Facilities:	T/A & R (L); P 100 cars; T; wheelchair access.
Fish finds:	Cod, haddock, huss, plaice, scampi, skate. Fish and chips to take-and-taste from around £1.90; sit-and-savour restaurant special around £4.00.
Fry:	Groundnut oil.
Side-lines:	Pickled gherkins, pickled onions. Other foods.
Wrapping:	Cartons, paper bags.

I wonder if Mother Hubbard would expect a telegram from the Queen if she were around today. However, the Oldham eaterie named after the fabled lady should be celebrating in grand style this year – for it first opened its doors to fish and chip fanatics one hundred years ago this year! Not long ago it became one of the northern jewels in the Merryweather empire of fried-fish emporia, bought from Associated Fisheries. Mother Hubbard, so the tale goes, was more polite to her dog. Not so at this fine fry-house. It's service par excellence. Mother Hubbard's is a 200-seater restaurant and employs no less than seventy personnel! With a name like this, of course children's parties are welcomed, as are coaches – with ample room to park. Special businessmen's lunches are also catered for.

Sale

CONWAY SUPPER BAR, 387 Washway Road.
Tel: 061 962 5362

Open:	Mon – Sat 11.30 – 2.00 p.m.; 4.30 p.m. – midnight. Sun 6.00 p.m. – midnight.

Facilities:	T/A; P near.
Fish finds:	Cod, haddock, plaice, whiting. Fish and chips to take-and-taste from around £1.20.
Fry:	Vegetable fat.
Side-lines:	Mushy peas. Other foods.
Wrapping:	Paper and boxes.

Since boundary changes became the fashion a few years ago, Sale is now a part of Greater Manchester. Just as long as we don't mistake it for the gold mining centre in Australia called Sale, but Mr Scruton's fish batter is certainly golden coloured, crisp and tasty. You'll find this traditional fish shop with its 16-seater diner on the Manchester side of the Pelican Hotel.

Winston Churchill referred to the 'Happy Couple' of fish and chips as 'Good Companions'.

Stockport

CHAMPION CHIP BAR, 167 Wellington Road South. Tel: 061 429 7101

Open:	Mon – Fri 11.30 a.m. – 2.30 p.m.; 4.30 p.m. – 7.30 p.m.; Sat 11.30 a.m. – 2.00 p.m.
Facilities:	T/A & R; T.
Fish finds:	Cod, haddock, plaice. Fish and chips to take-and-taste from around £1.30; sit-and-savour around £1.65.
Fry:	Oil.
Side-lines:	Mushy peas. Other foods.
Wrapping:	Trays, paper.

Mr Nicky McArdle and team ride the range and have built up a strong following and reputation for a reasonably-priced meal of excellent quality fresh fish at this establishment. You'll find them frying opposite Stockport Technical College about half a mile from Stockport town centre towards Buxton. Other foods are cooked, but not to the detriment of the most popular dish: fish and chips. Nicky is proud of his new 30-seater diner.

FRYERY, 452 Didsbury Road, Heaton Mersey. Tel: 061 432 1683

Open:	Mon – Sat 11.30 a.m. – 1.30 p.m. (Sat till 2.00 p.m.); 4.30 p.m. – 11.30 p.m. (Fri & Sat till midnight).
Facilities:	T/A; P.
Fish Finds:	Cod, haddock, plaice, scampi. Fish and chips to take-and-taste around £1.35.
Fry:	Palm oil.
Side-lines:	Mushy peas. Other foods.
Wrapping:	White news, bags.

This outlet forms part of the local conservation area and is run by David Steers, who's been here for fifteen years. The decor is in warm colours with terrazzo-tiled floor. The nearest pub is the Railway Inn a short way up the road, though for blue-blooded mortals, there is the Conservative Club next door.

Wigan

LITTLE CHIPPY, 543 Atherton Road, Hindley Green. Tel: 0942 55066

Open:	Mon 11.30 a.m. – 1.15 p.m.; Tue – Thu 11.30 a.m. – 1.15 p.m.; 4.15 p.m. – 6.15 p.m.; Fri 11.30 a.m. – 1.15 p.m.; 4.00 p.m. – 10.00 p.m.; Sat 11.30 a.m. – 1.15 p.m.; 4.15 p.m. – 6.15 p.m.

Facilities:	T/A; P; T; wheelchair access.
Fish finds:	Cod, haddock, plaice, whiting. Fish and chips to take-and-taste from around £1.30.
Fry:	Vegetable fat.
Side-lines:	Mushy peas. Other foods.
Wrapping:	Boxes, greaseproof, white news.

George Ernest Hinchcliffe's (Hinchy's) establishment has been frying for over seventy years. How long he's been there, on the corner of Long Lane, is another matter! Eighteen years, actually. He prides himself he could back his product, selling much cheaper, against any of the big names in the fast food industry. My guess is he'd win hands down, not only on product, but on friendly service as well. Actually, I think he's just looking to win the bet to pay for the recent refurbishment of his shop – which has always been clean and tidy. Good try, but no bet sir! You'll just have to stop wrapping chips in £5.00 notes! He says he's stopped – and still managed to instal a new Henry Nuttall range!

HAMPSHIRE
Alton

ALTON FISH BAR, 51 High Street. Tel: 0420 82225

Open:	Mon – Sat 11.30 a.m. – 2.00 p.m.; 4.30 p.m. – 11.00 p.m.; Sun 5.00 p.m. – 10.00 p.m.
Facilities:	T/A.
Fish finds:	Cod, haddock, rock, roe, plaice, scampi, skate. Fish and chips to take-and-taste from around £1.65.
Fry:	Oil.

Side-lines:	Pickled gherkins, pickled onions. Other foods.
Wrapping:	Paper, trays, bags.

No day out to Jane Austen's house at nearby Chawton or the Oates Memorial and Gilbert White Museum at Selborne would be complete without dining out on the superb fare served up at this fine, clean chippy. The outlet has been trading no less than forty years, going back to the time when the town was famous for ale and was the centre of the hop-growing business. There's also the interesting perpendicular church of St Lawrence which was restored in 1867. All in all, good things to see and good things to eat.

Andover

FRESH FRY, 11 Winchester Street. Tel: 0264 61025

Open:	Tue & Wed 11.30 a.m. – 1.45 p.m.; 5.00 p.m. – 10.00 p.m.; Thu 11.30 a.m. – 10.00 p.m.; Fri 11.30 a.m. – 2.00 p.m.; 5.00 p.m. – 10.00 p.m.; Sat 11.30 a.m. – 8.00 p.m.
Facilities:	T/A & R; P near; T; wheelchair friendly.
Fish finds:	Cod, haddock, plaice, rock. Fish and chips to take-and-taste from around £1.50; sit-and-savour around £1.85.
Fry:	Palm oil.
Side-lines:	Mushy peas, pickled gherkins, pickled onions. Other foods.
Wrapping:	Trays, greaseproof, white paper.

Go and do a bit of shopping at the open market, and have a quick drink at the Lamb public house before joining the queue at the fresh fry for a take-and-taste. Better still take a seat in the 20-seater-diner and enjoy a super plate of mouthwatering fish and chips with mushy peas.

Brockenhurst

RAINBOW FISH BAR, 30 Brookley Road. Tel: 0590 22747

Open:	Mon – Sat midday – 2.00 p.m.; Sat 5.00 p.m. – 10.00 p.m.; Sun (summer only) 5.00 p.m. – 10.00 p.m.
Facilities:	T/A; P; wheelchair access.
Fish finds:	Cod, cod's roe, haddock, plaice, scampi. Fish and chips to take-and-taste from around £1.75.
Fry:	100 per cent vegetable fat.
Side-lines:	Pickled gherkins, pickled onions. Other foods.
Wrapping:	Top quality bags.

Alan Beardsmore's family have been running this outlet for about six years, though the shop has been open for about ten. It is designed in an open-plan style, with the walls tiled from floor to ceiling. The overall impression is one of freshness and cleanliness. Their constant vigilance is on efficiency and reviewing their menu – they are currently including various vegetarian dishes. You'll find them near the Midland Bank on the main road.

Burlsedon (Nr Southampton)

CRISPINS, Hamble Lane. Tel: 042121 2824

Open:	Mon – Sat 11.45 a.m. – 1.45 p.m.; 5.00 p.m. – 11.00 p.m. (opens Fri 4.30 p.m.).
Facilities:	T/A; P near; wheelchair friendly (one step).

Fish finds: Cod, haddock, plaice. Fish and chips to take-and-taste from around £1.50.

Fry: Vegetable oil.

Side-lines: Pea fritters, pickled onions.

Wrapping: Greaseproof, bags.

Established over thirty years ago, Mr Downie is in charge of this 'top shop', taking in cleanliness, taste, presentation and sales. It's near the Tesco's store, close to the Portsmouth road, and well worth a visit. Then pop down to the Hamble river and sail your old canoe.

HAMPSHIRE

Drayton

CRISPINS, 161 Havant Road. Tel: 0705 76669

Open:	Mon – Wed, 11.30 a.m. – 2.00 p.m.; 5.00 p.m. – 10.30 p.m.; Thu – Sat 11.30 a.m. – 2.00 p.m.; 5.00 p.m. – 11.00 p.m.
Facilities:	T/A; P near; wheelchair friendly.
Fish finds:	Cod, haddock, plaice. Fish and chips to take-and-taste from around £1.50.
Fry:	Palm oil.
Side-lines:	Pickled onions. Other foods.
Wrapping:	Trays, white paper, greaseproof, bags.

About 2 miles from Portsmouth, you will find a little place called Drayton on the Havant Road, where you will find a nice little chippy selling really good fish and chips. A goodly portion of haddock and chips will cost around £1.50. Try some.

Emsworth

GOOD TASTE, 1 The Grove, Westbourne. Tel: 0243 372811

Open:	Tue & Wed 5.00 p.m. – 9.00 p.m.; Thur 11.30 a.m. – 1.30 p.m.; 5.00 p.m. – 9.00 p.m.; Fri 11.30 a.m. – 1.30 p.m.; 5.00 p.m. – 9.30 p.m.; Sat 11.30 a.m. – 1.30 p.m.; 5.00 p.m. – 8.00 p.m.
Facilities:	T/A; P near.
Fish finds:	Cod, haddock, huss, plaice. Fish and chips to take-and-taste from around £1.80.
Fry:	Oil.

Side-lines: Pickled onions.

Wrapping: White paper.

It's around thirteen years – lucky for some – since Jim Clarke took on this trade, and he's built quite a reputation in the area during this time. All fish is bought fresh, and the haddock and plaice can also be fried in breadcrumbs. You'll find Good Taste in the village square next to the White Horse pub in this seaport at the mouth of the Ems.

Fareham

HIGHLAND FISHERIES, 10 Fareham Park Road. Tel: 0329 42169

Open: Mon midday – 1.30 p.m.; Tue – Sat 11.30 a.m. – 2.00 p.m.

Facilities: T/A; P (street).

Fish finds: Cod, eel, haddock, plaice, skate. Fish and chips to take-and-taste from around £1.65.

Fry: Red Box oil.

Side-lines: Mushy peas, pickled gherkins, pickled onions. Other foods.

Wrapping: Greaseproof, white paper.

Perhaps it's because the shop is situated just off the Highlands Road, by the Post Office, that proprietors Mr and Mrs Moore count haggis as a 'regional speciality'! 'Hi Hi a haggis fry.' Anyway, he does an excellent fry, whatever! The shop is good for paint in and out, clean and friendly. The Highlands is also the name of the nearest pub. J. Martup recommends this outlet.

Farnborough

ELITE FISHERIES, 61 Cove Road, Cove. Tel: 0252 541742

Open:	Tue – Fri 11.45 a.m. – 2.00 p.m.; Tue & Wed 5.30 p.m. – 10.00 p.m; Thu & Fri 5.00 p.m. – 10.30 p.m.; Sat 11.30 a.m. – 9.30 p.m.
Facilities:	T/A; P (street).
Fish finds:	Cod, haddock, plaice, rock, skate. Fish and chips to take-and-taste from around £1.60.
Fry:	Vegetable oil.
Side-lines:	Mushy peas, pickled gherkins, pickled onions.
Wrapping:	Paper, bags.

This traditional Martin Collins' family chippy has been trading from between the Methodist church and the Tradesman's Arms for over forty years. Much is known about the Royal Aircraft Factory and aerodrome on Farnborough Common, and of course the famous air show. Less well remembered is that the remains of Napoleon III, the Prince Imperial and the Empress Eugenie are in a mausoleum in St Michael's Roman Catholic church in the town. Just the sort of thing to discuss while you're tucking in to a tasty take-away from the Elite.

Gosport

VILLAGE FISH BAR, 13 Little Lane, Alverstone. Tel: 0705 580766

Open:	Tue – Sat 11.30 a.m. – 1.30 p.m.; 5.00 p.m. – 9.00 p.m. (Sat till 7.30 p.m.).
Facilities:	T/A.
Fish finds:	Cod, haddock, plaice, rock eel, skate. Fish and chips to take-and-taste from around £1.40.

Fry:	Vegetable oil.
Side-lines:	Mushy peas, pickled eggs, pickled onions. Other foods.
Wrapping:	White off-cuts, greaseproof.

Though Susan and Bill Bridgeman have been running this traditional take-away, near St Mary's church at the junction of Church Road, for just under a decade, they've collected a large band of faithful followers. It must have something to do with the excellent value tasty fare consistently available here. The recommendations came in thick and fast: G.M. Gosley, Mrs Sarah Powlesland, Mr P. Martin (who even sent the Ordnance Survey Map reference): and Keith Hallam, the Tourism and Marketing Officer for the Borough of Gosport, all wrote. Yes folks, we heard you all – you all think the Bridgeman's shop is great! Who are we to argue?

Hartley Wintney

MARINERS, The Row, High Street. Tel: 025 126 2273

Open:	Mon (Bank Holidays only), Tue, Sat 11.30 a.m. – 2.00 p.m.; 5.00 p.m. – 10.00 p.m.
Facilities:	T/A & R (L); P near; T.
Fish finds:	Cod, haddock, lemon sole, plaice, rock, skate. Fish and chips to take-and-taste from about £1.70; sit-and-savour around £3.75.
Fry:	Groundnut oil.
Side-lines:	Pickled gherkins, pickled onions. Other foods.
Wrapping:	Paper tray, paper.

You see what happens when people with vision take over a simple village chippy? Martin Bourcier and Simon Butts took a long look at their trade, a deep breath, and built on an up-market fish restaurant seating just eighteen people. Then they took another breath and built on space for another sixteen and they're still bursting at the seams with custom. As they say, they offer the best product available, but where they score particularly is in presentation and style. Now customers travel from miles around to this picturesque village, just for a meal of good fish and chips. As well as the traditional fry the duo also serves steamed fish in various sauces with fresh croquette potatoes. Having said all this, don't let it detract from the take-away, where the standard is equally high. Clientele ranges from families (special children's meals) to antique dealers visiting the nearby shops, to local councillors and even other restaurant owners on busmen's holidays. They obviously know a good thing!

Lymington

CRISPINS, 130 High Street. Tel: 0590 677850

Open:	Daily 11.00 a.m. – 11.00 p.m. (summer); 11.30 a.m. – 2.00 p.m.; 4.30 p.m. – 10.00 p.m. (winter).
Facilities:	T/A & R; P near; T.
Fish finds:	Cod, haddock, halibut (restaurant only), plaice, scampi. Fish and chips to take-and-taste from around £1.50; sit-and-savour around £2.45.
Fry:	Vegetable oil.
Side-lines:	Fish cakes, pea and pineapple fritters, pickled onions. Other foods.
Wrapping:	White paper, trays, paper bags.

This seaport chippy has been trading for over thirty years. You'll find it easily at the bottom of the Masonic Hall. You won't be disappointed with the standard of fare served to their discerning clientele, which includes many yachtsmen and fishermen who know a thing or two about what comes out of the water! You can sit and swap stories with the locals in their comfortable 42-seater diner.

Portsmouth

CHURCHILL'S FISH BAR, 13 London Road, North End.
Tel: 0705 690123

Open: Mon – Fri 11.30 a.m. – 2.00 p.m.; Mon 5.00 p.m. – 8.30 p.m.; Tue & Wed 4.45 p.m. – 8.30 p.m.; Thu & Fri 4.45 p.m. – 9.00 p.m.; Sat 11.30 a.m. – 7.30 p.m.

Facilities: T/A & R; P near; T (emergencies only!); wheelchair access.

Fish finds: Cod, dogfish, haddock, plaice, scampi. Fish and chips to take-and-taste from around £1.45.

Fry: Palm oil.

Side-lines: Mushy peas, pickled gherkins, pickled onions. Other foods.

Speciality: Yorkshire fish cakes.

Wrapping: News, off-cuts.

Alf and Hermione Pickup are only the third incumbents of this fish and chip shop since it changed from being a pub backing on to the local brewery. But there's another pub, The Tap, two doors away and they don't sell fish and chips! The building dates back to 1878, and the chippy is immaculately done out with tiled floor and walls, orange fittings and pot plants to give the finishing touch. Adjustable-height lights hang over each of the tables in the pine-walled restaurant. Apart from raising a lot of money for numerous charities, the Pickups have one of the best captions I've seen on a business card – 'Nine out of ten cats say their owners prefer Churchill's.' Nice one, particularly with dogfish on the menu. Then we've got the two-legged recommendations from B. and F.C. Chase, Mrs G.A. Sanderson, A. O'Mahoney and Mr and Mrs R. Thompson. Carol Cleeve, who works there, also sings the praises of her bosses, but that doesn't count except to prove it's a friendly atmosphere! But they did come third in the Daloon U.K. Fish and Chip Shop Championships in 1988, and in the last ten last year. They do reductions for pensioners – and for anyone wanting to make a quick getaway, its only two minutes' walk from the Continental Ferry Port.

CRISPINS RESTAURANT, 3 Arundel Street. Tel: 0705 8200847

Open:	Daily 11.00 a.m. – 7.00 p.m. (take-away); 11.00 a.m. – 6.00 p.m. (restaurant).
Facilities:	T/A & R; T.
Fish finds:	Cod, cod roe, haddock, halibut, plaice, scampi. Fish and chips to take-and-taste from around £1.55; sit-and-savour around £2.25.
Fry:	Palm oil.
Side-lines:	Pickled onions.
Wrapping:	Cardboard boxes or trays with paper, personalized bags.

Phillip Spear runs this shop that's been frying for more than seventeen years. You'll find it in the pedestrian precinct opposite Allder's department store. For the history buffs, Portsmouth became a city in 1926, the seat of a bishop the following year and the chief magistrate became Lord Mayor in 1928. Add the magnificent Guildhall built in 1931, the numerous naval establishments and the Dickens Museum, and there's enough to work up an appetite for Crispins and relax in the large 100-plus-seater diner.

CRISPINS, 161 Havant Road, Drayton. Tel: 0705 376669

Open:	Mon – Sat 11.30 a.m. – 2.00 p.m.; 5.00 p.m. – 10.30 p.m.; Fri & Sat till – 11.00 p.m.
Facilities:	T/A; P near; wheelchair access.
Fish finds:	Cod, haddock, plaice. Fish and chips to take-and-taste from around £1.40, depending on size.
Fry:	Palm oil.

Side-lines: Mushy peas, pickled onions. Other foods.

Wrapping: Paper, trays, own bags.

Often frequented by Portsmouth Football Club players, the outlet is situated on the corner of Upper Drayton Lane. Mr Sidaway runs the shop and lives above the premises. Very clean, hygienic appearance with gold coloured tiles and illuminated menu and facia. The New Inn pub is just next door.

MAY'S OF COSHAM, 59 High Street. Tel: 0705 375870

Open: Tue 11.15 a.m. – 2.00 p.m.; Wed & Thu 11.15 a.m. – 2.00 p.m.; 4.15 p.m. – 9.30 p.m.; Fri 11.15 a.m. – 2.00 p.m.; 4.00 p.m. – 10.00 p.m.; Sat 11.00 a.m. – 10.00 p.m.

Facilities: T/A; wheelchair access.

Fish finds: Cod, haddock, huss, plaice, skate, sole. Fish and chips to take-and-taste from around 75p (small portion) to £1.70.

Fry: Palm oil.

Side-lines: Pickled onions. Other foods.

Wrapping: Greaseproof, white paper, polystyrene boxes.

Some people describe the chippy as being opposite Boots and the TSB – but even more say that these national names can be found across the street from May's. Reason? There's been a chippy on this site for over sixty years, and for the most part it's been called May's. First there was grandfather May who handed over to Arthur May in 1946. Then only a few years ago he passed the shop to his son, Stuart May. They sell different sizes of fried fish and also have a wet fish department which sells smoked fish and shellfish. There are four pubs nearby: The Swan, Red Lion, Portsbridge and the Rocket. Plenty of places in which to sit and ponder on which fine fish you will eat from May's.

Southampton

CAP'N COD, 245 Aldermoor Road, Lordswood. Tel: 0703 774227

Open:	Mon – Sat 11.30 a.m. – 1.30 p.m.; 5.00 p.m. – 10.00 p.m.
Facilities:	T/A; P near; wheelchair friendly.
Fish finds:	Cod, haddock, plaice, scampi. Fish and chips to take-and-taste from around £1.50.
Fry:	Vegetable oil.
Side-lines:	Pea fritters, pickled onions. Other foods.
Wrapping:	Greaseproof, bags, cartons.

This shop is called Cap'n Cod, not Cap'n Birdseye, so you might expect a sea shanty or two, or maybe a naval rating wanting some whiting. Whatever you want, this is the place. Super cod and chips or whatever takes your fancy. Clean and fresh with a friendly staff. The Cap'n is not too far from the Woodman pub.

CRISPINS, 328 Shirley Road. Tel: 0703 7713355

Open:	Mon – Sat 11.30 a.m. – 2.00 p.m.; 5.00 p.m. – 11.00 p.m.
Facilities:	T/A; wheelchair friendly.
Fish finds:	Cod, haddock, plaice. Fish and chips to take-and-taste from around £1.50.
Fry:	Vegetable oil.
Side-lines:	Pea fritters, pickled onions. Other foods.
Wrapping:	Greaseproof.

Even those leaving with their own private state-rooms on the big liners have been known to pop into Crispins for their last genuine British fish and chips before they set sail. You will find the Averley Bingo Club opposite, or there's the Rising Sun pub down the road. Whatever you do with your leisure time, don't forget your fish and chips.

HEMBER FISH AND CHIPS, 5 Upper Northam Road. Hedge End. Tel: 0489 782799

Open:	Mon – Fri 11.30 a.m. – 1.30 p.m.; 5.00 p.m. – 11.00 p.m.; Sat 11.30 a.m. – 2.30 p.m.; 5.00 p.m. – 11.00 p.m.; Sun 4.30 p.m. – 10.00 p.m.
Facilities:	T/A; P.
Fish finds:	Cod, haddock, plaice, scampi. Fish and chips to take-and-taste from around £1.60.
Fry:	Vegetable oil.
Side-lines:	Pickled onions. Other foods.
Wrapping:	Paper.

They've had the 'Frying Tonight' sign hanging above this fine establishment for nigh on fifty years. It's opposite the Post Office in the main road, near a small roundabout. Both prices and quality brought compliments, as did the charming and friendly service. The small shop is spotless at all times. Recommendations were endorsed by L. Clark who named it as tops with representative travellers, and Peter Hodge from Havant.

> *There have been over 2,000 varieties of potato, though few of these are worth cultivating, as most are highly vulnerable to a mould-like fungus disease.*

MIKE'S FISH BAR, 184 Burgess Road, Bassett. Tel: 0703 768546

Open:	11.30 a.m. – 2.00 p.m.; 5.00 p.m. – 11.00 p.m. (Fri & Sat till 11.30 p.m.).
Facilities:	T/A; P near; T.
Fish finds:	Cod, cod's roe, haddock, plaice. Fish and chips to take-and-taste from around £1.50.
Fry:	Vegetable oil.
Side-lines:	Pickled onions.
Wrapping:	Paper.

Southampton University was moved to its present site in 1914. That was fortunate for this chippy which gains much business from the campus being close at hand. This traditional chip shop recently won an award for the best value fare in the south – but still found sufficient funds to re-tile the floor, give the place a face-lift and fit a new range. Obviously they must have a healthy turnover, which speaks for itself. The nearest pub is the Crown and Sceptre.

Potatoes were first grown in Ireland, as a staple diet, in 1633.

Southsea

BEN'S FISH BAR, 79 Castle Road. Tel: 0705 827346

Open:	Mon – Fri 11.45 a.m. – 2.00 p.m.; 5.00 p.m. – 11.30 p.m.; Sat 11.45 a.m. – 2.00 p.m.; 5.00 p.m. – 8.30 p.m.
Facilities:	T/A with sit-down; wheelchair access.

Fish finds:	Cod, haddock, plaice, rock. Fish and chips to take-and-taste from around £1.10.
Fry:	Groundnut oil.
Side-lines:	Pickled gherkins, pickled onions. Other foods.
Wrapping:	White paper, trays.

Clive Reynolds, a staunch member of the Fish Fryers Association, took over this outlet seven years ago. You'll find this fine 70-year-old outlet across the common from the Hovercraft Ferry and the fun-fair. I counted five pubs within a couple of hundred yards – the Wheelbarrow, White Horse, Barley Mow, India Arms and Little's Wine Bar. Clive's a friendly fellow, who takes his frying seriously – though, like a colleague a few miles away, why he counts haggis as a speciality is beyond me. Still, the selection of alternatives he offers would fill a page. Incidentally, you can have your plaice either breaded or battered.

HEREFORD & WORCESTER
Bewdley

CATCHEM'S END FISH BAR, 134 Kidderminster Road. Tel: 0299 403615

Open:	Mon & Tue 4.00 p.m. – 11.30 p.m.; Wed & Thu 11.30 a.m. – 2.00 p.m.; 4.00 p.m. – 11.00 p.m.; Fri & Sat 11.30 a.m. – 2.30 p.m.; 4.00 p.m. – 12.30 a.m.
Facilities:	T/A; P near; T.
Fish finds:	Cod, cod's roe, haddock, plaice, scampi. Fish and chips to take-and-taste from around £1.60.
Fry:	Groundnut oil.

Side-lines:	Mushy peas, pickled onions.
Wrapping:	Trays, white paper.

This long-established fish shop is a very successful business. They have always put their customers' needs for a well cooked, fresh product served with courtesy at the top of their priorities. This outlet is based in an historic building next door to the Angel pub, right on the River Severn and not far from the Safari Park. Nice outlook, nice food, nice people.

Kidderminster

CAPTAIN COD, Station Place, Comberton Hill. Tel: 0562 753532

Open:	Mon – Sat 11.30 a.m. – 11.30 p.m.
Facilities:	T/A & R; P (opposite).
Fish finds:	Cod, cod's roe, haddock, plaice, scampi. Fish and chips to take-and-taste from around £1.55.
Fry:	Fat.
Side-lines:	Mushy peas, pickled gherkins, pickled onions. Other foods.
Wrapping:	Trays or wrapped in white news.

P.J. Webb, P. Webb, E. Prosser and M. Hawkins all have a finger in the batter at this fine establishment, opposite the railway station and Severn Valley Railway – preservers of fine steam trains. They've been frying here for nine years and recently made the top ten in the Daloon Fish and Chip Shop contest; runner-up in the Midlands and East Anglia Fish and Chip Shop of the Year; and winner of the Enterprise Award for the Midland Region in the same Sea Fish contest. Perhaps in future it will not only be for carpets that this town on the Stour is known – but for fine fried fish as well!

HERTFORDSHIRE
Baldock

TAYLOR'S MALTINGS FISH SHOP & RESTAURANT, 46A High Street. Tel: 0462 893393

Open:	Tue – Sat 11.30 a.m. – 2.00 p.m.; 4.45 p.m. – 10.30 p.m.; (R till 8.45 p.m.).
Facilities:	T/A & R (L); P; T.
Fish finds:	Cod, dogfish, haddock, plaice, skate. Fish and chips to take-and-taste from around £1.45; sit-and-savour around £2.00.
Fry:	FryMax fat.
Side-lines:	Mushy peas, pickled gherkins, pickled onions.
Wrapping:	Bags, white paper.

Paul Taylor's shop has been trading in the main street, next to the White Lion pub, for more than twenty years. Not long enough for him to remember the excitement hereabouts, when, in 1925, a Roman cemetery was unearthed. There's more excitement these days over the consistent good quality of Paul's fish and fry, and the excellent value so close to London.

Borehamwood

DYNASTY FISH AND CHIPS, 17 Howard Drive. Tel: 01 953 1706

Open:	Mon – Sat midday – 2.00 p.m.; 5.00 p.m. – 11.30 p.m.
Facilities:	T/A: P near.
Fish finds:	Cod, plaice, rock, scampi. Fish and chips to take-and-taste from around £2.05.

Fry:	Vegetable fat.
Side-lines:	Pickled gherkins, pickled onions. Other foods.
Wrapping:	Paper and bags.

Considering the postal address, I'm surprised Mr Pun has not re-named his cheerful outlet Howard's Way, which would also add nautical appeal. However, before I incur the wrath of Ms Collins – who has, no doubt, trod the boards at the nearby studios on more than one occasion – I shall endorse its twelve successful years under the current banner. Also well known is the Suffolk Punch pub, opposite, at the junction with Templeton Avenue. The chippy serves each of its fish portions in three sizes.

From one-time 'poor man's sustenance' the British chippy is crossing the social divide to become an institution as the national fast food of Britain.

Cheshunt

MERRYWEATHERS, 14 Newham Parade, College Road. Tel: 0992 24414

Open:	Mon – Sat 11.30 a.m. – 2.30 p.m.; 5.00 p.m. – 10.30 p.m.
Facilities:	T/A; P.
Fish finds:	Cod, haddock, huss, plaice, scampi, skate. Fish and chips to take-and-taste from around £2.20.
Fry:	Groundnut oil.
Side-lines:	Mushy peas, pickled onions.
Wrapping:	Cartons and paper bags.

This outlet became part of the successful chain headed by Carol Merryweather about a year ago – though they've been frying on this site for over fifteen years. Cheshunt is situated on the River Lea, 14 miles north of London. Cheshunt College, for training Nonconformist ministers, was removed to Cambridge in 1905. The building then became a training college for the Church of England. Whatever your faith or following, there's no shortage of good fare, on Fridays or any other day, at this spotless Merryweathers outlet, managed by Mrs Diane Gill, a super lady fryer.

Hemel Hempstead

LEMON PLAICE, 10 Bellgate, Fletcher Way, Highfields. Tel: 0442 41938

Open:	Mon – Thu 11.30 a.m. – 1.30 p.m.; 5.00 p.m. – 10.30 p.m.; Fri 11.30 a.m. – 2.00 p.m.; 4.30 p.m. – 10.30 p.m.; Sat 11.30 a.m. – 10.30 p.m.
Facilities:	T/A; P.
Fish finds:	Cod, haddock, plaice, rock, roe, skate, squid-rings. Fish and chips to take-and-taste from around £1.70.
Fry:	Palm oil.
Side-lines:	Pickled gherkins, pickled onions. Other foods.
Wrapping:	White news, off-cuts.

Vic Hastings believes in a traditional decor with lots of woodwork, plants and pictures to give the accent on warm, homely surroundings. Though only in his ownership for four years, the outlet has been trading well at the Bellgate Shopping Parade for around twenty-one. Vic has been frying for over fifteen years and you can be sure he keeps to a high standard when fellow chippies, Terry and Doreen Macklin from Beaconsfield, recommend the outlet. Vic, you owe them a drink in your local, the Royal Stag opposite!

MERRYWEATHERS, 126 The Marlowes. Tel: 0442 42513

Open:	Mon – Thu 11.00 a.m. – 11.00 p.m.; Fri & Sat 11.00 a.m. – midnight.
Facilities:	T/A & R; P at rear (80+ cars); wheelchair friendly.
Fish finds:	Cod, cod's roe, haddock, halibut, plaice, rock, skate. Fish and chips to take-and-taste from around £2.00; sit-and-savour around £2.85.
Fry:	Groundnut oil.
Side-lines:	Pickled gherkins, pickled onions. Other foods.
Wrapping:	Cartons, paper bags.

There are still many fine houses and inns to be found in this much expanded area that was once a sleepy market town on the river Gade. Merryweathers ensures that the highest standard is maintained at this busy outlet, where there has been a chippy trading for the last fifteen years. The 38-seater diner is a must for a family fish and chip feast. Situated opposite the Gateway Foodmarket.

Rickmansworth

CORNER PLAICE, 309 Baldwins Lane, Croxley Green. Tel: 0923 775221

Open:	Mon – Sat 11.30 a.m. – 2.00 p.m.; 5.00 p.m. – 10.30 p.m. (Thu – Sat from 4.30 p.m.).
Facilities:	T/A; P.
Fish finds:	Cod, haddock, plaice, rock – and at weekends, scampi, skate to order. Fish and chips to take-and-taste from around £1.85.
Fry:	Groundnut oil.
Side-lines:	Pickled gherkins, pickled onions. Other foods.
Wrapping:	White news.

Steve Kyriakou has been frying for eleven years, wrapping his fine fare the traditional way in white paper – with chip cones for the 'eat now' brigade. You'll find this neat outlet at the top of Baldwins Lane, on the corner of a parade of shops beside the recreation ground and playing fields. Last year Steve was rewarded for all his fine efforts with an Enterprise Award for London and the south, and second place in the area finals of the Sea Fish Fish and Chip Shop of the Year contest.

Watford

EBB TIDE FISH AND CHIPS, 97 Market Street. Tel: 0923 33484

Open:	Mon – Sun 11.30 a.m. – midnight; Sun 3.00 p.m. – midnight.
Facilities:	T/A & R; P near; T; wheelchair access.

Fish finds:	Cod, haddock, plaice, rock, scampi, skate. Fish and chips to take-and-taste from around £1.80; sit-and-savour £2.05.
Fry:	Groundnut oil.
Side-lines:	Pickled gherkins, pickled onions. Other foods.
Wrapping:	Greaseproof bags, paper.

I'm sure it had nothing to do with the tasty rock and bread roll served up at this fine shop that made Elton John dispose of his interest in the local football club. This good chippy has a 24-seater diner, and the Crown pub is nearby. Mrs Beatrice Griffiths of King's Langley recommends the outlet, particularly for the friendly staff, the spotless surroundings and most of all the beautifully cooked food.

HUMBERSIDE
Cleethorpes

COUNTY FISHERIES, 277 Grimsby Road. Tel: 0472 693424

Open:	Mon – Sat 11.30 a.m. – 1.30 p.m.; 4.30 p.m. – 11.30 p.m.
Facilities:	T/A; P near.
Fish finds:	Haddock, skate. Fish and chips to take-and-taste from around £1.70.
Fry:	Fat and dripping.
Side-lines:	Mushy peas, pickled onions. Other foods.
Wrapping:	Double white wrap.

The Barwick family can thank the Grimsby fishermen for landing their catches just a few miles down the road. There has been frying at this location near the Darlelis Hotel and the Co-op block of shops for well over fifty years. Currently the shop walls are tiled from floor to ceiling in beige.

Grimsby

RIVERSIDE, 1 Alexandra Road. Tel: 0472 356282

Open:	Tue – Fri 11.30 a.m. – 2.00 p.m.; 5.30 p.m. – 10.00 p.m.; Sat 11.30 a.m. – 10.00 p.m.
Facilities:	R (L); P near; T; wheelchair friendly.
Fish finds:	Haddock, plaice, scampi, skate. Fish and chips to sit-and-savour around £4.20.
Fry:	Vegetable fat.
Side-lines:	Fish cakes, mushy peas. Other foods.
Wrapping:	Trays, paper, greaseproof, bags.

Mr Leon Marklew knows a thing or two about the price of fish: he's been wholesaling for over forty years, so only the freshest of fish is served in the restaurant, superbly cooked from the pan to the plate. Try the special fish and chips, roll and butter, cup of tea or coffee (or a bottle of wine or lager, which is extra) for around £4.20.

Patrington

PATRINGTON FISHERIES, 14 Market Place. Tel: 0964 630401

Open:	Mon 4.00 p.m. – 6.00 p.m.; Tue 11.00 a.m. – 1.15 p.m.; Wed 11.00 a.m. – 1.15 p.m.; 8.00 p.m. – 11.15 p.m.; Thu 4.00 p.m. – 6.00 p.m.; Fri 11.00 a.m. – 1.15 p.m.; 8.00 p.m. – 11.30 p.m.; Sat 11.00 a.m. – 1.15 p.m.; 8.00 p.m. – midnight.

Facilities:	T/A; P; wheelchair access.
Fish finds:	Cod, haddock, plaice, skate. Fish and chips to take-and-taste from around £1.50.
Fry:	Fat.
Side-lines:	Mushy peas.
Speciality:	Home-made potato and sage cakes (patties).
Wrapping:	Parchment bags with white paper.

They've been 'Frying Tonight' in this conservation-area shop for over fifty years. It's next to the antique shop and opposite the Midland Bank. Alan Glaholm's your friendly fryer, ruling over his Triumph range of yellow and stainless steel. Over a quarter of a century ago the art master of Withernsea High School painted a trawler mural to cover one wall. The others are green and cream with an olde-worlde ceiling. There are several pubs close at hand, including the Hildyard Arms and the Station Hotel. The proprietors are Brenda and Bob Garbutt, who've owned the premises for the last five years.

Scunthorpe

EXCEL FISHERIES, 126 Rowland Road. Tel: 0724 844231.

Open:	Mon – Thu 11.30 a.m. – 1.45 p.m.; 4.30 p.m. – 11.30 p.m.; Fri – Sat 11.30 a.m. – 1.45 p.m.; 4.30 p.m. – 11.45 p.m.
Facilities:	T/A; P near.
Fish finds:	Cod, haddock. Fish and chips to take-and-taste from around £1.50.
Fry:	Dripping.
Side-lines:	Mushy peas, pickled eggs and onions. Other foods.
Wrapping:	Greaseproof, white paper.

Sukhjinder Singh Kaila took on this outlet only five years ago, but by 1987 had already won a 'Chippy of the Year' award in his region, for the biggest portion of chips at the keenest price. What's more the chips, and the fish, are firm and dry. The award brought useful publicity to this shop on the corner of Rowland Road, opposite the Coronation Club. Recently refitted and extended, it is decorated throughout with pale brown tiles and has a new aluminium shop front. Apart from the club opposite, there's the Queen's pub a couple of hundred yards away.

ISLE OF MAN
Douglas

ISLANDER, 82 Bucks Road. Tel: 0624 76797

Open:	Mon – Sat midday – 2.00 p.m.; 5.00 p.m. – midnight; Sun 8.00 p.m. – 11.30 p.m.
Facilities:	T/A; P.
Fish finds:	Cod, haddock, plaice, scampi and a fish of the day special. Fish and chips to take-and-taste from around £1.40.
Fry:	Vegetable fat.
Side-lines:	Pickled onions. Other foods.
Wrapping:	Polystyrene trays, news.

If you stick a pin in a map exactly 27 miles from England, Scotland and Northern Ireland, you'd have that pin in the Isle of Man. The island is a lot bigger than many 'mainlanders' think – about five times the size of Jersey. It may have its own government and constitution, but they still fry the British way at the Baxter's corner chippy. Mr and Mrs Baxter have been serving delicious fish in light, dry batter for going on seven years. The portions are good, though I wouldn't bet there is much left for the old

Manx cat – unless you buy him a special piece! The outlet is tiled from floor to ceiling in off-white, beige and brown, with tinted windows and stainless steel fittings. It is always spotless. Find the shop on the corner with Christian Road.

Ramsey

HARBOUR BISTRO, East Street. Tel: 0624 814182

Open:	Tue – Sat midday – 1.45 p.m.; 7.00 p.m. – 10.30 p.m.
Facilities:	R (L); T; wheelchair access.
Fish finds:	Smoked salmon about £5.00; Manx queenies around £5.50. Cod, halibut, salmon around £3.00.
Fry:	Own recipe.
Side-lines:	Various.

The famous Manx queenies are just one of a wonderful array of locally-caught seafood available at this friendly, harbour-side bistro. Don't stand on ceremony – enjoy a full meal or a snack with a variety of white fish cooked in any one of many ways. Try langoustines and salmon baked in puff pastry. Other foods are also available. Ramsey is 14 miles from Douglas, on the north-east coast, at the mouth of the River Sulby.

KENT

Bexley Heath

SEA LION FISH BAR, 152 Brampton Road. Tel: 01 303 1155

Open:	Tue – Thu midday – 1.30 p.m.; Fri & Sat midday – 2.00 p.m.; Mon – Thu 5.00 p.m. – 10.30 p.m.; Fri 4.30 p.m. – 10.30 p.m.; Sat 5.00 p.m. – 9.00 p.m.

Facilities:	T/A; P.
Fish finds:	Cod, haddock, plaice, rock, skate. Fish and chips to take-and-taste from around £2.05.
Fry:	Groundnut oil.
Side-lines:	Pickled gherkins, pickled onions. Other foods.
Wrapping:	Paper bags.

Local demand results in a menu that includes the London delicacies of pie and mash. Like the man says, if they wan' it, they can 'ave it, and like it. And like it they do at this traditional chippy run by Dennis, Gordon and Monica Beasley. The decor's red and white, the ambience clean and bright, the food good and tasty. One warning: if you fancy a drink either before or after your nosh, call into the off-licence next door to the Sea Lion – 'cos there's not a boozer for 'alf a mile.

Bromley

TOM BELL FISH & CHIPS, 1 Market Parade, East Street.
Tel: 01 460 6328

Open:	Mon – Sat 11.00 a.m. – 11.00 p.m.
Facilities:	T/A & R; P near; T; wheelchair access.
Fish finds:	Cod, cod's roe, haddock, huss, plaice, scampi, skate. Fish and chips to take-and-taste from around £2.05; sit-and-savour around £2.40.
Fry:	Vegetable fat.
Side-lines:	Pickled gherkins, pickled onions. Other foods.
Wrapping:	Trays, paper.

To consider this area without Bell's would be rather like vinegar without salt. The family have been associated with the trade for around 100 years – which must be some form of a record. The family acquired this outlet twenty years ago, and their fish and chips then cost around 6½p. It's nice to find that one thing hasn't changed, at least – the quality of the fare – and Mr Bell tells me the Bromley Council have recently awarded them a certificate for good hygiene. I hope they'll still be frying in another 100 years. There is seating for forty in this spotless diner. Have a nice day!

Chatham

MERRYWEATHERS, 288 High Street. Tel: 0634 843093

Open:	Mon – Sat 11.30 a.m. – 6.00 p.m.
Facilities:	T/A & R; P near.
Fish finds:	Cod, cod's roe, haddock, halibut, plaice, rock eel, scampi, skate. Fish and chips to take-and-taste from around £1.75; sit-and-savour around £2.45.
Fry:	Groundnut oil.
Side-lines:	Pickled gherkins, pickled onions. Other foods.
Wrapping:	Cartons, paper bags.

Chatham, of course, is the home of the world-famous St Bartholomew's Hospital, winner of countless awards in the field of medicine. This chippy, which now belongs to Merryweathers, also won an award when it first opened – for its design. Since then it has had designs of frying consistently good fare. It's to be found at the end of the High Street between Fine Fare and Tesco.

Folkestone

BOATING POOL ROTUNDA RESTAURANT, Marine Parade.
Tel: 0303 51145

Open:	Summer: daily 10.00 a.m. – 10.00 p.m.; winter: weekends only 11.45 a.m. – 5.00 p.m.

Facilities:	T/A & R; P near.
Fish finds:	Cod, plaice, scampi. Fish and chips to take-and-taste from around £2.30; sit-and-savour around £2.45.
Fry:	Vegetable oil.
Side-lines:	Pickled gherkins, pickled onions. Other foods.
Wrapping:	Paper bags, polystyrene trays, cardboard cones.

Dave and Dominic Moore are rushed off their feet most of the time in this busy cafeteria, in one of the twin rotundas on Folkestone sea front. They serve up quality fresh fish at amazingly good value. Don't be put off if you don't find a take-away counter, because there isn't one: just look and make a selection from the menu. Pop into the rotunda amusement park next door if the weather's bad, or just to pass the time while you await the cross-channel ferry. Don't forget your sou'wester!

OLYMPIA FISH BAR, 71 Foord Road. Tel: 0203 52095

Open:	Mon 5.00 p.m. – midnight; Tue – Sat 11.30 a.m. – 2.00 p.m.; 5.00 p.m. – midnight.
Facilities:	T/A; P.
Fish finds:	Cod, haddock, huss, plaice, skate, squid. Fish and chips to take-and-taste from around £1.55.
Fry:	Palm oil.
Side-lines:	Pickled gherkins, pickled onions. Other foods.
Wrapping:	White bags, white paper, newspaper.

They've been frying in this establishment for over half a century, though proprietor S. Pieri only took over a few years ago. Previously it was known as Goodenoughs – a motto Mr Pieri has set out to even better! He turned the former front garden into a small car park – a service his increasing clientele appreciate. You'll find this fine fry-house at the end of Blackbull Road, next to the Castle Inn.

Hythe

TORBAY OF HYTHE, 81 High Street. Tel: 0303 269531

Open:	Tue 11.30 a.m. – 9.30 p.m.; Wed 11.30 a.m. – 2.30 p.m.; Thu – Sat 11.30 a.m. – 9.00 p.m.
Facilities:	T/A & R (L); P near; wheelchair access.
Fish finds:	Cod, cod's roe, dabs, haddock, hake, halibut, huss, lemon sole (Dover sole in summer only), monkfish, plaice, skate. Fish and chips to take-and-taste from around £1.75; sit-and-savour from £3.10.
Fry:	Fat.
Side-lines:	Pickled gherkins, pickled onions. Other foods.
Wrapping:	Paper.

A thoroughly British chippy of the highest standard. Although the Gilberts have only been frying at this location for about five years, the family have been in the trade for three generations. Before that they were fishermen out of Brixham – hence the name of this outlet. Among the not-so-usual specialities served here are mussels in batter, with chips and tartare sauce as a take-out. A school of musketry was set up in the town in 1854 – but with fare fried to this standard I don't see anyone from this establishment being put before the firing squad! The chippy is next to the National Westminster Bank.

Maidstone

SEVEN SEAS FISH BUFFET, 4 Union Street. Tel: 0622 56123

Open:	Mon 11.00 a.m. – 6.30 p.m.; Tue & Thu 11.00 a.m. – 7.00 p.m.; Wed 11.00 a.m. – 3.00 p.m.; Fri 11.00 a.m. – 8.00 p.m.; Sat 10.30 a.m – 6.30 p.m.

Facilities: T/A & R (L); P near; T; wheelchair friendly.

Fish finds: Cod, haddock, huss, plaice. Fish and chips to take-and-taste from around £1.50; sit-and-savour around £1.85.

Fry: Vegetable oil.

Side-lines: Pickled onions. Other foods.

Wrapping: Greaseproof bags, white paper.

This outlet opened for business just when the Kaiser was declaring war on everybody in 1914. In those days Maidstone was a bustling market town in the middle of the hop fields, with beer, malting and agricultural machinery manufacture among its main businesses. The Seven Seas building dates back to 1550 and still retains many of the original beams. The restaurant seats eighty and the furniture matches the building's date, with dark oak benches along the walls, and tapestry back-rests. The fish is well cooked and the chips are nice and dry. If you're feeling thirsty, the Duke of Marlborough is the nearest pub, which is just of Week Street.

Margate

DANE VALLEY FISH BAR, 52 Dane Valley Road. Tel: 0843 295307

Open: Mon – Fri midday – 1.30 p.m.; 5.00 p.m. – 10.30 p.m; Sat 11.30 a.m. – 2.00 p.m.; 5.00 p.m. – 10.00 p.m.

Facilities: T/A; P; wheelchair access.

Fish finds: Cod, haddock, plaice, rock. Fish and chips to take-and-taste from around £1.35.

Fry: Oil.

Side-lines: Mushy peas, pickled gherkins, pickled onions. Other foods.

Wrapping: Paper, boxes.

In a town where fishing, other than tourism, was considered the main industry, it is natural that the standard of any chippy must be high. Bob and Coral Steele recognize this, and therefore only cook to order – so a quick telephone call is advised if you are in a hurry. The result is well worth the extra couple of minutes, with beautifully crisp batter and piping hot chips. You'll find this outlet a couple of hundred yards past the King Edward pub. Look for the sign 'Real men have a Moby Dick' – that sells many large cod pieces!

New Romney

ROD & LINE FISH BAR, 21 Littlestone Road. Tel: 0679 63059

Open:	Thu 11.30 a.m. – 1.30 p.m.; 5.00 p.m. – 8.30 p.m.; Fri 11.30 a.m. – 1.30 p.m.; 5.00 p.m. – 9.30 p.m.; Sat 11.30 a.m. – 1.30 p.m.; 5.00 p.m. – 9.00 p.m.
Facilities:	T/A; P; wheelchair access.
Fish Finds:	Cod, haddock, huss, plaice, skate. Fish and chips to take-and-taste from around £1.20.
Fry:	Vegetable oil.

Side-lines:	Pickled gherkins, pickled onions. Other foods.
Wrapping:	Containers or paper.

You'll always find plenty of parking space around this outlet – it's opposite the Romney-Hythe-Dymchurch railway station. This typically British chippy has been trading from this spot for forty-five years. Not only do they have wet fish sales – always a sign of freshness for a chippy – but the haddock and skate is only included on the menu when it has been caught locally. Well worth a try.

Orpington

CRISPINS, 344 Orpington High Street. Tel: 0689 29104

Open:	Mon – Thu 11.00 a.m. – 2.30 p.m.; 4.00 p.m. – 10.30 p.m.; Fri & Sat 11.00 a.m. – 10.30 p.m.
Facilities:	T/A & R; T.
Fish finds:	Cod, haddock, plaice, rock, scampi, skate. Fish and chips to take-and-taste from around £2.10; sit-and-savour around £2.60.
Fry:	Oil.
Side-lines:	Pickled gherkins, pickled onions. Other foods.
Wrapping:	Paper, own-label bags.

One of those areas where the residents were perfectly happy being where they were until the Boundary Commission came along and moved them. Orpington used to be in Kent, surrounded by large fruit areas. Now it's in Greater London, inside the orbital M25, with little more than half a dozen golf courses to prevent total urbanization. With the river Cray not too far, this 20-seater super fish and chip shop has a well-earned reputation for consistent quality and pleasant service.

Sevenoaks

FOUR WENTS FISH BAR, 1 Sevenoaks Road, Borough Green.
Tel: 0732 884884

Open:	Tue – Thu 11.30 a.m. – 1.30 p.m.; 5.00 p.m. – 10.00 p.m.; Fri 11.30 a.m. – 1.30 p.m.; 4.45 p.m. – 10.00 p.m.; Sat 11.30 a.m. – 2.00 p.m.; 5.30 p.m. – 10.00 p.m.
Facilities:	T/A; P.
Fish finds:	Cod, haddock, plaice, rock, scampi. Fish and chips to take-and-taste from around £1.60.
Fry:	Palm oil.
Side-lines:	Pickled gherkins, pickled onions. Other foods.
Wrapping:	Paper, greaseproof bags.

I've no idea what the shop name is about – it existed long before the ancient trees blew down, so it can't be that! Perhaps if I had attended Sevenoaks' well-known 15th-century grammar school I'd know. Perhaps it has something to do with Sevenoaks reputedly having one of the country's oldest cricket grounds? Anyway, to fish and chips: Roly and Sue Twitchett look after a fine establishment that has been frying for over twenty years. The decor is sea blue and spotless white, hence the clean food award. Take Mrs Barbara King's word for it: the fare is first class. You'll find them on the corner with Quarry Hill Road, at the A25 cross-roads.

SEVEN SEAS FISH BAR, 93 St John's Hill. Tel: 0732 451308

Open:	Daily 11.30 a.m. – 2.00 p.m.; 5.00 p.m. – 10.00 p.m. (Fri from 4.30 p.m.).
Facilities:	T/A; P near; T.

Fish finds: Cod, haddock, huss, plaice, scampi, skate. Fish and chips to take-and-taste from around £1.50.

Fry: Vegetable oil.

Side-lines: Pickled gherkins, pickled onions. Other foods.

Wrapping: Double paper then brown bags.

There's been a chippy on this site for over fifty years. It's opposite the Post Office, near the pedestrian crossing. Mr M. Campbell is in charge of the range, with excellent results. The shop recently underwent a complete refurbishment. The walls are now light brown board, with white gloss paint and cream ceilings. There are several pubs close at hand for the thirsty: the Castle and the New Inn are just two.

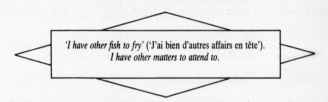

'I have other fish to fry' ('J'ai bien d'autres affairs en tête').
I have other matters to attend to.

Snodland

PETE'S PLACE, 113 Malling Road. Tel: 0634 240308

Open: Tue – Sat 11.30 a.m. – 1.30 p.m.; 4.30 p.m. – 9.30 p.m. (Sat till 7.30 p.m.).

Facilities: T/A; P; wheelchair access.

Fish finds: Cod, haddock, plaice, rock, skate. Fish and chips to take-and-taste from around £1.70.

Fry: Palm oil.

Side-lines: Mushy peas, pickled gherkins, pickled onions. Other foods.

Wrapping: Greaseproof bags, white paper.

If you're still on that journey back from the ferry at Folkestone, and you didn't eat earlier, take exit 4 off the M20 and pop into this well-run, clean and efficient chippy, where they've been frying for over half a century. Peter Crowhurst has only been in charge for the last few years, but he consistently keeps up the traditional high standard with fine food. It's easy to find on the main road and well worth the detour. Nice selection of wet fish also available if you fancy DIY.

Tunbridge Wells

SEALAND FISH BAR, 69c London Road, Southborough. Tel: 0892 29487

Open: Mon – Sat 11.30 a.m. – 2.00 p.m.; 5.00 p.m. – 10.00 p.m.

Facilities: T/A; wheelchair access.

Fish finds: Cod, fishburgers (100 per cent fish) plaice, rock salmon, scampi, skate. Fish and chips to take-and-taste from around £1.80.

Fry: Vegetable fat.

Side-lines: Pickled gherkins, pickled onions. Other foods.

Wrapping: Greaseproof, double white paper, cones.

Greenery adorns the large shop front, giving an atmosphere of freshness and airiness even before you enter. The decor is brown and beige tiles with beige roller blinds on the windows. Very smart. As a service to customers they display posters on the walls advertising local events. Solon Charilaou has been frying here for ten years and had earned recommendations for both quality and service from Mrs Pam Smith, which were confirmed on our inspection. The Crown and the Imperial pubs and the Hand and Sceptre Hotel are all nearby to this main road outlet between Tonbridge and Tunbridge Wells.

Welling

MERRYWEATHERS, 9 Upper Wickham Lane. Tel: 081 304 4557

Open: Mon – Sat 11.00 a.m. – 10.00 p.m.

Facilities: T/A & R; P (street); T; wheelchair friendly.

Fish finds: Cod, haddock, plaice, rock and more. Fish and chips to take-and-taste from around £1.95; sit-and-savour around £2.90.

Fry: Groundnut oil.

Side-lines: Pickled gherkins, pickled onions.

Wrapping: Cartons, paper bags.

A very lively team run the Merryweathers branch in Welling, under the watchful eye of Michelle. Everything freshly prepared and freshly cooked. Each shop has its own individuality and the team of ten make it all happen. A 20-seater diner in which to sit-and-savour awaits you.

LANCASHIRE
Blackburn

MICHELLE'S CHIP SHOP, 34 King Street, Whalley. Tel: 025 482 3971

Open: Mon – Sat 11.30 a.m. – 1.30 p.m.; Tue & Wed 4.30 p.m. – 6.30 p.m.; Thu & Fri 4.30 p.m. – 7.00 p.m.

Facilities: T/A; P near.

Fish finds: Fish cakes, haddock, plaice. Fish and chips to take-and-taste from around £1.15.

Fry: Vegetable oil.

Side-lines: Mushy peas, pickled onions. Other foods.

Wrapping: Trays.

Paul Frost does the frying here now, though there's been a chippy here for many a long year. The first grammar school was established by Queen Elizabeth I in the town in 1567. Those first schoolchildren though would probably have eaten black pudding, and they wouldn't have known the delights of fried fish and chips. Certainly not anything as delicious as those served up in King Street, Whalley. The outlet is opposite the Post Office, near the new Health Centre. More important, if you fancy a pint to wash down your meal, the Whalley Arms pub is also nearby.

Blackpool

THE COTTAGE, 31 Newhouse Road, Marton. Tel: 0253 64081

Open: Mon – Sat 11.45 a.m. – 2.00 p.m.; 5.00 p.m. – midnight; Sun 5.00 p.m. – midnight (summer) – 8.00 p.m. (winter).

Facilities: T/A & R (L); P; T; wheelchair access.

Fish finds: Cod, Dover sole, haddock, hake, halibut, plaice, prawns, salmon, swordfish, trout, whitebait. Fish and chips to take-and-taste from around £1.50; sit-and-savour about £2.05.

Fry: Master oil.

Side-lines: Mushy peas, pickled onions. Other foods.

Wrapping: Trays, white paper.

The setting befits the name, or vice versa. The premises were once an old farmhouse, dating back to 1856. The decor is that of a farmhouse kitchen and the fare has that fresh, just cooked taste – though the imported fish must be bought in frozen. Any size fish will be cooked to order. You'll find fryer Enid Needham and owners Jay and Eileen Patel ready and willing to serve you at this delightful establishment near the Oxford Square roundabout, on the corner past the Midland Bank. It's been trading for over forty-five years and visited by many of the celebrities who have appeared in the town over that time. Recommended by Yvonne Bentham and Mr and Mrs Charles Morby.

FIELDINGS FISH BAR, 10 Simpson Street, South Shore.
Tel: 0253 42201

Open: Daily 11.30 a.m. – 10.30 p.m. (Easter – Nov).

Facilities: T/A & R; T; P; limited wheelchair access.

Fish finds: Cod, haddock, plaice. Fish and chips to take-and-taste from around £1.30; sit-and-savour about £1.80.

Fry: Vegetable fat.

Side-lines: Mushy peas, pickled onions. Other foods.

Wrapping: Polystyrene trays, greaseproof paper, white news.

The fact that the outlet has been frying for over eighty years – probably the longest of any in Blackpool – doesn't mean Tricia and Brian Cummings and their sons have been here all that time! They've been hosts here for nine years to numerous show biz luminaries among others, as it's just behind the Beach Hotel, opposite the south pier. And it doesn't take show folk two shakes of a salt-cellar to find the best frys. The restaurant has seating for sixty-two, with a decor of orange seats, yellow tables, grey floor and wood-panelled walls. Altogether very gay! Recommended by Mr and Mrs F. Christmas of Shipston-on-Stour.

GRASMERE FISH & CHIPS, 27A Grasmere Road. Tel: 0253 24985

Open: Mon – Sat 11.45 a.m. – 2.00 p.m.; 4.45 p.m. – midnight; Sun 7.30 p.m. – midnight.

Facilities:	T/A & R; P.
Fish finds:	Calamari, cod, haddock. Fish and chips to take-and-taste from around £1.20.
Fry:	Palm oil.
Side-lines:	Mushy peas, pickled onions. Other foods.
Wrapping:	Greaseproof or tray, white paper and brown.

You may not need to know that the Blackpool Tower is 500 ft high, but you will want to know how to get to a really good chippy. This one's on the corner of Grasmere Road and Westmorland Avenue – where it has been for more than sixty years. Stuart Cottam and wife Janet have been there for the last fourteen or so, well settled in to the trade after twenty years frying. It doesn't even worry them when the large parties arrive in town for the famous illuminations, and they suddenly get orders for 100 servings at a time! What's more, the last serving comes out just as fresh, tasty and crisp as the first.

SENIORS, 106 Normoss Road, Normoss. Tel: 0253 33529

Open:	Tue – Sat 11.30 a.m. – 2.00 p.m.; 4.30 p.m. – 7.00 p.m. (Fri till 8.00 p.m.).
Facilities:	T/A & R; P near; T.
Fish finds:	Cod, haddock, plaice, scampi. Fish and chips to take-and-taste from around £1.40; sit-and-savour around £2.00.
Fry:	Oil.
Side-lines:	Mushy peas.
Wrapping:	Greaseproof, white news, brown paper, trays.

John Alwyn Proctor heads a large staff in this busy outlet opposite the Newton Arms Hotel. A teak dado is topped by green and white paper, with green curtains. Similar-coloured floor tiles complete the smart, fresh appearance. Their consistent good service and quality product was rewarded recently by local radio, plus a Sea Fish Industry runner-up award. The shop has been trading for over thirty years.

Chorley

PAWSON'S GOLDEN PLAICE, 4–6 Livsey Street. Tel: 02572 73489

Open:	Mon & Thu 11.30 a.m. – 1.30 p.m.; Tue & Sat 11.00 a.m. – 2.15 p.m.; Wed 11.30 a.m. – 1.15 p.m.; Fri 11.00 a.m. – 2.00 p.m.
Facilities:	T/A & R; P near.
Fish finds:	Codling, haddock, plaice. Fish and chips to take-and-taste from around £1.20; sit-and-savour from £1.95.
Fry:	Vegetable fat.
Side-lines:	Mushy peas. Other foods.
Wrapping:	Greaseproof, white news, plus new newspaper.

The Pawsons took on this lunchtime only outlet a few years ago, and ever since have been working hard at building up the trade. If you're out for the day, say to have a look at Astley Hall, the Elizabethan structure and park given to Chorley as a war memorial by R.A. Tatton, then do pop into this pleasant chippy for lunch. It's got an attractive beamed ceiling and pine panelling. The dining room is papered in white anaglypta with more pine, elm tables and stools. If you're thirsty after eating their fine fare, there's the Prince of Wales pub opposite.

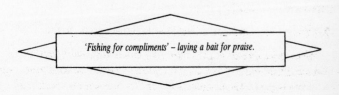

'Fishing for compliments' – laying a bait for praise.

Didsbury

BURNS FISH RESTAURANT, 12 Warburton Street. Tel: 061 434 0538

Open:	Tue – Sun midday – 2.00 p.m.; 5.30 p.m. – 10.30 p.m.
Facilities:	R (L); P; T.
Fish finds:	Brill, crayfish, Dover and lemon sole, haddock, hake halibut, mullet, plaice, red snapper, salmon, turbot. Fish and chips to sit-and-savour around £5.50.
Fry:	Own recipe.
Side-lines:	Mushy peas, gherkins. Other foods.

As you can see, the fish on offer is both varied, fresh and plentiful. The chef will be delighted to cook any fish of your choice as you like it – grilled, poached, deep fried. Nothing is too much trouble, and if you still have room for more, try my favourite, pecan nut pastry. A fine selection of wines are also on offer.

There were over 25,000 chippies in the UK from before the First to the end of the Second World War.

Heywood

WIGHTMAN'S, 47 Manchester Street. Tel: 0706 60166

Open:	Mon – Fri 11.30 a.m. – 1.30 p.m.; Mon, Wed & Thu 8.45 p.m. – midnight; Fri 4.30 p.m. – 6.30 p.m.; 8.45 p.m. – midnight.
Facilities:	T/A & R; P near; T.

156

Fish finds:	Cod, haddock occasionally, silver hake rarely. Fish and chips to take-and-taste from about £1.20.
Fry:	Palm oil.
Side-lines:	Mushy peas. Other foods.
Wrapping:	Greaseproof bags, white news.

We asked Bert and Elsie Wightman, who have been ensconced in this 80-year-old chippy for over twenty-eight years, if they cooked any national or regional specialities? Quick as a flash, this endearing couple came back with: 'Surely fish, chips and mushy peas is THE national dish.' Quite right Sir, and long may they be so – particularly when they are served up as well as they always are in your fine establishment. Until quite recently Mr Wightman worked a six-day week. Now he's taking a well earned rest – he only works five! On any of these days you'll find this fine fryer – who counts many friends in the National Fish Fryers Federation – at the range at the juction of Manchester Street and Rochdale Lane, but at the end of 1990, when Bert reaches sixty-five, he'll be hanging up his spatula for the last time and putting the chippy up for sale. Have a long, happy retirement Bert – you've earned it.

Kirkham

WESHAM FISH SHOP, 1 Garstang Road, Tel: 0772 682673

Open:	Tue – Sat 11.30 a.m. – 1.15 p.m.; 8.30 p.m. – 11.45 p.m.; also teatime Thu & Fri 4.30 p.m. – 6.15 p.m.
Facilities:	T/A; P near; wheelchair friendly.
Fish finds:	Cod, fish-cakes, haddock, rock, scampi. Fish and chips to take-and-taste from around £1.25.
Fry:	Vegetable oil.

Side-lines: Mushy peas. Other foods.

Wrapping: Trays, paper, greaseproof, bags.

Mr Shorrock is the master fryer, ably assisted by his wife at this traditional chippy, not far from Exit 3 on the M55. So if you are feeling tired, stop off and have a feast at the Wesham Fish Shop. Cod and chips will set you back around £1.25. Spend a bit more and you can have mushy peas.

Nelson

A.J.P. & P.J. HALL, 'Fish & Chips', 4 Hibson Road. Tel: 0282 601886

Open: Mon & Tue 11.15 a.m. – 1.45 p.m.; Wed – Fri
                  11.15 a.m. – 1.45 p.m.; 4.00 p.m. – 6.00 p.m.;
                  Sat 11.15 a.m. – 6.00 p.m.

Facilities: T/A; P.

Fish finds: Cod, cod's roe, haddock, hake, lemon sole, plaice,
                  scampi. Fish and chips to take-and-taste from around
                  £1.45.

Fry: Hard oil – FryMax.

Side-lines: Mushy peas. Other foods.

Speciality: Fish scones.

Wrapping: Greaseproof, white news, newspaper.

Alistair Hall and wife Pauline took over this outlet five years ago and the selection of fresh fish available indicates the way he has built on the trade. Incidentally, there are many more Nelsons dotted around the world than the old Admiral had eyes. There's the town in New Zealand, for example, and Canada boasts both a river and town in British Columbia. But the one that matters is three miles from Burnley and is a former textile town that has a growing tourist industry. The Leeds–Liverpool canal is an attraction and much of our industrial heritage is to be seen in the area. The

Lancashire Witches are also likely to become one of the subjects for a theme park nearby. Among all of this history is the small, end-of-terrace property adjacent to F.W. Woolworth and the Station Hotel, where they do some great frys! The decor is simple but the food is good and the service friendly.

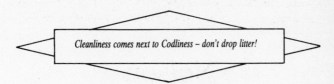

Cleanliness comes next to Codliness – don't drop litter!

Ormskirk

SKIPPERS, 128 Burscough Street. Tel: 0695 573036

Open: Mon – Thu 11.30 a.m. – 2.00 p.m.; 5.00 p.m. – 11.00 p.m.; Fri 11.30 a.m. – 2.00 p.m.; 4.45 p.m. – midnight; Sat 11.30 a.m. – 2.00 p.m.; 5.00 p.m. – 11.30 p.m.; Sun 5.00 p.m. – 10.00 p.m.

Facilities: T/A; P near.

Fish finds: Cod, haddock, plaice, king prawns, rock salmon (when available), scampi, skate, squid. Fish and chips to take-and-taste from around £1.20.

Fry: Palm oil.

Side-lines: Mushy peas, pickled gherkins, pickled onions. Other foods.

Wrapping: Greaseproof, white news.

Not only does this outlet encourage 'phone calls so that your order will await your arrival, it will even deliver it, providing it comes to more than £4.00. Ormskirk has a fine parish church with a tower and spire side-by-side. It is the burial place of the Stanley family, whose former home, Lathom House, is nearby. There are also 17th-century school buildings.

Oswaldtwistle

JOHN'S CHIPPY, 31 Moscow Mill Street. Tel: 0254 383747

Open:	Mon & Tue 11.30 a.m. – 1.00 p.m.; Wed & Thu 11.30 a.m. – 1.00 p.m.; 4.30 p.m. – 6.00 p.m; Fri 11.30 a.m. – 1.00 p.m.; 4.15 p.m. – 6.15 p.m.
Facilities:	T/A.
Fish finds:	Cod. Fish and chips to take-and-taste from about £1.00.
Fry:	Fat.
Side-lines:	Mushy peas. Other foods.
Wrapping:	White news, newspaper.

John Fenton has been behind the range for a few years, and features a different 'Special' each week – mainly non-fish, like black pudding. By sticking to cod-only he is able to offer one of the most reasonably priced meals of fresh fish and piping hot, firm chips that we list in this book. Once famous as an area for making cotton goods and pottery, now you'll find John's fry-house next to a small carpet factory.

Penwortham (Preston)

GODWINS, 89 Pope Lane. Tel: 0772 742068/745371

Open:	Mon 11.30 a.m. – 1.30 p.m.; 4.00 p.m. – 6.30 p.m.; 8.00 p.m. – midnight; Tue & Wed 8.00 p.m. – midnight; Thu – Sat 11.30 a.m. – 1.30 p.m.; 4.00 p.m. – midnight.
Facilities:	T/A; P near.
Fish finds:	Cod, haddock, plaice, scampi. Fish and chips to take-and-taste from around £1.35.

Fry:	Vegetable oil.
Side-lines:	Mushy peas. Other foods.
Wrapping:	Trays, white paper.

Two miles south of Preston, a mile from the main roads (if you get lost ask a local – they all know) is Godwins, where they've been for over fifty-five years. Mrs S. Bradley's family have been at the helm since 1957. The building was the original Post Office, but it's fingers, not stamps, that get licked regularly now, after a feed on the delicious fare served up at this fine chippy. To show how good news travels fast – an Australian couple turned up on the Godwins' doorstep, having cycled from London as part of a round-the-world trek. They'd been told of the fine fry by a New Zealand couple, and made the journey specially to fill their tucker bag.

Preston

DERIK'S PLAICE, 48 Plungington Road. Tel: 0772 27001

Open:	Mon – Sat 11.15 a.m. – 1.30 p.m.; Mon – Wed & Sat 4.15 p.m. – 9.00 p.m.; Thu & Fri 4.15 p.m. – midnight.
Facilities:	T/A & R; P; T; wheelchair access.
Fish finds:	Cod, haddock, plaice, scampi. Fish and chips to take-and-taste from around £1.30.
Fry:	Vegetable fat.
Side-lines:	Mushy peas.
Speciality:	Black pudding.
Wrapping:	Greaseproof, clean news, newspaper.

Derrick Cray has been in the business less than four years – having previously worked for British Leyland – but is already making his mark. This century-old building was only recently converted into a chippy with fully-tiled walls in beige and brown, and a light brown floor. The tables are marble Formica in a style to match the range, with seating in beige and brown cushions. Overall very smart, but it was the quality of the fare, the presentation and cleanliness and friendliness of the staff that was brought to our attention by Mr and Mrs Edwards of Preston. Incidentally, Preston North End were one of the original twelve football clubs who formed the Football League in 1889 and won the cup themselves the following year. There'd be a few frys served if the occasion could be repeated 100 years on!

Ribchester (Preston)

RIBCHESTER CHIPPY, 32 Water Street. Tel: 025 878 788

Open: Tue – Sat 11.45 a.m. – 1.30 p.m.; Tue 8.30 p.m. – 11.30 p.m.; Wed & Fri 4.30 p.m. – 6.00 p.m.; Thu & Fri 8.30 p.m. – midnight; Sat 6.00 p.m. – midnight.

Facilities: T/A & small café; P near; wheelchair access.

Fish finds: Cod, haddock, plaice, scampi. Fish and chips to take-and-taste from around £1.60; sit-and-savour from £1.75.

Fry: Palm oil.

Side-lines: Mushy peas, pickled onions. Other foods.

Wrapping: Bags, plain news.

Nestling in this small village in the Ribble Valley with its Roman Fort and Baths, on the Ribble Way Nature Trail, is Carole and Jenny's chippy. It's been in existence as a fry-house for as long as anyone around can remember – though the girls only recently took over. They mainly fry haddock bought fresh the same day from Fleetwood, but as supplies require they switch to cod or hake. Certainly an enterprising establishment and well worth the stop, or even detour, if you're in the area.

St Annes

THREE FISHES, 26 Alexandra Road. Tel: 0253 724377

Open:	Tue – Sat 11.45 a.m. – 1.30 p.m.; Tue – Fri 4.30 p.m. – 6.30 p.m.; 8.30 p.m. – 11.45 p.m.; Sat 9.00 p.m. – 11.45 p.m.
Facilities:	T/A; P near; wheelchair friendly.
Fish finds:	Cod, haddock. Fish and chips to take-and-taste from around £1.30.
Fry:	Vegetable oil.
Side-lines:	Mushy peas, pickled gherkins, pickled onions. Other foods.
Wrapping:	White paper, greaseproof.

St Annes is about a mile or so from Blackpool, very pleasant with nice shops for a bit of a browse or a bracing walk along the sea front. But don't forget to visit the Three Fishes for a packed lunch of fish and chips. A frequent visitor is the 'sprightly' Les Dawson.

LEICESTERSHIRE

Barrow-upon-Soar

RIVER SOAR FISH BAR, 59 North Street. Tel: 0509 414004

Open:	Mon 5.00 p.m. – 11.30 p.m.; Tue & Wed midday – 1.30 p.m.; 5.00 p.m. – 11.30 p.m.; Thu midday – 1.30 p.m.; 5.00 p.m. – midnight; Fri & Sat midday – 2.00 p.m.; 5.00 p.m. – midnight.

Facilities:	T/A; P.
Fish finds:	Cod, haddock, plaice. Fish and chips to take-and-taste from around £1.85.
Fry:	Vegetable oil.
Side-lines:	Mushy peas, pickled gherkins, pickled onions. Other foods.
Wrapping:	Greaseproof, white news.

The B591 from exit 22 on the M1 will take you straight into Barrow-upon-Soar – and it's well worth the detour for some of the best fish and chips in the area. Mr Michael has been running this outlet next door to the library for a few years. With the river on your doorstep and excellent fare to feed on, what more could anyone ask? Ms Y. Coates agrees, for she used to travel regularly to this shop from Cornforth in Durham. Mind you, her parents were also living in the town!

Leicester

ANDREW'S FISH & CHIPS, 130 Fosse Road, South Leicester.
Tel: 0533 556047

Open:	Mon & Tue 5.00 p.m. – 11.00 p.m.; Wed – Fri 11.45 a.m. – 1.45 p.m.; 5.00 p.m. – 11.00 p.m.; Sat 6.00 p.m. – 11.00 p.m.
Facilities:	T/A; P.
Fish finds:	Cod, haddock, plaice. Fish and chips to take-and-taste from around £1.70.
Fry:	Vegetable fat.
Side-lines:	Mushy peas, pickled gherkins, pickled onions. Other foods.

Wrapping: Greaseproof, white paper, newspaper.

Mr A.E. Kyprianou's shop, opposite the Mobil petrol station, has been frying regularly for over a quarter of a century. It's nicely decorated with a white ceiling and patterned, brown tiled walls. If you are visiting Leicester, points of interest are the Assize Courts made up of the remains of the Great Hall of the castle and the ruins of the Abbey of St Mary, in which Cardinal Wolsey died in 1530. A walk in Bradgate Park to work up an appetite for Andrew's fare will unearth the remains of the house in which Lady Jane Grey was born. After all this history, as well as the fine fish and chips, you may like a drink. There's the Merry Monarch close to Mr Kyprianou's fine chippy.

BRADGATE FISHERIES, 3 Bradgate Road, Anstey. Tel: 0533 362878

Open: Tue – Thu midday – 1.30 p.m.; 5.00 p.m. – 11.30 p.m.;
              Fri & Sat midday – 2.00 p.m.; 5.00 p.m. – midnight.

Facilities: Fish cakes, haddock, plaice, scampi. Fish and chips to
              take-and-taste from around £1.80.

Fry: Vegetable fat.

Side-lines: Mushy peas, pickled gherkins, pickled onions. Other
              foods.

Wrapping: White newspaper, trays.

*There's been a chippy on this site for well over ninety years. Jack Zafiri
has run this very smart shop for the last eight, though he's been in the
trade for twenty years. He won a 'best kept business' award the only time
the local council entered a 'best kept village' competition. He was also
runner-up in the 1988 Daloon 'Fish and Chip Shop of the Year' contest.
From the hanging flower-baskets outside to the the yellow, beige and
brown interior, it really is a picture of cleanliness. Images of Anstey in
Victorian times adorn the walls. Staff uniforms are in green with check
highlights to match the menu boards. Altogether a pleasing experience
which, together with the fine fare, is recommended by Mrs E. Helps.*

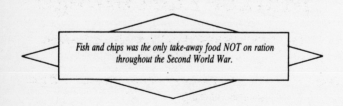

*Fish and chips was the only take-away food NOT on ration
throughout the Second World War.*

GRIMSBY FISHERIES, 334 Welford Road. Tel: 0533 709175/702374

Open: Fri 11.30 a.m. – 2.30 p.m.; 4.15 p.m. – 11.30 p.m.;
              Sat 11.00 a.m. – 11.00 p.m.

Facilities: T/A & R (L) ; T.

Fish finds:	Cod, haddock, plaice (breaded, stuffed or battered), salmon, scampi, seafood platter. Fish and chips to take-and-taste from around £2.10; sit-and-savour from £3.25.
Fry:	Oil.
Side-lines:	Mushy peas, pickled gherkins, pickled onions. Other foods.
Wrapping:	Paper.

One of the Radio Trent 945 'Jocks' told us about this super chippy just a little way from the station – though the prison and the infirmary are also in the same long road! 'Lefty' Eleftheriou's shop on the corner of Gainsborough Road has been frying for nearly forty years, and does a rapid turnover of fresh fish. Don't be surprised if you have to queue, though the wait will be worth it. The fish is lightly battered and the chips nice and firm. 'Lefty' has owned the outlet for fifteen years, winning the Radio Leicester 'Best Fish and Chip Shop 1987' award, best in the Midlands in 1988 and regional finalist last year in the Sea Fish Industry survey.

Market Harborough

TAYLOR'S FISH RESTAURANT, 10 Adam & Eve Street.
Tel: 0858 63043

Open:	Tue – Sat midday – 2.00 p.m.; 5.00 p.m. – 9.00 p.m. (later in summer).
Facilities:	T/A & R (L); P near; T; off-licence; wheelchair access.
Fish finds:	Cod, dogfish, haddock, halibut, lemon sole, plaice, skate. Fish and chips to take-and-taste from around £1.60; sit-and-savour around £2.20.
Fry:	Blended oil.

| Side-lines: | Mushy peas, pickled gherkins, pickled onions. Other foods. |
| Wrapping: | Bags, paper, trays. |

Hmm . . . interesting! They claim to be the second oldest chippy in the world: with a starting date of 1902 I would not like to pass judgement, although since they're in a deeded building going back to 1707 I'll certainly accept the account of the resident ghost! Whatever the history, Frank Taylor has certainly built up one of the best and most interesting outlets in the country, since he took over from his father in 1967. Hidden away in a back street near the old grammar school it may be, but they come from miles around to sample the take-away, or the cosy diner (seating eighty-six) or the Upstairs Restaurant and Coffee Shop. The restaurant has a fascinating historical decor, built in the attics of three adjoining cottages, which had been derelict for nearly a century. The spirits I preferred came in glasses, along with the wines, usefully graded from dry to sweet on the menu to match your meal. A thoroughly enjoyable eating experience. Oh dear, I'm so full . . .

Ratby (Nr Leicester)

RATBY FISH BAR, 93 Main Street. Tel: 0533 392772

Open:	Mon & Thu 6.00 p.m. – 11.30 p.m.; Fri 5.00 p.m. – midnight; Sat 6.00 p.m. – midnight.
Facilities:	T/A; P; T.
Fish finds:	Cod, haddock, plaice. Fish and chips to take-and-taste from around £1.90.
Fry:	Vegetable fat.
Side-lines:	Mushy peas, pickled gherkins, pickled onions. Other foods.
Wrapping:	White news.

The building that houses this chippy dates back a century and a half – long before the M1 forged a barrier between Ratby and Leicester. John Millington set up his fry-house in the three storey building over twenty years ago. The black woodwork outside is set off by white brickwork. There's a panelled dado inside, with tiling in the working area. The church is opposite, and the Plough pub not far away. Comes highly recommended by Mr and Mrs L. & W. Hart who regularly make a ten-mile trek from Whitwick because they say these fish and chips are simply 'the best'.

Rutland

FISH-N-GRILL, 51–53 Dean Street, Oakham. Tel: 0572 72429

Open:	Mon – Thu 11.45 a.m. – 1.30 p.m.; 5.00 p.m. – 11.30 p.m.; Fri & Sat 11.45 a.m. – 1.45 p.m.; 5.00 p.m. – 10.00 p.m.
Facilities:	T/A & R (L); P (street); T.
Fish finds:	Cod, haddock, plaice (breaded or battered), prawns, scampi. Fish and chips to take-and-taste from around £1.40; sit-and-savour around £2.50.
Fry:	Vegetable fat.
Side-lines:	Mushy peas, pickled gherkins, pickled onions. Other foods.
Wrapping:	Greaseproof, white news.

The Bostocks' chippy may be tucked away behind Victor Wood's garage, but it has been doing very nicely, thank you, for over twenty years. Why? First, because it's an ultra-clean outlet with two doors to ease the flow of customers. Then there's the restaurant with its wood-panelled dado and papered upper that has ample room to accommodate about fifty people (don't forget to get in before the coach parties). Finally, and most importantly, comes the quality of fare that many will put up against any in the country – and prices are reasonable.

LINCOLNSHIRE
Boston

TATE'S FISH RESTAURANT, 4 & 6 New Street. Tel: 0205 62753

Open:	Mon & Thu 11.30 a.m. – 1.30 p.m.; Tue 11.00 a.m. – 2.00 p.m.; Wed 10.30 a.m. – 3.00 p.m.; 4.00 p.m. – 7.00 p.m.; Fri 11.00 a.m. – 2.00 p.m.; 4.30 p.m. – 10.00 p.m.; Sat 10.30 a.m. – 8.00 p.m.
Facilities:	T/A & R; P; T; wheelchair access.
Fish finds:	Cod, haddock, plaice, skate wings. Fish and chips to take-and-taste from around £1.70; sit-and-savour around £2.25.
Fry:	Pure lard.
Side-lines:	Mushy peas.
Wrapping:	Greaseproof, white paper.

Hanging baskets outside and principal features picked out in contrasting colours went towards winning this traditional chippy the town's award for a good shop front. Find it by following the queue along the pedestrianized shopping precinct, in the shadow of the historical Boston Stump – the famed tower of St Botolph's, the largest parish church in all England. Otherwise ask, for any Bostonian knows Tate's: they have been frying in the town for nearly fifty years, and at this site for nearly thirty years. (Robert and David Tate admit they don't believe in change for change's sake. A local antique dealer, for instance, got nowhere when he offered to buy the basic formica-topped tables used at ground and first floor eating levels.) It's the consistency of good frys that people come for – among them D. Robotham from Nottingham and Mrs V. Ingham from Skegness. All cod is skinned and boned on the premises. Restaurant seats 150.

Grantham

GRIMSBY FISHERIES, 59 London Road. Tel: 0476 60344

Open:	Mon – Wed 11.00 a.m. – 2.00 p.m.; 4.00 p.m. – 11.30 p.m.; Thu & Fri 11.00 a.m. – 2.30 p.m.; 4.00 p.m. – midnight; Sat 11.00 a.m. – 11.30 p.m.
Facilities:	T/A & R (L); P; T.
Fish finds:	Cod, haddock, plaice, prawns, scampi. Fish and chips to take-and-taste from around £1.85; sit-and-savour around £2.30.
Fry:	Vegetable oil.
Side-lines:	Mushy peas, pickled gherkins, pickled onions. Other foods.
Wrapping:	Greaseproof, white news, trays.

A former corner-shopkeeper's daughter from Grantham has been firmly ensconced at No. 10 Downing Street for some years. She believes in the 'enterprise economy', something very much to the fore here, with stiff competition keeping everyone on their toes. The result: an extra clean shop, friendly staff and prices kept stable to the benefit of the consumer. Mrs M. Barber opened this outlet close to the Grantham football ground just a few years ago.

WINDSOR RESTAURANT & TAKE-AWAY, 53 London Road. Tel: 0476 64061

Open:	Mon – Thu 11.30 a.m. – 2.00 p.m.; 4.30 p.m. – midnight; Fri & Sat 11.30 a.m. – midnight; Sun 4.30 p.m. – midnight (restaurant last orders 10.00 p.m.).
Facilities:	T/A & R (L); P near; T; wheelchair access.

Fish finds:	Cod, haddock, halibut, lemon sole, plaice, scampi, shark, squid, swordfish. Fish and chips to take-and-taste from around £1.75; sit-and-savour from £2.75.
Fry:	Vegetable oil.
Side-lines:	Mushy peas, pickled onions. Other foods.
Wrapping:	White news.

When William and Vera Kirby opened their small shop over half a century ago, the Great North Road carried traffic past their door. Things change: their son Gordon and his son Heil now run the much enlarged Windsor, and a bypass takes traffic clear of the town. But one thing hasn't changed – the quality of fare fried up for up to 100 diners and queues of take-away customers at this truly traditional chippy. The Kirby family have always had close community ties with the town, including helping to build the Baptist Chapel and maintaining the highest standards at the football club. Gordon is a keen member of the Fish Fryers Federation, and sees a future not only for his son, but also for his two grandsons in the business locally.

Louth

MR CHIPS FISH RESTAURANT, 17–21 Aswell Street.
Tel: 0507 603756

Open:	Mon – Sat 9.00 a.m. – 11.00 p.m. (Fri & Sat till 11.30 p.m.).
Facilities:	T/A & R (L); P; T; wheelchair access (wide aisles and specially designed seats), plus disabled toilets and mother and baby room.
Fish finds:	Cod, haddock, plaice, scampi, skate. Fish, chips and peas to take-and-taste from around £1.75.
Fry:	Vegetable oil.

Side-lines: Mushy peas. Other food.

Wrapping: Greaseproof, white paper, trays.

*Patrick is the third generation of the Hagan family to enter the trade –
adding up to nearly seventy years of non-stop frying! The outlet was
purpose-built. The air-conditioned, self-service restaurant must be one of
the largest in the country – seating no fewer than 300 diners, all at ground
level. Plenty of plants and original oil paintings give the place a fresh and
clean appearance. Let's hope there are future generations to carry on the
friendly, efficient service with prime quality products at reasonable prices.
Find it from Market Place into Queen Street, then first right into Aswell
Street. The Turks Head pub is close at hand. Outlet recommended by
M.F. Johnson of Grantham.*

'*I do profess . . . to serve him truly . . . and to eat no fish.*'
Shakespeare: King Lear I.iv.

Sleaford

SCOFFERS, Lincoln Road. Tel: 0529 303313

Open: Mon 11.30 a.m. – 2.00 p.m.; 4.30 p.m. – 7.00 p.m.;
                 Tue – Fri 11.30 a.m. – 2.00 p.m.; 4.30 p.m. – 10.30 p.m.;
                 Sat 11.30 a.m. – 2.00 p.m.; 4.45 p.m. – 10.30 p.m.

Facilities: T/A & R (L); P near; T.

Fish finds: Cod, haddock, plaice. Fish and chips to take-and-taste
                 from around £1.50; sit-and-savour around £2.35.

Fry: Dripping.

Side-lines: Other foods.

Wrapping: Paper, bags.

This outlet was recommended to me as 'the best in England' by Tracy Ardito of Grimsby. Unfortunately, many others make that claim. But everybody who visits Scoffers has nothing but praise and if you don't want to queue for a take-away, then take your place in the 34-seater diner and watch Mr and Mrs Sleaford go by. For what it's worth Sleaford celebrated its centenary in 1988. It became the capital of Kesteven, one of the three administrative divisions of Lincolnshire, in 1888.

Wainfleet All Saints

J.E. SUTTON & SON, 45 High Street, Tel: 0754 880357

Open:	Mon & Tue 6.30 p.m. – 11.00 p.m.; Wed & Fri 10.45 a.m. – 1.00 p.m.; 6.30 p.m. – 11.00 p.m.; Sat 10.45 a.m. – 1.30 p.m.; 6.30 p.m. – 11.30 p.m.
Facilities:	T/A & R (L); P near; T; wheelchair access.
Fish finds:	Cod, haddock, lemon sole, plaice, rock, skate. Fish and chips to take-and-taste from around £1.00; sit-and-savour around £1.20.
Fry:	Fat.
Side-lines:	Mushy peas, pickled onions. Other food.
Wrapping:	Newspaper.

When talking about a 'traditional' chippy, first visit Russell James and Elizabeth Sutton's establishment. She and her late husband started the business, about five miles from Skegness, sixty years ago! The shop was set up in Quaker Buildings dating back to 1773, opposite the Post Office. Frying still takes place on a coal-fired range (one of the last), which customers claim adds to the flavour. The business is now run by a second generation, who still like to keep to the old ways with prices that are a thing of the past in most outlets.

MERSEYSIDE
Birkenhead

HIPPO'S, 579 Borough Road. Tel: 051 652 1689

Open: Mon – Fri 11.00 a.m. – 1.30 p.m.; 4.30 p.m. – midnight;
Sat midday – 2.00 p.m.; 4.30 p.m. – midnight; Sun
5.00 p.m. – 11.00 p.m. (times change in the summer).

Facilities: T/A; P; T.

Fish finds: Cod, haddock, plaice. Fish and chips to take-and-taste
from around £1.45.

Fry: Vegetable oil.

Side-lines: Mushy peas, pickled gherkins, pickled onions. Other foods.

Wrapping: Paper.

You don't need a 'Full House' at the nearby bingo club to take in this outlet's very reasonably priced fare. There has been frying at this location for several years now, and they claim to be the first in the Wirral to combine several different take-away menus – although of them all, fish and chips still comes out top of the list with its customers. That can only be a compliment to the way the fresh fish are cooked. For the thirsty, there's a Povalls off-licence three doors away.

Southport

HARPERS FISH RESTAURANT, 29 East Bank Street. Tel: 0704 37370

Open: Mon – Sat 11.30 a.m. – 6.30 p.m.; Easter Sunday 11.30 a.m. – 6.30 p.m.

Facilities: T/A & R (L); off-sales; P near; T; wheelchair friendly.

Fish finds: Cod, haddock, plaice. Fish and chips to take-and-taste from around £1.50; sit-and-savour around £2.05.

Fry: Vegetable oil.

Side-lines: Mushy peas. Other foods.

Wrapping: Trays, paper, greaseproof.

Why don't you take your holidays in Southport and visit Harpers Fish Restaurant, where fish is freshly cooked in the old-fashioned way. Relax in the 56-seater diner and enjoy the special: fish and chips, pot of tea, bread and butter, for around £2.55. You can't miss Harpers, just follow the aroma.

Wallasey

PAUL'S, 25 Poulton Road. Tel: 051 638 8696

Open: Mon – Sat 11.30 a.m. – 1.45 p.m.; 4.30 p.m. – 11.30 p.m.; Sun 8.00 p.m. – midnight.

Facilities: T/A; P near.

Fish finds: Cod, haddock, plaice. Fish and chips to take-and-taste from around £1.55.

Fry: Bestfry fat.

Side-lines: Mushy peas, pickled onions. Other foods.

Wrapping: Paper.

This shop, opposite the Dale public house, has a traditional Victorian atmosphere. They keep up a standard they have set themselves at this outlet: friendly service, attractive and clean surroundings, and above all quality fresh fish.

MIDDLESEX
Bedfont

W.R. GRANT, 499 Staines Road. Tel: 081 890 3845

Open: Mon 11.00 a.m. – 2.00 p.m.; 4.00 p.m. – 8.00 p.m.; Tue – Sat 11.00 a.m. – 2.00 p.m.; 4.00 p.m. – 10.30 p.m.

Facilities: T/A; P; T; wheelchair access.

Fish finds: Cod, huss, plaice, scampi, skate. Fish and chips to take-and-taste from around £1.80.

Fry: Vegetable oil.

Side-lines: Mushy peas, pickled gherkins, pickled onions. Other foods.

Wrapping: Trays, white paper, bags.

If you want to know the time, ask a policeman; if you want to know about fried fish, ask Mr Grant. His family have been in the trade fifty-three years and they're now on their third generation of fryers. The outlet, in the middle of a parade of shops, is tiled throughout in a black and white chequered pattern. The staff are turned out in white coats, blue tabards, and boaters or forage hats. Just as much care is taken in the cooking and serving of the beautifully fresh fish and firm chips that look, and taste, a treat. Fresh wet fish is also available and, if you fancy a pint, there's the Load of Hay pub just down the road.

Edgeware

CAPTAIN'S CABIN, 120 Burnt Oak, Broadway. Tel: 081 952 3071

Open: Mon – Thu 11.30 a.m. – midnight; Fri & Sat 11.30 a.m. – 1.00 a.m.

Facilities: T/A & R (L – wine); T.

Fish finds: Cod, haddock, plaice, rock, skate. Fish and chips to take-and-taste from around £1.70.

Fry: Groundnut oil.

Side-lines: Pickled gherkins, pickled onions. Other foods.

Wrapping: Trays, paper, bags.

The golden wall tiles match the crispy batter at Abdel Omar's shop at the junction with Watling Road. There's seating on red leatherette for fifty-four, around thirteen tables. Even the conveniences are spotlessly painted in pink and grey, and there's an air of hygiene throughout. The shop has been trading under the current ownership for over seven years, with only fresh fish being used. The Bald Faced Stag is the nearest watering hole. For those who think of Edgeware only as a suburban outpost eight miles from the metropolis, here was the forge of William Powell, whose work on the anvil is said to have suggested Handel's 'Harmonious Blacksmith' when, in the early eighteenth century, he was organist at the church of St Lawrence, Whitchurch. No doubt an ingenious composer could make something from the delicious sounds of Omar's fish at the frier!

Enfield

FISH BASKET, 149 Lancaster Road. Tel: 081 366 8246

Open:	Daily 11.30 a.m. – 1.45 p.m.; 5.00 p.m. – 11.00 p.m. (Sat till 10.00 p.m.).
Facilities:	T/A.
Fish finds:	Cod, cod's roe, haddock, plaice, rock, skate. Fish and chips to take-and-taste from around £2.30.
Fry:	Vegetable oil.
Side-lines:	Pickled onions. Other foods.
Wrapping:	White paper.

Queuing can be expected at this popular shop, where the service is friendly and the fare first class. For those who wish to know, the Enfield Rifles were, in fact, made in the town at the Royal Small Arms Factory.

A fisherman who was father of three kings was Abu Shujar al Bouyah, a Persian from the Delem province. His three sons, Imad, Ruken and Moez, all rose to sovereignty.

GEORGE'S FISH BAR, 8 Savoy Parade, Southbury Road. Tel: 081 363 0723

Open:	Daily 11.30 a.m. – 2.00 p.m.; 4.30 p.m. – 10.00 p.m.
Facilities:	T/A & R (L); P near; T.
Fish finds:	Cod, haddock, plaice, rock, scampi, skate. Fish and chips to take-and-taste from around £2.25; sit-and-savour around £3.25.
Fry:	Groundnut oil.
Side-lines:	Pickled gherkins, pickled onions. Other foods.
Wrapping:	Greaseproof, white paper.

This shop boasts fresh cooked fare, pleasantly presented in clean and inviting surroundings, plus twenty-five seats in the dining section. Enfield Town station is just down the block and it's almost next door to the Cannon cinema, and when you've got customers like Mr J. Wingate of Mafeking Road nearby, it's no wonder. He writes that he remembers buying fish and chips for tuppence in Bloomsbury and Covent Garden when he was a boy. 'I have eaten them anywhere and everywhere since, but not till I sat in George's had I eaten so well!' With customers like him, who needs advertising?

Hillingdon

MERRYWEATHERS, 372 Long Lane. Tel: 0895 33749

Open:	Mon – Sat 11.30 a.m. – 9.30 p.m.
Facilities:	T/A & R; P; T; wheelchair access.
Fish finds:	Cod, haddock, huss, plaice, skate. Fish and chips to take-and-taste from around £1.90; sit-and-savour from £2.50.
Fry:	Groundnut oil.

Side-lines: Mushy peas, pickled onions. Other foods.

Wrapping: Cartons, paper bags.

This long-established outlet was taken over by the Merryweathers chain only eighteen months ago. Manager Brian Batchelor has been frying for more than six years, and has no problem keeping the premises and fare up to the standard expected by his bosses and, more important, his customers. The dining area is big enough to seat you and everybody else.

Hounslow

RAINBOW FISH BAR, 63 Hanworth Road. Tel: 081 570 5894

Open: Sun – Fri 11.30 a.m. – 2.15 p.m.; 5.00 p.m. – 10.00 p.m.; Sat 11.30 a.m. – 2.30 p.m.; 5.00 p.m. – 9.30 p.m.

Facilities: T/A & R; P near; T.

Fish finds: Cod, haddock, plaice, rock, scampi, skate. Fish and chips to take-and-taste from around £2.25; sit-and-savour around £2.55.

Fry: Fat and groundnut oil.

Side-lines: Pickled gherkins, pickled onions. Other foods.

Wrapping: Paper, bags, newspaper.

Cod is the most popular dish at this traditional chippy, situated behind Marks and Spencer. In the 18th century nearby Hounslow Heath was infested with highwaymen. These days there are more 'cowboys' committing 'highway robbery' by turning out junk food with fancy names than anything else. Therefore it's good to be able to recommend well-cooked, pleasantly served fare, dished up at reasonable prices for this part of the country, by people who know their trade. After a day's shopping, rest your weary bones in the 40-seater diner.

Northolt

MERRYWEATHERS, 496 Church Road. Tel: 081 845 9268

Open:	Mon – Sat 11.30 a.m. – 9.30 p.m.
Facilities:	T/A; P.
Fish finds:	Cod, haddock, huss, plaice, scampi, skate. Fish and chips to take-and-taste from around £2.00.
Fry:	Groundnut oil.
Side-lines:	Mushy peas, pickled onions. Other foods.
Wrapping:	Cartons, paper bags.

For years when anyone thought of Northolt, they'd think either of the airfield or the racecourse. That means high-fliers and winners – the sort of words used these days to describe the very successful fish and chip chain Merryweathers. They bought out this long-established outlet two years ago, and put Mark McKitten in charge, giving it their special treatment that makes take-away food more of an experience than just 'fast food'.

Ruislip

CORAL BAY, 160 High Street. Tel: 08956 32445

Open:	Mon – Thu 11.30 a.m. – 2.00 p.m.; 4.30 p.m. – 10.00 p.m.; Sun midday – 8.00 p.m.; Fri & Sat open all day.
Facilities:	T/A & R; P; T; wheelchair access.
Fish finds:	Cod, cod's roe, haddock, halibut, plaice, rock, salmon, scampi, sole. Fish and chips to take-and-taste from around £1.90; sit-and-savour around £2.95.

Fry:	Oil.
Side-lines:	Mushy peas, pickled gherkins, pickled onions. Other foods.
Wrapping:	White paper, bags.

I wonder how many fishermen, after a fruitless day on the Grand Union Canal, the Pin Brook or even Ruislip Lido have called into this fine chippy, and then told the tale at home of how they had their catch cooked for them! Stranger things have happened, even though I see no freshwater fish on the menu! This quintessentially British outlet has been trading for many years near Ruislip underground station, and has a reputation for good fare, which is reasonably priced and pleasantly presented with cheerful service. The outlet, which has recently come under the ownership of Clive Carmichael, a fryer with twenty years' experience, serves only the freshest fish delivered direct from Grimsby market.

Twickenham

HAROLD'S PISCATORIUM, 106 Heath Road. Tel: 081 892 7774

Open:	Tue – Sat midday – 2.30 p.m.; 5.30 p.m. – 10.30 p.m.
Facilities:	T/A & R (L); T; wheelchair friendly.
Fish finds:	Cod, Dover and lemon sole, haddock, hake, halibut, monkfish, plaice, skate and many more. Fish and chips to take-and-taste from around £2.50; sit-and-savour around £4.50.
Fry:	Vegetable oil.
Side-lines:	Mushy peas, pickled gherkins, pickled onions. Other foods.
Wrapping:	Cartons, paper bags.

Ask directions to this fine eatery run by David Coles. Not that it's actually that hard to find – just 500 yd west of the town centre on the A305. Their English-style cooking of the highest standard attracts a discerning clientele.

But for those just back from their Spanish package junket, why not try your meal 'A la plancha' in the 35-seater diner? A glance at the long menu will correctly deduce that he will cook anything the sea or river gives up, in any way you like. Just don't ask him for chips solo – he doesn't do them.

By the way, he is a first class chef. If you want further recommendation that this is one of the best in west London, ask 73-year-old Pat Pelly who eats there regularly and says, 'Every type of fish he cooks is superb.'

EGYPTIAN 2000 BC

MERRYWEATHERS, 113 St Margarets Road. Tel: 081 892 2117

Open:	Mon – Sat midday – 2.30 p.m.; 5.00 p.m. – 10.30 p.m.
Facilities:	T/A & R; T; wheelchair access.
Fish finds:	Cod, haddock, huss, plaice, scampi, skate. Fish and chips to take-and-taste from around £2.20; sit-and-savour around £3.10.
Fry:	Groundnut oil.
Side-lines:	Mushy peas, pickled onions. Other foods.
Wrapping:	Cartons, paper bags.

There's been a chippy on this site for over a quarter of a century. But it was only two years ago that Merryweathers took over, converted things to their swish, clean, fresh approach and put Mark and Dawn Davidson at the helm. The queues speak for themselves. They call Twickenham Eyot 'Eel Pie Island' – but the fare at Merryweathers is far more sophisticated! Alexander Pope lived and was buried in the Borough, and there are many now who would not count a visit complete, win or lose at the famous 'Twickers' ground, without a touch-down at this scrummy outlet.

West Drayton

MERRYWEATHERS, 6 Station Road. Tel: 0895 442337

Open:	Mon – Sat 11.30 a.m. – 9.30 p.m.
Facilities:	T/A; P; wheelchair access.
Fish finds:	Cod, haddock, huss, plaice, scampi, skate. Fish and chips to take-and-taste from around £2.00.
Fry:	Groundnut oil.
Side-lines:	Mushy peas, pickled onions. Other foods.
Wrapping:	Cartons, paper bags.

You'll find V.J. Broughton, S. Sayer and T. Brennan (sorry to be so formal folks!) in charge of the range at this recently acquired Merryweathers outlet. When some companies get bigger the individual parts tend to lose their identity; not so with Merryweathers, where the standards are set to be kept.

NORFOLK
Botesdale

FISH SHOP, Market Place. Tel: 0379 898543

Open: Tue & Fri 11.30 a.m. – 1.30 p.m.; 4.30 p.m. – 7.00 p.m.; Thu & Sat 11.30 a.m. – 1.30 p.m.; 4.30 p.m. – 11.30 p.m.

Facilities: T/A & R; P (road); T.

Fish finds: Cod, cod's roe, haddock, plaice, rock, scampi, skate. Fish and chips to take-and-taste from around £1.35; sit-and-savour around £1.50.

Fry: Beef dripping.

Side-lines: Mushy peas, pickled onions. Other foods.

Wrapping: White paper.

They're still using a 40-year-old coal-fired range at this traditional shop on the A143. Mr Richard Lewis' fine establishment is opposite Market Place and seats just sixteen in the supper room. Only fresh fish is fried, so if you have a preference, it's as well to 'phone in your order. There is a choice of three hostelries close by, with the Greyhound right next door. Margaret Gower told me nice things about this shop, particularly how kind and friendly Mr and Mrs Lewis are to their customers. We are pleased to recognize their chivalry, together with their fine food.

Downham Market

QUALITY FISH AND CHIPS, 9 Wales Court. Tel: 0366 382605

Open:	Mon – Sat 11.00 a.m. – 2.00 p.m.; 4.00 p.m.. – 8.00 p.m. (Tue morning only).
Facilities:	T/A & R; T; wheelchair friendly.
Fish finds:	Cod, haddock, plaice, scampi, skate. Fish and chips to take-and-taste from around £1.40; sit-and-savour around £1.60.
Fry:	Vegetable oil.
Side-lines:	Mushy peas, pickled onions. Other foods.
Wrapping:	White paper.

This little Downham Market friendly fish shop serves super fish and chips, and the staff are very helpful and work hard in their quest to satisfy. There is seating for approximately twenty-four in the small but neat diner.

Dereham

BIG FRY, 6 Market Place. Tel: 0362 693177

Open:	Mon 11.30 a.m. – 2.00 p.m.; 4.30 p.m. – 11.15 p.m.; Tue & Wed 11.45 a.m. – 1.45 p.m.; 4.30 p.m. – 11.15 p.m.; Thu 11.00 a.m. – 2.00 p.m.; 4.00 p.m. – 11.30 p.m.; Fri & Sat 10.30 a.m. – 11.45 p.m.; Sun 4.00 p.m. – 10.00 p.m.
Facilities:	T/A; P near; wheelchair access.
Fish finds:	Cod, haddock, plaice, rock, scampi, skate. Fish and chips to take-and-taste from around £1.50.

Fry:	Dripping.
Side-lines:	Mushy peas, pickled onions. Other foods.
Wrapping:	White off-cuts.

You will find this traditional Norfolk village chippy between King's Lynn and Norwich in East Dereham Market Place, just off the A47. The fish is freshly cooked to order and very good value. If you have the time North Eltham is worth a visit to see the old Saxon cathedral.

Nearly a quarter of all meals eaten outside the home are fish and chips.

Fakenham

MR CHIPS, Bridge Street. Tel: 0328 863018

Open:	Mon – Wed 11.00 a.m. – 2.00 p.m.; 4.00 p.m. – 11.00 p.m.; Thu & Sat 11.00 a.m. – 11.00 p.m.; Fri 11.00 a.m. – 2.00 p.m.; 4.00 p.m. – 11.30 p.m.
Facilities:	T/A & R; P near; wheelchair access.
Fish finds:	Cod, haddock, plaice, rock, scampi, skate. Fish and chips to take-and-taste from around £1.35.
Fry:	Dripping.
Side-lines:	Pickled onions. Other foods.
Wrapping:	White paper.

Fakenham is half-way between King's Lynn and Crome, where Fakenham folk and others spend glorious sunny days at the race course, and after a goodly win they descend on the fish and chip shop for a fish and chip supper. The staff here are kind and friendly, taking pride in the cooking of king-size cod and chips. Try some.

Great Yarmouth

W.M. MASTERSON & SON LTD, 113 Regent Road. Tel: 0493 842747

Open:	Summer only (1 May – 31 October) Mon – Sat 11.30 a.m. – 3.00 p.m.; Sun by chance.
Facilities:	T/A & R (L); P; T; wheelchair access.
Fish finds:	Cod, haddock, plaice, rock, skate. Fish and chips to take-and-taste from around £2.65; sit-and-savour around £1.60.
Fry:	Groundnut oil.
Side-lines:	Mushy peas, pickled gherkins.
Wrapping:	Polystyrene trays, paper.

When your outlet is situated opposite McDonalds, with Kentucky Fried Chicken on the corner, you have to be good, very good. But then, this family firm have had plenty of practice at getting it right – sixty years, in fact! They are so good that their shop, which also retails wet fish, has a Sea Fish Quality Award, so you can eat here in the 40-seater diner, and while you are waiting for a table you can arrange to send kippers and bloaters to your friends by post.

SEAFOOD RESTAURANT, 85 North Quay. Tel: 0493 856009

Open:	Mon – Fri midday – 2.00 p.m.; 7.00 p.m. – 10.45 p.m.; Sat 7.00 p.m. – 10.45 p.m.
Facilities:	R (L); T.

Fish finds:	Whatever the nearby Lowestoft fishermen land, from turbot to whitebait, shellfish and more. A super meal with wine around £25.00.
Fry:	Own recipe.
Side-lines:	Salads, vegetables.

After a day at the races or visiting Caister Castle or the Roman town, what better than a nice, relaxing fish meal in pleasant surroundings with friendly service? You'll get all this and good, varied food here. The restaurant only seats forty so, if possible, book ahead. The standard is high and the variety both of fish and cooking methods worthwhile. Music and children's portions are laid on. It's not your actual fish and chip shop, dear.

Hunstanton

DON'S PLACE, 8 Le Strange Terrace. Tel: 04853 33747

Open:	Mon – Thu 11.30 a.m. – 2.30 p.m.; 5.00 p.m. – 7.00 p.m. (Thu morning only); Fri 11.30 a.m. – 2.30 p.m.; 4.00 p.m. – 8.00 p.m.; Sat 11.30 a.m. – 8.00 p.m.; Sun 11.00 a.m. – 8.00 p.m.; April to September 11.00 a.m. – 11.00 p.m.
Facilities:	T/A & R; P near; wheelchair friendly.
Fish finds:	Cod, cod's roe, fish cakes, haddock, plaice, scampi. Fish and chips to take-and-taste from around £1.45; sit-and-savour around £3.35.
Fry:	Dripping.
Side-lines:	Pickled onions. Other foods.
Wrapping:	White paper.

If you take the A149 from King's Lynn and follow the coast road, you will pass through Dursingham and Heacham and on to Hunstanton and Don's Place. The staff work very hard in this spotlessly clean fish and chip shop with its 28-seater diner. The menu is limited but the fish is excellent.

Norwich

BIG FRY, 130 Dereham Road. Tel: 0603 622946

Open: Mon – Fri 11.30 a.m. – 2.00 p.m.; 4.30 p.m. – 11.45 p.m.; Sat 11.30 a.m. – 11.45 p.m.; Sun 5.00 p.m. – 10.30 p.m.

Facilities: T/A; P near; wheelchair access.

Fish finds: Cod, haddock, plaice, rock, scampi, skate. Fish and chips to take-and-taste from around £1.30.

Fry: Dripping.

Side-lines: Pickled onions. Other foods.

Wrapping: White paper, trays.

Take a left for Norwich and the Norfolk Broads, straight on for Great Yarmouth and the seaside. That's after you have sampled the mouthwatering fish and chips from Big Fry. A very busy shop serving only the best. Enjoy yourself.

Roughton

FISH SHOP, Norwich Road. Tel: 0263 761289

Open: Tue – Sat midday – 2.00 p.m. (Fri & Sat from 11.30 a.m.) all year; Sun, Tue – Thur 4.30 p.m. – 10.00 p.m.; Fri 4.30 p.m. – 11.00 p.m.; Sat 4.30 p.m. – midnight May – Sept.

Facilities:	T/A & R (L); P; T.
Fish finds:	Cod, haddock, plaice, rock, skate, others on request. Fish and chips to take-and-taste from around £1.60; sit-and-savour from £3.50.
Fry:	Vegetable fat.
Side-lines:	Mushy peas, pickled gherkins, pickled onions.
Wrapping:	Paper or cartons.

Dave and Linda Thake (no, not hake!) have been running this busy thirty-year-old outlet for five years. They've built a good reputation for fresh, quality fare at reasonable prices, served in pleasant surroundings. The comfortable restaurant seats just two dozen. It's easy to find, on the A140 three miles from Cromer, with the New Inn opposite.

Mrs I. Bowman travels regularly from Peterborough to sample the menu, and gives it full marks also for cleanliness, generous portions and the friendliness of all concerned.

The name Billingsgate either originated from Belin, an ancient king around 400 BC, or it could be associated with a water gate owned by a man named Biling.

Swaffam

MR CHIPS, 48 Market Place. Tel: 0760 721792

Open:	Mon – Thu 11.30 a.m. – 2.00 p.m.; 4.30 p.m. – 11.15 p.m.; Fri 11.00 a.m. – 2.00 p.m.; 4.00 p.m. – 11.30 p.m.; Sat 11.00 a.m. – 11.45 p.m.
Facilities:	T/A & R; P near; wheelchair access.

Fish finds:	Cod, haddock, plaice, rock, scampi, skate. Fish and chips to take-and-taste from around £1.50; sit-and-savour around £1.75.
Fry:	Dripping.
Side-lines:	Pickled onions. Other foods.
Wrapping:	White paper, trays.

Swaffam has the historic Oakleigh House in its midst, reminding everybody of days gone by when fish and potatoes were prepared and cooked below stairs by Mrs Bridges. But now fish and potatoes in the shape of chips are cooked on the ground floor at 48 Market Place where you can relax in the 50-seater diner.

Thetford

MR CHIPS, 9 Market Place. Tel: 0842 753018

Open:	Mon – Wed 11.00 a.m. – 2.00 p.m.; 4.00 p.m. – 11.00 p.m.; Thu 11.00 a.m. – 11.00 p.m.; Fri 10.30 a.m. – 11.00 p.m.; Sat 10.30 a.m. – 11.30 p.m.
Facilities:	T/A; P near; T; wheelchair access.
Fish finds:	Cod, haddock, plaice, rock, scampi. Fish and chips to take-and-taste from around £1.35.
Fry:	Dripping.
Side-lines:	Pickled onions. Other foods.
Wrapping:	White paper, trays.

Apart from a superb fish and chip shop, the bustling market town of Thetford boasts a castle and a priory, so pick up a cod and chips and explore.

Wymondham

BIG FRY, 36 Market Place. Tel: 0953 603210.

Open: Mon 11.30 a.m. – 2.00 p.m.; 4.30 p.m. – 11.00 p.m.;
Tue – Thu 11.30 a.m. – 2.00 p.m.; 4.30 p.m. –
11.30 p.m.; Fri & Sat 11.00 a.m. – 2.00 p.m.; 4.30 p.m.
– 11.45 p.m.

Facilities: T/A; P near; wheelchair access.

Fish finds: Cod, fish cakes, haddock, rock, scampi, skate. Fish and
chips to take-and-taste from around £1.35.

Fry: Dripping.

Side-lines: Pickled onions. Other foods.

Wrapping: White paper, trays.

*On the A11 from Norwich to Thetford road, you will find the little village
of Wymondham, steeped in ecclesiastical history, and the famous village
chippy. The manager and his staff beaver away, happy at work, serving up
the most delicious fish and chips at a very reasonable price.*

NORTHAMPTON-
SHIRE
Northampton

COLLEGE CHIPPY, 9–11 College Street. Tel: 0604 30298

Open: Mon, Tue, Thu 11.00 a.m. – 2.00 p.m.; Wed & Fri
10.30 a.m. – 2.30 p.m.; Sat 10.30 a.m. – 3.00 p.m.

Facilities:	T/A & R; T.
Fish finds:	Cod, haddock, plaice. Fish and chips to take-and-taste from around £1.65; sit-and-savour around £1.85.
Fry:	Oil.
Side-lines:	Mushy peas. Other foods.
Wrapping:	Bags, polystyrene trays.

A truly traditional British chippy and, not to put too fine a point on it, one of the old school – established no less than ninety years ago. Generations of students have had their staple diet from this establishment – and it would not have survived this long had it not consistently kept up a standard that met with approval throughout. Find it opposite Jeyes Jetty, with George Maoudis, a chippy of some twenty-two years' experience, behind the range – where he has been these last eight years.

ALBERT J. RAMSBOTTOM, 94 Abington Street. Tel: 0604 35236

Open:	Mon – Fri 11.30 a.m. – 2.30 p.m.; 5.00 p.m. – 9.00 p.m.; Sat 11.30 a.m. – 9.00 p.m.
Facilities:	T/A & R (L); P; T; wheelchair access.
Fish finds:	Cod, haddock, plaice, rock, skate. Fish and chips to take-and-taste from around £1.60; sit-and-savour around £3.00.
Fry:	Oil.
Side-lines:	Mushy peas, pickled gherkins, pickled onions. Other foods.
Wrapping:	Polystyrene trays, white news, printed bags.

'Traditional Fish 'n' Chips with a Touch of Class' is what it says on the front of their menu – and that is just what you get! Anyone who trades from premises near a local radio station (Northants '96') must be more than confident his product will consistently stand up to the closest scrutiny! Graeme Cook's 76-seater restaurant with waitress service, maroon and grey decor, and prints of Northampton adorning the walls, plus Albert Ramsbottom stories, does just that. He sets out to be good – and succeeds. Special children's menu available.

> *Mushy (marrowfat) peas have a very high fibre content – making an excellent, balanced meal with fish and chips.*

NORTHUMBERLAND
Amble

CHARLIE'S, 36 Albert Street. Tel: 0665 710206

Open:	Mon – Wed 7.00 p.m. – 11.00 p.m.; Thu – Sat 11.30 a.m. – 1.30 p.m.; 7.00 p.m. – 11.00 p.m.; Sun 6.30 p.m. – 10.00 p.m.
Facilities:	T/A & R; P near; wheelchair friendly.
Fish finds:	Cod, haddock, lemon sole, plaice, rock, shark, skate. Fish and chips to take-and-taste from around £1.50; sit-and-savour £2.00.
Fry:	Jennings FatMix.
Side-lines:	Mushy peas, pickled onions. Other foods.
Wrapping:	Trays, paper, greaseproof.

Why don't you amble into Charlie's chip shop and treat yourself to some super, succulent fish and chips or shark steak. Just relax in the 21-seater diner and the staff will serve you whatever's your pleasure. You will find Amble just off the A1 between Alnwick and Morpeth.

Ashington

KIELDER'S FISH BAR. Tel: 0670 812527

Open:	Mon & Tue 11.30 a.m. – 1.30 p.m.; 7.30 p.m. – 11.30 p.m.; Wed & Thu 11.30 a.m. – 1.30 p.m.; 4.30 p.m. – 11.30 p.m.; Fri 11.15 a.m. – 1.45 p.m.; 4.30 p.m. – 11.45 p.m.; Sat 11.15 a.m. – 1.45 p.m.; 7.30 p.m. – 11.45 p.m.; Sun 8.00 p.m. – 11.30 p.m.

Facilities: T/A; P near; wheelchair friendly.

Fish finds: Cod, haddock, plaice, skate. Fish and chips to take-and-taste from around £1.10.

Fry: Vegetable oil.

Side-lines: Mushy peas, pickled onions. Other foods.

Wrapping: Paper, trays, greaseproof, bags.

The north-east is packed with traditional fish and chip shops, serving up real honest-to-goodness food with no airs and graces, and friendly service. Fish and chips with prices averaging around £1.10–£1.50; what more do you want?

NOTTINGHAMSHIRE
Hucknall

ROY'S FISH AND CHIPS, 125 Portland Road. Tel: 0602 633622

Open: Daily 11.00 a.m. – 2.00 p.m.; 6.00 p.m. – midnight: (Sun morning only).

Facilities: T/A & R; P near; wheelchair access.

Fish finds: Cod, haddock, plaice, scampi. Fish and chips to take-and-taste from around £1.50; sit-and-savour around £1.90.

Fry: Vegetable oil.

Side-lines: Mushy peas, pickled onions. Other foods.

Wrapping: Polystyrene trays, white news, carriers.

Family-run business with Roy, wife Edna, son Alan and two nieces trading at this spot on the corner of Sherwood Street for over sixteen years. The building dates back to 1889 and Roy goes out of his way to keep the shop traditional. This also helps to hold down prices, while retaining the very high standard of fresh fish, delivered mainly from Scarborough and Aberdeen. They do all their own filleting and also sell wet fish, particularly for the home freezer. They often get large orders for 100 or more take-outs to local factories. The small 20-seater diner is excellent.

Old Basford

LAST & MARSHALL, 45 Arnold Road. Tel: 0602 783103

Open: Wed – Sat 11.45 a.m. – 1.30 p.m.; 5.00 p.m. – 10.00 p.m. (Sat morning only).

Facilities: T/A; P.

Fish finds: Cod, fish cakes (home-made), haddock, plaice, scampi. Fish and chips to take-and-taste from around £1.40.

Fry: Oil.

Side-lines: Mushy peas.

Wrapping: Polystyrene trays, white paper, bags.

More than a quarter of a century ago the Marshall family started trading from this site, opposite St Aiden's Church. A smart little chippy that prides itself in its cleanliness – acknowledged as such with a commendation from the local council. They aim to make only top quality fries, so do not single out any particular meal as 'special'. The same applies to the customers, each of whom is treated with courtesy and made to feel 'individual'.

'The best fish smell when they are three days old' – don't outstay your welcome.

OXFORDSHIRE

Chipping Norton

IN PLAICE, Horsefair. Tel: 0608 644303

Open: Tue – Sat 11.30 a.m. – 2.00 p.m.; 5.00 p.m. – 10.30 p.m. (June & July: Sat all day).

Facilities: T/A; P near.

Fish finds: Cod, haddock, plaice, scampi. (Friday special rock salmon, battered squid, shark steak.) Fish and chips to take-and-taste from around £1.60.

Fry: Vegetable oil.

Side-lines: Mushy peas, pickled gherkins, pickled onions. Other foods.

Wrapping: White news off-cuts.

This fish and chip shop is in the old Red Cross building, adjacent to the Blue Boar pub, one of the oldest buildings in the town. It's a small, attractively tiled chippy, clean and neat. A popular innovation is the Senior Citizen Lunch each Wednesday, with reduced price fish and chips. The Rugby Club lads always pop in for a jumbo-size take-away after training.

Headington

MEDITERRANEAN FISH BAR, 150 London Road. Tel: 0865 65894

Open: Mon – Sat 10.00 a.m. – 11.30 p.m.; Sun midday – 11.00 p.m.

Facilities:	T/A & R; P; T; wheelchair access.
Fish finds:	Cod, haddock, lemon sole, plaice, shark, skate. Fish and chips to take-and-taste from about £1.20; sit-and-savour around £2.80.
Fry:	Vegetable fat.
Side-lines:	Other foods.
Wrapping:	White wrap, trays.

Mr I. Malta (I wonder how he thought of the name for his outlet!) has been trading from this address for going on three years, though he's in his tenth year as a fryer. His prices and portions are very reasonable – in fact the only thing you could call a bit of a shark is the one on the menu.

SMART'S, 81 London Road. Tel: 0865 64920

Open:	Mon – Thu 11.30 a.m. – 2.00 p.m.; 4.30 p.m. – 11.30 p.m.; Fri & Sat 11.30 a.m. – 2.00 p.m.; 4.30 p.m. – midnight; Sun 5.00 p.m. – 11.30 p.m.
Facilities:	T/A.
Fish finds:	Cod, haddock, plaice. Fish and chips to take-and-taste from around £1.50.
Fry:	Vegetable fat.
Side-lines:	Mushy peas, pickled gherkins, pickled onions. Other foods.
Wrapping:	White wrap paper.

Smart by name, smart by appearance is this cheerful shop that has only been trading a couple of years. The proprietors are Italian and you'll find the outlet opposite Boots and next to Lloyds Bank in this town on the A4142, off the A40 on the London side of Oxford. This shop comes very well recommended – Mama Mia . . .

SHROPSHIRE
Gobowen (Nr Oswestry)

GOBOWEN FISH & CHIP SHOP, Sunny Bank, Old Whittington Road.
Tel: 0691 661307

Open:	Mon – Wed 11.30 a.m. – 1.30 p.m.; 7.30 p.m. – 11.30 p.m.; Thu 11.30 a.m. – 1.30 p.m.; 5.30 p.m. – 10.30 p.m.; Fri & Sat 11.30 a.m. – 1.30 p.m.; 4.45 p.m. – 11.45 p.m.; Sun 5.30 p.m. – 10.30 p.m.
Facilities:	T/A; P near.
Fish finds:	Cod, haddock, plaice, scampi. Fish and chips to take-and-taste from around £1.65.
Fry:	Vegetable fat.
Side-lines:	Mushy peas, pickled onions. Other foods.
Wrapping:	Polystyrene trays and white paper wrap.

Originally the old Post Office, but don't try posting a letter there – they've moved around the corner! The business has been in Mrs K. Tinsley's family since 1968. It is now run by Mrs Tinsley, her husband and father-in-law. The decor is grey, beige and brown with overhead fans. Staff are smartly turned out: men in pale blue shirts, dark ties, white smocks and trilbies; ladies in white smocks with red and white paper hats. A smart set-up, with very fine fare, deserving of all the praise given by Mrs P. Jones of Ellesmere Port.

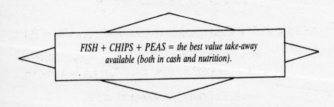

FISH + CHIPS + PEAS = the best value take-away available (both in cash and nutrition).

Newport

ZACH'S PLAICE, 77 High Street. Tel: 0952 825654

Open:	Mon – Thu 11.30 a.m. – 2.00 p.m.; 4.30 p.m. – 11.30 p.m.; Fri & Sat 11.30 a.m. – 11.30 p.m.
Facilities:	T/A & R (L); P; T.
Fish finds:	Cod, haddock, plaice. Fish and chips to take-and-taste from around £1.60; sit-and-savour from £3.00.
Fry:	Vegetable oil.
Side-lines:	Mushy peas, pickled onions. Other foods.
Wrapping:	Greaseproof, white wrap or trays.

They first started selling fish on these premises in 1856 – but it was not until five years ago that they were fried here also! John Thompson first sold wet fish here, followed by the Plant family between 1885 and 1929. Zach Yiacoumis had been in the fish and chip trade for a number of years when he arrived in Newport as a visitor – and ended up fulfilling a dream to set up a modern and clean take-away and luxurious, comfortable 50-seater restaurant. So attractive is the decor that the local Civic Society made an award for the sympathetic restoration of the premises. It gives the appearance of an up-market Continental taverna, that somehow makes the fish taste even fresher than they already are. Recommended by Mrs Jean Clewlow of Whitchurch.

Shrewsbury

CHIPPIE FISH & CHIPS, 244 Monkmoor Road. Tel: 0743 57574

Open:	Mon – Wed midday – 2.00 p.m.; 5.00 p.m. – 10.45 p.m.; Thu – Sat midday – 2.00 p.m.; 5.00 p.m. – 11.00 p.m.
Facilities:	T/A & R; P near; T; wheelchair access.

Fish finds:	Cod, haddock, plaice, scampi. Fish and chips to take-and-taste from around £1.60; sit-and-savour around £1.90.
Fry:	Vegetable oil.
Side-lines:	Mushy peas, pickled onions. Other foods.
Wrapping:	Paper double-wrap.

The shop has been trading for nearly twenty years, though Robert Witterick only took over a few years ago. The decor emphasizes the British aspect to the trade – with red seats and tables, blue floor and white walls. Find it on the corner of the Telford Estate opposite the Motorway Tyre Services in this market town on the River Severn. If you fancy a cuppa with your fish fare, Robert goes out of his way to make it to your taste, served in white china cups. Alternatively, for those with a wish for something stronger, there's the Monkmoor Hotel 100 yd down the road.

SOMERSET
Bridgwater

ADMIRAL BLAKE FISH BAR, 6 St Mary Street. Tel: 0278 423798

Open:	Mon – Thu midday – 2.00 p.m.; 5.00 p.m. – 11.30 p.m.; Fri & Sat 11.30 a.m. – 2.00 p.m.; 5.00 p.m. – midnight.
Facilities:	T/A & R (L); P near; T.
Fish finds:	Cod, fish cakes (home-made), haddock, plaice, seafood platter, scampi. Fish and chips to take-and-taste from around £1.50.
Fry:	Oil.
Side-lines:	Various foods.

Speciality: Potato scallops.

Wrapping: Paper, trays.

Bridgwater's most famous son, Admiral Sir Robert Blake (1598–1657) might have enjoyed this credit to his memory. The Ingram family have traded under the banner for thirty years. The shop recently underwent a complete refit, and is now decorated in white tiles and cream formica. Fixed seating in the restaurant is in cream and brown, with attractive use of wall and menu boards. Staff wear red tabards with the house name emblazoned on them, plus white overalls. Located a couple of hundred yards past St Mary's Church.

WEST QUAY FISH BAR, 8 West Quay. Tel: 0278 424648

Open:	Mon – Fri 11.30 a.m. – 2.00 p.m.; 5.00 p.m. – 11.30 p.m. (Fri till midnight); Sat 11.30 a.m. – midnight.
Facilities:	T/A; small dining area; P.
Fish finds:	Cod, haddock, plaice. Fish and chips to take-and-taste from around £1.45; sit-and-savour £1.90.
Fry:	Vegetable oil.
Side-lines:	Mushy peas. Other foods.
Wrapping:	Chippy trays, white news.

A real traditional chippy that first opened its doors over eighty-five years ago. The present proprietor Mr Len Gunn took over this, his first frying venture, a year ago. The outlet has a strong local following as well as tourist visitors. If you are a fish who wishes to avoid being fried, note the outlet is situated on the River Parrett, less than 100 yd from the Town Bridge. Bridgwater was the only town in the country engaged in making Bath brick, and it was here, in 1685, that the Duke of Monmouth was proclaimed king, only to be captured by James, Duke of York at Ringwood, and beheaded by him in London later that same year. The Duke of Monmouth should have stayed in Bridgwater and waited for this fine outlet to open!

Cheddar

BAYS FISH & CHIP RESTAURANT, Cliff Street. Tel: 0934 742392

Open:	Summer: daily midday – 2.30 p.m.; 5.00 p.m. – 10.30 p.m.; winter: Tue – Sat midday – 2.00 p.m.; 5.00 p.m. – 10.00 p.m.
Facilities:	T/A & R; P; T.

Fish finds:	Cod, haddock, plaice, scampi. Fish and chips to take-and-taste from around £1.50; sit-and-savour around £2.00.
Fry:	Groundnut oil.
Side-lines:	Mushy peas, pickled gherkins, pickled onions. Other foods.
Wrapping:	White wrap paper.

It seems the Bays has been established in Cheddar almost as long as the caves and the cheese! Not quite, just a mere fifty years or so. I certainly remember it from coach trips in my younger days, and the fare is as good now as ever. It's now run by John and Chris Marsh, who pride themselves in cooking only fresh fish to order. They say their customers prefer a few minutes' wait to being given food that has been left standing. The premises were rebuilt some years ago at the bottom of the gorge, near the Butcher's Arms pub. The restaurant – nothing elaborate or fussy about the decor and furnishings, but clean and bright – seats sixty-four, meaning coach parties are welcome, so get there early. They cook the fare the way you like it.

Crewkerne

WEST END FISH SALOON, 3 Hermitage Street. Tel: 0460 72678

Open:	Tue, Fri & Sat 11.30 a.m. – 1.30 p.m.; Mon, Tue & Sat 6.00 p.m. – 9.30 p.m.
Facilities:	T/A; wheelchair access.
Fish finds:	Cod, haddock, plaice. Fish and chips to take-and-taste from around £1.30.
Fry:	Oil.
Side-lines:	Various foods.
Wrapping:	Greaseproof, white paper.

Talk about living and working in harmony. There are two shops in Crewkerne, and the odd opening hours listed above are because they alternate with one another! The premises at West End have been established for half a century, have been run by the same family for nearly forty years and by Mike and Val Studley for nearly the last twenty-five years. If they don't know how to work things by now they never will! It's at the end of Market Street opposite F.W. Woolworth.

Glastonbury

TAYLOR'S PLAICE, 76 High Street. Tel: 0458 31139

Open: Mon, Tue, Thu – Sat midday – 2.00 p.m.; Mon, Tue & Thu 5.30 p.m. – 10.30 p.m. (summer extended hours).

Facilities: T/A; P.

Fish finds: Cod, fish cakes, fish fingers, haddock, plaice, scampi. Fish and chips to take-and-taste from around £1.45.

Fry: Vegetable oil.

Side-lines: Pickled gherkins, pickled onions. Other foods.

Wrapping: White wrap, chip bags.

Mr and Mrs Taylor are the names of the proprietors. Though they haven't been in the land of King Arthur for long, they have plans to make this shop the best in the west. Already many locals have claimed they have come to their rescue – particularly with their OAP special meals on Tuesdays and Thursdays. The shop is right next door to the Baptist church, which perhaps explains why it does not open on Sundays. No mention about 21 June, summer solstice! Major and Mrs G.W. Nation would rather talk about the excellence of their fare.

Taunton

CRISPINS, 20 East Reach. Tel: 0823 284983

Open:	Mon – Thu midday – 2.00 p.m.; 5.30 p.m. – 11.00 p.m.; Fri 11.30 a.m. – 2.00 p.m.; 5.00 p.m. – 11.00 p.m.; Sat 11.30 a.m. – 11.00 p.m.
Facilities:	T/A.
Fish finds:	Cod, plaice, scampi. Fish and chips to take-and-taste from around £1.55.
Fry:	Vegetable oil and fat.
Side-lines:	Mushy peas, gherkins, pickled onions.
Wrapping:	Paper then Crispins bag.

I notice they don't sell sole – which is just as well, as St Crispin is the patron saint of shoe-makers, and it might invite unjust comment! In fact the fare, though limited, is first-rate. The chippy is located in a listed building and run by a great team, led by Mr Harkham – who isn't listed!

CRISPINS RESTAURANT, 31–33 Station Road. Tel: 0823 275028

Open:	Daily 11.30 a.m. – 2.15 p.m.; 5.30 p.m. – 11.00 p.m.; Sat 11.30 a.m. – 11.00 p.m.
Facilities:	T/A & R (L); T.
Fish finds:	Cod, haddock, plaice, scampi. Fish and chips to take-and-taste from around £1.55; sit-and-savour around £2.60.
Fry:	Vegetable oil.
Side-lines:	Pickled gherkins, pickled onions. Other foods.
Wrapping:	Paper and own bag.

'And Crispin Crispian shall ne'er go by . . . But we in it shall be remembered.' Shakespeare: Henry V, *iv. 3.*

The Bard combined, with poetic licence, the two fabled Roman saints into one being for his purposes. For our purpose it serves to emphasize the quality of this outlet, why it should not be passed by, and how the friendly staff led by K. Markham will do everything to make sure your visit is truly remembered! You'll find them frying near the Royal Ashton Hotel. The large diner caters for around 100.

Wells

CRISPINS, 17 Broad Street. Tel: 0749 72340

Open:	Mon – Thu 11.30 a.m. – 11.00 p.m.; Fri & Sat 11.30 a.m. – 11.30 p.m.
Facilities:	T/A & R; P near; T; wheelchair friendly.
Fish finds:	Cod, haddock, halibut, plaice, rock, scampi, skate, swordfish. Fish and chips to take-and-taste from around £1.60; sit-and-savour around £2.10.
Fry:	Palm oil.
Side-lines:	Mushy peas, pickled onions. Other foods.
Wrapping:	White paper, bags, cartons.

Wells should be called a city, as it boasts a very fine cathedral. (Milton Keynes' developments corporation want to call their town a city, and they don't have a cathedral.) Anyway, Crispins is a first class fish and chip shop, serving everybody from all walks of life and all parts of the world, so on your next pilgrimage, pop into the chip shop and take a seat – there are thirty-two in all.

STAFFORDSHIRE
Hanley (Stoke-on-Trent)

GOLDFISH BOWL, 32–34 Goodson Street. Tel: 0782 23240

Open:	Daily 11.00 a.m. – 5.00 p.m.
Facilities:	T/A & R (L); P near; T.
Fish finds:	Cod, haddock, plaice. Fish and chips to take-and-taste from around £1.50; sit-and-savour around £2.00.
Fry:	Fat and oil.
Side-lines:	Mushy peas.
Wrapping:	White news.

They've been frying at this location for nearly thirty years, and still cod, chips and peas is the favourite dish. There's always plenty of room in this 172-seater super-diner. A.J. Moorhouse's bright and cheerful outlet is all decked out in gold and tan. You'll find it, and enjoy the fare, at the rear of the British Home Stores in this district of Stoke-on-Trent, where pottery was the main industry for centuries.

SUFFOLK
Aldeburgh

ALDEBURGH FISH & CHIP SHOP, 226 High Street. Tel: 0728 452250

Open:	Tue, Thu & Sat 11.45 a.m. – 1.45 p.m.; 5.00 p.m. – 9.00 p.m.
Facilities:	T/A; P.

Fish finds:	Cod, plaice, rock eel, skate, smoked salmon. Fish and chips to take-and-taste from around £1.50.
Fry:	Fat.
Side-lines:	Other foods.
Wrapping:	Bags, paper.

Proprietor Peter Cooney's establishment has been trading for over forty years. He has an unusual side-line – he cures his own salmon on the premises. I thought for a minute he was going to tell me he sold live crabs, to be synonymous with the poet George Crabbe who was born in the town in 1754! Anyway, you'll find the chippy, smoked salmon and all, at the lower end of the High Street. Recommended by T. Shemmins of Ipswich.

Beccles

KNELL'S, 23 Blyburgate. Tel: 0502 717632

Open:	Mon 11.00 a.m. – 2.00 p.m.; Tue – Sat 11.00 a.m. – 2.00 p.m.; 4.00 p.m. – 10.30 p.m. (Fri & Sat till 10.00 p.m.). Winter: Tue – Thu till 7.00 p.m.
Facilities:	T/A & R (L); T.
Fish finds:	Cod, haddock, halibut, lemon sole, plaice, rock, skate. Fish and chips to take-and-taste from around £1.50; sit-and-savour around £2.40.
Fry:	Vegetable oil.
Side-lines:	Mushy peas, pickled gherkins, pickled onions. Other foods.
Wrapping:	Polystyrene trays, paper.

Beccles stands on a navigable part of the Waveney, eight miles west of Lowestoft. The church of St Michael is interesting as it has a detached

*belfry tower. After your sightseeing drop into Knell's, which is situated in a
Grade II listed building that was built in 1700. Already building a good
reputation for quality of service and fare, it was recommended by
W.A. Bell of Woodbridge. A 40-seater diner awaits you and your friends,
so come sit and sample one of the prides of Beccles.*

Bury St Edmonds

MR CHIPS, St Andrews Street. Tel: 0284 754589

Open:	Mon & Tue 11.00 a.m. – 9.00 p.m.; Wed 10.30 a.m. – 9.00 p.m.; Thu – Sat 11.30 a.m. – 9.00 p.m.
Facilities:	T/A & R; P near; wheelchair access.
Fish finds:	Cod, haddock, plaice, rock, scampi, skate. Fish and chips to take-and-taste from around £1.35; sit-and-savour around £1.75.
Fry:	Dripping.
Side-lines:	Pickled onions. Other foods.
Wrapping:	White news.

*You must call at Bury St Edmonds, the gateway to Norfolk. But don't just
drive straight through. It's just off the A45 about half-way between
Newmarket and Stowmarket. Bury has lots of interesting features, fine
buildings, a lovely theatre and a very good fish and chip shop restaurant
serving succulent, appetizing fish. Take-and-taste or sit-and-savour in the
36-seater diner.*

Uncooked potatoes contain only about twenty-two calories
per ounce.

Felixstowe

BOUNTY FISHERIES, 115 High Road West. Tel: 0394 283356

Open:	Mon – Sat 11.30 a.m. – 2.00 p.m.; 4.45 p.m. – 10.00 p.m.
Facilities:	T/A; P near.
Fish finds:	Cod, cod's roe, haddock, plaice, rock eel, scampi, skate. Fish and chips to take-and-taste from around £1.55.
Fry:	Groundnut oil.
Side-lines:	Mushy peas, pickled gherkins, pickled onions. Other foods.
Wrapping:	Cartons and paper.

Mrs S.P. Wicks has been trading for some time at this seaside resort and ferry port on the Orwell, having built up a reputation for fine fare well served. All the fish is bought fresh and cooked fresh. Trade is brisk at this location, so don't be surprised if you have to queue. The wait is worth it: super portions of succulent fish with an abundance of chips.

Ipswich

MARIANI'S FISH AND CHIPS, 342 Nacton Road. Tel: 0473 727174

Open:	Tue – Sat 11.30 a.m. – 2.00 p.m.; 4.30 p.m. – 11.15 p.m.
Facilities:	T/A; P near; wheelchair access.
Fish finds:	Cod, haddock, plaice (on and off the bone), rock eel, skate, whiting (when available). Fish and chips to take-and-taste from about £1.45.
Fry:	Fat.

Side-lines: Pickled gherkins (in jars only), pickled onions. Other foods.

Speciality: Potato scallops.

Wrapping: Greaseproof, white wrap, newspaper.

Luigi Mariani started as a fryer in 1962, but gave it up in 1975. He couldn't keep away from the range, however, and opened this outlet in 1980. You'll find him at the end of a shopping parade, in this busy seaport where Cardinal Wolsey once planned, and just began, a great college. But for students of Britain's favourite take-away, there's plenty of fine fish to choose from at this spotless outlet.

POPLAR FISH BAR, 39 Woodbridge Road. Tel: 0473 258358

Open: Mon – Sat midday – 2.00 p.m.; 5.00 p.m. – midnight.

Facilities: T/A; P near.

Fish finds: Cod, haddock, lemon sole (when available), plaice, rock eel, skate, whiting. Fish and chips to take-and-taste from around £1.50.

Fry: Beef dripping.

Side-lines: Mushy peas, pickled gherkins, pickled onions. Other foods.

Speciality: Potato scallops.

Wrapping: Greaseproof, white paper, bags.

Bernie Fosdike's fine shop is close to the centre of Ipswich, near the rear of the Odeon Theatre. During the twenty or so years he has been frying, he's served many stars and artistes of theatre. I think he must have greasepaint rather than blood in his veins; in fact, as he has been known still to be serving the show-folk at past 2.00 a.m. – though he officially closes at midnight. Live theatre may be getting less frequent, but with the standard of fare Bernie dishes up, he will never go short of customers. Particularly liked are the potato scallops – slices of potato dipped in batter.

Lowestoft

S.M. BIRD, 6 Stradbroke Road, Pakefield. Tel: 0502 65727

Open:	Mon & Tue 11.30 a.m. – 1.30 p.m.; 4.30 p.m. – 11.00 p.m.; Thu 11.30 a.m. – 1.30 p.m.; 7.30 p.m. – 11.00 p.m.; Fri 11.30 a.m. – 1.30 p.m.; 4.30 p.m. – 11.30 p.m.; Sat 11.30 a.m. – 2.00 p.m.; 7.30 p.m. – 11.30 p.m.
Facilities:	T/A; P near.
Fish finds:	Cod, dabs, haddock, plaice, rock salmon, scampi, skate. Fish and chips to take-and-taste from around £1.35.
Fry:	Fat.
Side-lines:	Mushy peas, pickled onions.
Wrapping:	White paper, newspaper (bought from local journal).

Mr Stanley Bird and his wife Marcella run this spotlessly clean shop with its white decor and tiled floor, with the help of two friendly part-time staff. They've been trading here, on the Ipswich side of Lowestoft near the A12, for going on thirty-six years. They always buy fresh fish when available for this fine selection, which should be most of the time with the town's famous fish market not so far away. The shop is opposite the Tramway Hotel.

Saxmundham

FLORA TEA ROOMS, Dunwich Beach. Tel: 072873 433

Open:	Daily 10.00 a.m. – 6.00 p.m.
Facilities:	T/A; P; T.

Fish finds:	Cod, Dover and lemon sole, haddock, plaice, prawns, fresh salmon, skate. Fish and chips to take-and-taste from about £2.85.
Fry:	Oil.
Side-lines:	Various foods.
Wrapping:	White bags, white paper.

Sarah Elsley and Daphne Gill, who run this 70-year-old outlet, call the decor 'bright and basic'. But then, with magnificent views over the sea and countryside, in an unspoiled, uncommercialized area, who needs distraction close to the eye? There are also many places of historic interest, plus a bird sanctuary and National Trust property, all close at hand. The Ship Inn is the nearest pub. With free parking for up to 700 cars they can cope with all the publicity they have had over the years from London press to television and even the New York Times. *But then, when you serve up fare of this high standard, what more do you expect? Recommended by T.E. Robinson from Carlisle (a long way to come for a take-away!), and B.W. Holmes from Loughton.*

Stowmarket

CHIP INN, 5 Comb's Ford. Tel: 0449 677744

Open: Mon – Sat 11.30 a.m. – 1.30 p.m.; 4.30 p.m. – 10.00 p.m. (Mon till 9.00 p.m.).

Facilities: T/A; T; wheelchair access.

Fish finds: Cod, haddock, huss, plaice, skate. Fish and chips to take-and-taste from around £1.25.

Fry: Oil.

Side-lines: Mushy peas, pickled gherkins, pickled onions. Other foods.

Wrapping: White paper, trays, boxes with lids.

You'll find this cheerful chippy at the rear of the new Esso garage in this market town on the Gipping, 12 miles from Ipswich. Ron Lewis is behind the range, where he's been for five of his ten years as a fryer. He fries only fresh fish, which is also available in his wet fish department. The steady increase in turnover illustrates the standard of fare he offers his customers.

Wickham Market

EAT INN, 73 High Street, Woodbridge. Tel: 0728 746361

Open: Daily 11.30 a.m. – 1.45 p.m.; 4.30 p.m. – 10.00 p.m.

Facilities: T/A & R (L); P near; T; wheelchair access.

Fish finds: Cod, haddock, huss, plaice, scampi, skate. Fish and chips to take-and-taste from around £1.65; sit-and-savour around £2.20.

Fry: Oil.

Side-lines: Pickled gherkins, pickled onions. Other foods.

Wrapping: White bags, white paper. Large orders: free carrier.

Local people in a local business – that's the Pearce family, who have been trading from this shop for over twenty years. The premises, part of a conservation area, date back to the 16th century. However, a few years ago the interior of both shop and restaurant were completely refitted – while retaining the magnificent, old feature beams. Wooden tables have been installed in keeping with the traditional surroundings and the whole place is kept spotless. Find it on the main road next to the Co-op. Mrs J. Mayo compliments them on their speedy service and the way they always seem to 'bring out the best' in their frys.

Woodbridge

CASTLE KITCHEN, 64 Castle Street. Tel: 03943 6809

Open: Tue – Sat 11.30 a.m. – 1.30 p.m.; 4.45 p.m. – 9.45 p.m. (Thu till 7.00 p.m.).

Facilities: T/A; P near.

Fish finds: Cod, haddock, plaice, rock eel, skate. Fish and chips to take-and-taste from around £1.45.

Fry: Beef dripping.

Side-lines: Pickled onions.

Wrapping: White paper, printed bags.

They're friendly folk at the Castle Kitchen, and serve tasty frys using only fresh fish. This bright, clean shop has built up a keen following of regulars. Located on the corner of Mill Lane, opposite the recreation ground, the colour scheme here is beige, blue and orange with both In and Out doors to cope with the ever-increasing flow of traffic. The nearest pub is the Wagon and Horses in Bredfield Street.

SURREY
Banstead

SEINE RIGGER, 11 Nork Way. Tel: 0737 351168

Open:	Mon – Sat 11.45 a.m. – 2.00 p.m.; 5.15 p.m. – 10.30 p.m. (Mon till 10.00 p.m.).
Facilities:	T/A & R (L); P; T.
Fish finds:	Cod, haddock, huss, plaice, scampi, skate. Fish and chips to take-and-taste from around £1.95; sit-and-savour around £3.50.
Fry:	Groundnut oil.
Side-lines:	Pickled gherkins, pickled onions. Other foods.
Speciality:	Skate middles.
Wrapping:	Polystyrene trays, white paper, printed bags.

You'll find W.J. Lofthouse's 20-year-old outlet four doors from the junction with Firtree Road. Very smart decor with olive green carpet, imitation gas lamps with brass fittings and old prints of Billingsgate Market on the walls. The nearest pub is the Drift Bridge, half a mile away; the distance should encourage you to sit in at the Seine Rigger's 28-seater diner, rather than take-out, because they are licensed anyway.

Beddington

MR CHIPS, 178 Croydon Road.Tel: 081 681 7356
Also at 21 Cheam Common Road, Worcester Park. Tel: 081 337 5786

Open:	Mon – Fri midday – 2.00 p.m.; 5.00 p.m. – 11.00 p.m.; Sat 11.30 a.m. – 2.00 p.m.; 5.00 p.m. – 11.00 p.m.

Facilities:	T/A; P; T; wheelchair access.
Fish-finds:	Cod, haddock, plaice, rock, skate. Fish and chips to take-and-taste from around £1.50 (pensioners £1.00).
Fry:	Vegetable oil.
Side-lines:	Pickled gherkins, pickled onions. Other foods.
Wrapping:	Paper.

Mr P.M. Scroggs has owned Mr Chips for over fifteen years. It's on the Broadway, opposite the Plough pub. The decor is blue and white tiles throughout, with illuminated price signs and attractive prints of some of the dishes sold which look as good as the real thing – but the real thing tastes that much better! Children's portions of cod are served and all prices are very reasonable for this part of the country. A third outlet has been opened at 15 Langley Green Parade, Crawley, West Sussex. Tel: 0293 20790.

Carshalton

FISH 'R' US, 17 The Market, Wrythe Lane. Tel: 081 644 8574

Open:	Mon – Fri 11.00 a.m. – 1.30 p.m.; 4.00 p.m. – 10.00 p.m.; Sat 11.00 a.m. – 10.00 p.m.
Facilities:	T/A & R (L); T; wheelchair access.
Fish-finds:	Cod, haddock, plaice, rock salmon, scampi, skate. Fish and chips to take-and-taste from around £2.00; sit-and-savour around £3.00.
Fry:	Palm oil.
Side-lines:	Mushy peas, pickled gherkins, pickled onions. Other foods.
Wrapping:	Bags, paper.

The shop is in the middle of the shopping parade, but the decor of the restaurant, with its small bar, is definitely 'olde worlde', with beamed ceilings and walls. The friendly staff are dressed in red uniforms with the fryers in white shirts, ties and red trousers covered with red and white striped aprons. The name may have connotations with a certain toy shop, but I'm certain children of all ages will get worthwhile satisfaction from the fare on sale here. Recommended by Steve Robins of Sutton. Ami and Cecil Darvishi have been frying here for four years.

Cheam Village

SUPERFISH, 64 The Broadway. Tel: 081 643 6906

Open:	Mon – Sat 11.30 a.m. – 2.00 p.m. (Sat till 2.30 p.m.); 5.30 p.m. – 11.00 p.m. (Fri & Sat till 11.30 p.m.).
Facilities:	T/A & R; P near; T; wheelchair access.
Fish finds:	Cod, haddock, halibut, huss, lemon sole and plaice on the bone when available, scampi. Fish and chips to take-and-taste from around £1.80; sit-and-savour around £3.75.
Fry:	Beef dripping.
Side-lines:	Mushy peas, pickled gherkins, pickled onions.
Wrapping:	Greaseproof, white paper, bags.

Alan Archer runs this bright and cheerful fish shop near the centre of the town for Mr Rhodes' Superfish Co. Cheam was immortalized by one Anthony Hancock, a very funny man. I can't recall what comments he had about an area that has a park called Nonsuch; perhaps you could find out by taking the children there prior to a meal at Superfish. It doesn't matter if you have a big family, they have seating for about twenty-two. Special portions for children.

Croydon

McDERMOTT'S FISH & CHIPS, 6 Forestdale Centre, Addington. Tel: 081 651 1440

Open:	Mon – Sat midday – 2.00 p.m.; 5.00 p.m. – 9.30 p.m.
Facilities:	T/A & R; P (100 cars); T; wheelchair access.
Fish finds:	Cod, fish cakes, haddock, huss, plaice, scampi. Fish and chips to take-and-taste from around £1.60; sit-and-savour around £3.00.
Fry:	Groundnut oil.
Side-lines:	Mushy peas, pickled gherkins, pickled onions. Other foods.
Wrapping:	Greaseproof-lined paper bags.

Tony McDermott has been trading in the small shopping centre since 1987, building an increasing reputation for fine food and friendly service. All fish, in fact, is only fried to order, yet they are well organized to cut waiting time down to four minutes. Cod and haddock are both boned and skinned on the premises. It's on the corner of Featherbed Lane, and has recently opened the restaurant to seat thirty-five. The nearest pub is the Dales, also in the shopping centre. Last year they were London and South East regional winners of the Sea Fish 'Fish and Chip Shop of the Year' contest. By the way, if you want to drink and dine, there's no objection, nor corkage charged, to customers bringing their own wine.

SEAFARER, 65 Church Street. Tel: 081 688 7026

Open:	Mon – Wed 11.30 a.m. – 6.30 p.m.; Thu & Fri 11.00 a.m. – 8.00 p.m.; Sat 11.00 a.m. – 7.00 p.m.
Facilities:	T/A & R (L); T.

Fish finds: Cod, cod's roe, haddock, plaice, rock eel, scampi, skate.
Fish and chips to take-and-taste from around £1.75;
sit-and-savour around £2.80.

Fry: Vegetable oil.

Side-lines: Pickled gherkins, pickled onions. Other foods.

Wrapping: Cartons, paper.

*I wonder how many seafarers tramped along the old Brighton to London
road through Croydon in days of yore, to collect new ships' bells cast at
the foundries for which the area was once famous? These days the bells are
more likely to be in bottles containing whisky and the only seafarers in the
district, skateboard sailors. Nevertheless this establishment, with seating for
sixty in the diner, serves up fine fare next to Currys and Argos and 100 yd
from the Allders store. It was first opened nearly twenty years ago.*

Dorking

SEVEN SEAS FISH BAR, 59 Dene Street. Tel: 0306 889672

Open: Tue – Sat 11.30 a.m. – 2.00 p.m.; 5.00 p.m. – 9.30 p.m. (Sat till 9.00 p.m.).

Facilities: T/A.

Fish finds: Cod, haddock, huss, plaice. Fish and chips to take-and-taste from around £1.50.

Fry: Vegetable oil.

Side-lines: Mushy peas, pickled gherkins, pickled onions. Other foods.

Wrapping: White paper, bags.

Why not build up an appetite for your take-away with a walk in Glory Woods, which were given to the town in 1927 by Lord Francis Hope (Hope and Glory!) who later became Duke of Newcastle. When you are hungry enough the chippy is opposite the Post Office. It has light grain wood panels inside. The outlet has been there for a quarter of a century. Not quite as long as the woods, but long enough to serve up some excellent frys on a regular basis.

SUPERDISH, 245 High Street. Tel: 0306 889600

Open: Mon – Sat 11.30 a.m. – 10.00 p.m.

Facilities: T/A & R; P near; T; wheelchair friendly.

Fish finds: Cod, haddock, plaice, rock, skate. Fish and chips to take-and-taste from around £1.80; sit-and-savour around £2.10.

Fry: Vegetable oil.

Side-lines:	Mushy peas, pickled gherkins, pickled onions. Other foods.
Wrapping:	Greaseproof, paper, bags.

Here comes Superdish! Sounds almost like a flying saucer. I'll have my large cod and super supersonic chips on a plate, though, please! This is a very reasonably priced shop, with seating for about forty in the diner. Everything is cooked fresh, sizzling and delicious. Bring a bottle, they don't charge corkage. Coke on tap for the kids.

East Molesey

SUPERFISH, 90 Walton Road. Tel: 081 979 2432

Open:	Mon – Thu 11.30 a.m. – 2.00 p.m.; 5.30 p.m. – 11.00 p.m.; Fri 11.30 a.m. – 2.00 p.m.; 5.00 p.m. – 11.00 p.m.; Sat 11.30 a.m. – 2.30 p.m.; 5.00 p.m. – 11.30 p.m. (closed some Bank Holidays).
Facilities:	T/A & R; P near; T; wheelchair friendly.
Fish finds:	Cod, haddock, huss, plaice, scampi and more. Fish and chips to take-and-taste from around £1.85; sit-and-savour around £2.70.
Fry:	Beef dripping.
Side-lines:	Pickled gherkins, pickled onions. Other foods.
Wrapping:	Greaseproof, paper bags.

There's plenty of foot traffic around to make up the queues at this shop in the middle of a parade of shops. They make a particular effort to satisfy the children at this one, with special portions just for them. The outlet is bright, cheerful and spotless and gets very busy: a testament to the quality of food and service. Seating in the diner for thirt-five.

Esher

MERRYWEATHERS, 10 High Street. Tel: 0372 69807

Open:	Daily midday – 2.30 p.m.; 5.30 p.m. – 10.30 p.m.
Facilities:	T/A & R (L); P; T.
Fish finds:	Cod, haddock, huss, plaice, seafood platter, scampi. Halibut, lemon sole, skate when available. Fish and chips to take-and-taste from around £2.00; sit-and-savour around £4.25.
Fry:	Groundnut oil.
Side-lines:	Bread rolls baked on the premises, pickled gherkins, pickled onions.
Wrapping:	Reprint of 1946 *Surrey Advertiser*.

The name Merryweathers has been synonymous with good fish frying in Surrey for over forty years. The genuine, traditional fish and chips are well cooked and very tasty. The shop is situated mid-way between the cinema and Sandown Park racecourse. Compliments come from every quarter on the standard service and cleanliness.

Ewell

SUPERFISH, 9 Castle Parade, By-Pass Road. Tel: 081 393 3674

Open:	Mon 11.30 a.m. – 2.00 p.m.; Thu 5.30 p.m. – 11.00 p.m.; Fri 11.30 a.m. – 2.00 p.m.; 5.00 p.m. – 11.30 p.m.; Sat 11.30 a.m. – 2.30 p.m.; 5.00 p.m. – 11.30 p.m.
Facilities:	T/A & R; T; wheelchair access.
Fish finds:	Cod, haddock, halibut steaks, huss, whole lemon sole

when available, plaice on-the-bone, scampi, skate. Fish and chips to take-and-taste from around £1.65; sit-and-savour around £2.70.

Fry: Beef dripping.

Side-lines: Mushy peas. Other foods.

Wrapping: Bags, cartons, greaseproof, trays.

Where the A24, A240 and A232 join, there you will find Ewell. There you will also find this bright and cheerful fish restaurant with reasonable menu prices. The staff are always pleasant and courteous, with super service in the 36-seater diner.

Guildford

SEAFARE, 147 Worplesdon Road. Tel: 0483 62547

Open: Mon – Fri 11.30 a.m. – 2.00 p.m.; 5.00 p.m. – 11.00 p.m. (Fri till 11.30 p.m.); Sat 11.30 a.m. – 11.00 p.m.; Sun 5.00 p.m. – 11.00 p.m.

Facilities: T/A; P near; wheelchair friendly.

Fish finds: Cod, haddock, huss, plaice, scampi. Fish and chips to take-and-taste from around £1.90.

Fry: Palm oil.

Side-lines: Pea fritters, pickled gherkins, pickled onions. Other foods.

Wrapping: Fibre cartons, news off-cuts, white newspaper.

They've been frying at this outlet on the corner with Byrefield Road for more than eight years. It's opposite the Amoco petrol station in this town on the River Wey, 29 miles from London. Archbishop Abbot founded an almshouse in 1619 in what was to become Abbot's Hospital, in a magnificent Jacobean building. But we're more interested in the consistently succulent quality of the fare dished up by the owner of this busy take-away. Expect to queue, but it's worth it.

Mitcham

BUNTERS, 1–3 Upper Green West. Tel: 081 648 1549

Open: Tue – Fri 11.30 a.m. – 2.30 p.m.; 4.30 p.m. – 9.30 p.m. (Thu & Fri till 10.00 p.m.); Sat 11.45 a.m. – 8.00 p.m.

Facilities: T/A & R; P near; T.

Fish finds: Cod, haddock, hake, plaice, rock, scampi, skate. Fish and chips to take-and-taste from around £1.95; sit-and-savour around £2.55.

Fry: Groundnut oil.

Side-lines: Pickled gherkins, pickled onions. Other foods.

Wrapping: Polystyrene trays, paper.

'You must be one of the newer fellas?' Bing Crosby said to Frank Sinatra in High Society. *Mr Etheridge is the comparatively new owner, compared with his predecessor, who fried at this traditional outlet for over half a century. You'll find the shop on the Fair Green, next door to the King's Arms pub. Do they still hold which was the charter fair first founded in ancient times? That must be good for business!*

> *Early chippies were usually located in poorer parts of towns as deodorized cooking mediums did not come into their own until the beginning of this century.*

Morden

SUPERFISH, 20 London Road. Tel: 081 648 6908

Open: Mon – Fri 11.30 a.m. – 2.00 p.m.; Sat 11.30 a.m. – 2.30 p.m.; 5.00 p.m. – 11.30 p.m.

Facilities: T/A & R; P near; T; wheelchair friendly.

Fish finds: Cod, halibut, huss, lemon sole when available, plaice (whole on the bone), scampi, skate. Fish and chips to take-and-taste £1.65; sit-and-savour around £2.70.

Fry: Beef dripping.

Side-lines: Mushy peas, pickled gherkins, pickled onions. Other foods.

Wrapping: Greaseproof, trays, white paper.

With boundary changes some years ago, Morden became part of Greater London. They're a cheerful bunch of people in a bright and breezy outlet that is 10 miles from the centre of the Metropolis by road, rail or underground. They encourage families by providing ample seating, and always have a special children's menu available. Another of Mr Rhodes' value for money chippies.

New Malden

ROCK-N-ROE, 19 High Street. Tel: 081 949 3781
Also at 281 Putney Bridge Road, SW15. Tel: 081 949 3781

Open: Mon – Fri 11.30 a.m. – 2.30 p.m.; 5.00 p.m. – 11.30 p.m.; Sat 11.30 a.m. – 11.30 p.m.

Facilities: T/A & R (Putney (L)); P; T; wheelchair facilities.

Fish finds:	Cod, haddock, plaice, rock, skate. Fish and chips to take-and-taste from around £2.10; sit-and-savour from £2.35.
Fry:	Primol vegetable oil.
Side-lines:	Mushy peas, pickled gherkins, pickled onions. Other foods.
Wrapping:	Paper.

Music while you munch; snapper, crackle and pop; hake, rattle and roll; 'There's a Plaice For Us' – the puns are endless. What it frys down to is a unique eat-in-or-out experience. Proprietor Bob Hinton (Captain Bob to his customers and crew, for he sports a natty line in naval kit most of the time) is not only a third generation fryer, but a singer of some note. In the past he has toured with many top stars. Now he's home at the range, ready to serenade his customers at the drop of a chip, while simultaneously raising money for his favourite children's charity. Good food; good entertainment; well done. On a Saturday night at New Malden he holds a singalong (bring your own wine) at £5.00 a head.

Oxted

SEAFOOD (Oxted), 19 Station Road East. Tel: 0883 712689

Open:	Mon – Sat midday – 2.00 p.m.; 4.30 p.m. – 10.00 p.m.
Facilities:	T/A & R (L); P near; T.
Fish finds:	Cod, haddock, huss, plaice, skate. Fish and chips to take-and-taste from around £2.10; sit-and-savour around £3.30.
Fry:	Palm oil.
Side-lines:	Pickled gherkins, pickled onions.
Wrapping:	Bags and paper.

Our very own British Hart to Hart – Mr and Mrs A & D – have been trading next door to F.W. Woolworth for nearly twenty years. Unfortunately, the only sign of 'Freeway' is the M25 which you leave at the A22 turn-off to reach Oxted. I was going to say the only Rolls you see have sausage in them, but that is not true in this stockbroker belt – many of the customers arrive in them. The Hoskins pub is down the road and fine frys are available nearly all day in the nice little diner, which seats thirty-two.

Redhill

THE MASTER FRYER, 2 Linkfield Corner. Tel: 0737 766091

Open:	Mon – Sat 11.30 a.m. – 2.00 p.m.; Mon – Thu 4.00 p.m. – 11.30 p.m.; Fri & Sat 4.00 p.m. – midnight.
Facilities:	T/A; P near; wheelchair friendly.
Fish finds:	Cod, haddock, lemon sole, plaice, rock, skate. Fish and chips to take-and-taste from around £1.65.
Fry:	Palm oil.
Side-lines:	Mushy peas, pickled gherkins, pickled onions. Other foods.
Wrapping:	Trays, white paper, greaseproof, bags.

Yes, it's the Master Fryer by name and by nature with nice friendly staff. They used to dig red sand on the common here; I'd rather dig into the very tasty rock at this fine eatery! Or jump aboard a portion of skate wings and chips. Delicious!

One in three potatoes consumed in Britain is eaten as chips.

Tolworth

SUPERFISH, 59 The Broadway. Tel: 081 390 2868

Open:	Mon – Thu 11.30 a.m. – 2.00 p.m.; 5.30 p.m. – 10.30 p.m.; Fri & Sat 11.30 a.m. – 2.00 p.m.; (Sat till 2.30 p.m.); 5.00 p.m. – 11.00 p.m.
Facilities:	T/A & R (L); P near; T; wheelchair friendly.
Fish finds:	Cod, haddock, halibut, lemon sole, plaice, scampi, skate. Fish and chips to take-and-taste from around £1.85; sit-and-savour around £2.70.
Fry:	Beef dripping.
Side-lines:	Pickled gherkins, pickled onions. Other foods.
Wrapping:	Greaseproof, trays, white paper.

Another branch of Superfish which never fails to give good value in spotless surroundings. You can dine out in style with a family of four here for under £20.00. One lemon sole and chips, one plaice on the bone and chips, two children's platters, two Colas, one bottle of liebfraumilch or house wine, French bread and butter, a choice of pickles and sauces from the trolley. Could anyone ask for more? Then you can take the kids to Chessington World of Adventures, which is not too far away. Have a nice day!

Walton-on-Thames

MERRYWEATHERS, 109 Hersham Road. Tel: 0932 221105

Open:	Mon – Sat 11.30 a.m. – 2.30 p.m.; 5.00 p.m. – 10.30 p.m.
Facilities:	T/A; P near; wheelchair access.

Fish finds:	Cod, haddock, huss, plaice, skate. Fish and chips to take-and-taste from around £1.95.
Fry:	Groundnut oil.
Side-lines:	Mushy peas, pickled onions. Other foods.
Wrapping:	Own styled paper and cartons.

Somehow it was to be expected that a place like Walton-on-Thames would be high on the 'acquisition list' of Merryweathers, when they started out to build their chain of fry-houses several years ago. Why? Well, an up-market residential area with the super-swish, yet traditional, Merryweathers operation seems a natural marriage. They'd been frying at these premises for over thirty years when Carol and her colleagues came along three years ago. Barry and Carol Howarth now run the successful outlet for the company.

West Byfleet

SUPERFISH, 51 Old Woking Road. Tel: 09323 40366

Open:	Mon – Thu 11.30 a.m. – 2.00 p.m.; 5.30 p.m. – 10.30 p.m.; Fri & Sat 11.30 a.m. – 2.30 p.m.; 5.30 p.m. – 11.00 p.m. (Closed some Bank Holidays; opening times differ slightly in the two dining areas.)
Facillities:	T/A; R(L); P near; T; wheelchair friendly
Fish finds:	Cod, haddock, halibut, huss, lemon sole, plaice, scampi and more. Fish and chips to take-and-taste from around £1.65; sit-and-savour around £2.00.
Fry:	Beef dripping.
Side-lines:	Mushy peas, pickled gherkins, pickled onions. Other foods.
Wrapping:	Greaseproof, trays, white paper.

*There are two diners, one upstairs, one down. It would be wrong to
separate these two establishments, as Jane's 'Upstairs' is run by a member
of the family who own the Superfish chain, and she also uses the main
courses of freshly-fried fish from the downstairs restaurant in her outlet.
Several home-made sweets not available downstairs are available upstairs in
her pretty little domain. Downstairs has a clean, cheerful and welcoming
atmosphere that makes one think more of the sea and fresh air than the
mainly residential district that surrounds.*

Weybridge

FISHERMAN'S NET, 11 The Broadway. Tel: 09323 49791

Open: Tue – Thu 11.30 a.m. – 2.00 p.m.; 5.00 p.m. –
10.00 p.m.; Fri & Sat 11.30 a.m. – 2.30 p.m.; 5.00 p.m.
– 10.00 p.m.

Facilities: T/A & R; P; T.

Fish finds: Cod, haddock, huss, plaice, scampi, skate. Fish and
chips to take-and-taste from around £1.80.

Fry: Groundnut oil.

Side-lines: Pickled gherkins, pickled onions. Other foods.

Wrapping: White bag, white paper, white tray.

*If you are going to have a chippy in one of the most up-market areas of
the stockbroker-belt, with St George's Hill Estate and its homes of the
stars, then it is natural that one of the best known names in frying should
own it – Carol Merryweather. To say she is a 'Mermaid' of British fish
fryers should be sufficient also to emphasize that both her establishment
and fare, together with the service, is exemplary. The outlet has been
trading from the corner of Broadway, two doors from the National
Westminster Bank and opposite the V.G. Food Store, for around twenty
years. The decor of grey wall tiles with red seating gives a light, clean, airy*

appearance – borne out by two winning awards for health and hygiene. The nearest pub is Woody's in Woodham Road. Ms Merryweather's name now adorns the shop-front of a large group of outlets, who count among their assets one Harry Ramsden's of Guiseley, Yorks.

Whyteleafe

WHYTELEAFE FISH BAR, 2 Station Road. Tel: 0883 622510

Open:	Tue – Sat midday – 2.00 p.m.; 5.00 p.m. – 10.00 p.m.; (Sat till 9.00 p.m.).
Facilities:	T/A; P opposite; T (near).
Fish finds:	Cod, haddock, plaice, rock, scampi, skate. Fish and chips to take-and-taste from around £1.85.
Fry:	Palm oil.
Side-lines:	Pickled gherkins, pickled onions. Other foods.
Wrapping:	Greaseproof paper.

Dave Harris and Ted Stroud have been frying happily on the corner of Godstone Road, opposite the free car park, for a few years. They pride themselves in sticking to traditional ways with a reputation for quality. The shop enjoys a very good family lunch and tea-time trade, backed up with the baking done on the premises. They supply all your needs for a fresh fish dinner at home, other than a drink – which is obtainable at either the Whyteleafe Tavern or the Augustus Barnett off-licence – both nearby.

Potatoes are said to have been introduced from Peru into Europe by Spaniards early in the 16th century, and into Great Britain by Sir Walter Raleigh about 1585.

SUSSEX
Bexhill-on-Sea

TRAWLERS, 60 Sackville Road. Tel: 0424 210227

Open: Mon – Sat 11.30 a.m. – 1.50 p.m.; T/A: Mon 5.00 p.m.
                   – 9.00 p.m.; Tue – Sat 5.00 p.m. – 10.00 p.m.; R: Mon
                   5.00 p.m. – 7.50 p.m.; Tue – Sat 5.00 p.m. – 8.50 p.m.

Facilities: T/A & R; P near; T.

Fish finds:	Cod, haddock, huss, plaice, scampi, skate. Fish and chips to take-and-taste from around £1.45; sit-and-savour around £2.30.
Fry:	Vegetable oil.
Side-lines:	Pickled gherkins, pickled onions. Other foods.
Wrapping:	Polystyrene trays, paper.

Kevin Bland is running this establishment at the south end of Sackville Road. It's near the De La Warr Pavilion, which derives its name from an old Sussex land-owning family, a member of which, Thomas West, was the first governor of Virginia and gave his name, Delaware, to the state and river in the US. The 5th Earl married the heiress of the 4th Duke of Dorset and took the additional name of Sackville – hence the name of the road in which stands David's fine chippy. The fish for this outlet are mainly caught locally and he always tries to fry only to order.

Brighton

ALLAN JOHN'S, 8 Church Street. Tel: 0273 683087

Open:	Mon – Thu 10.00 a.m. – 5.30 p.m.; Fri 9.30 a.m. – 6.00 p.m.; Sat 9.00 a.m. – 6.00 p.m.; Sun 10.30 a.m. – 3.00 p.m.
Facilities:	R; P; wheelchair access.
Fish finds:	Cod, haddock, range of shellfish, seafood platter. Fish and chips to sit-and-savour from around £2.50.
Fry:	Vegetable oil.
Wrapping:	Containers.

In days gone by, the town was known as Brighthelmstone. That was a mouthful, but not tasty like those obtainable from this long-established

238

outlet. It's been here for over seventy-five years, long before NCP put up a car park next door, or Peter Dominic opened an off-licence at No. 2. But then, proprietor John Haslem wasn't around at the first fry either. He and his staff have given an excellent service since he took over seven years ago.

CAPTAIN'S TABLE, 83/85 Lustrells Vale, Saltdean. Tel: 0273 305577

Open:	Tue – Sat midday – 1.30 p.m.; 5.00 p.m. – 9.30 p.m.
Facilities:	T/A; P near.
Fish finds:	Cod, haddock, huss, plaice, scampi, skate. Fish and chips to take-and-taste from around £1.60.
Fry:	Palm oil.
Side-lines:	Mushy peas, pickled gherkins, pickled onions. Other foods.
Wrapping:	Boxes, paper.

Trevor Gee has fried his way to a Diploma of Merit inside two short years. He was also nominated as one of the eighteen national finalists for the Sea Fish Authority's 'Fish and Chip Shop of the Year Award 1989'. His shop's to be found next to the Circle K Superstore, a quarter of a mile inland from the A249 coast road.

GOLDEN FRY FISH BAR, 51 St James' Street. Tel: 0273 693467

Open:	Mon – Fri 11.30 a.m. – 7.30 p.m.; Sat 11.30 a.m. – 6.30 p.m.
Facilities:	T/A & R; P near; T; wheelchair access.
Fish finds:	Cod, haddock, huss, plaice, scampi, skate. Fish and chips to take-and-taste from around £1.50; sit-and-savour around £1.85.
Fry:	Vegetable oil.

Side-lines:	Pickled gherkins, pickled onions.
Wrapping:	Greaseproof bags, paper.

Gary Mason and his wife Carole manage this Numitor (Ross) outlet just a block back from the seafront near the Palace Pier. The place was completely refurbished just a couple of years ago. It now has seating for forty-two with waitress service. Dark wood tables and chairs contrast with the light wood panelling around the walls. A Welsh dresser to house the crockery is a nice touch in this open-plan shop. The Battle of Waterloo pub is close by. You're sure to get a friendly welcome from Sheila, the waitress, who hails from Stratford-upon-Avon but has worked at the Golden Fry for ten years.

RAINBOW FISH BAR, 191 Elm Grove. Tel: 0273 603969

Open:	Tue – Sat 11.45 a.m. – 2.00 p.m.; 5.00 p.m. – 10.00 p.m.
Facilities:	T/A; P near; wheelchair friendly.
Fish finds:	Cod, haddock, plaice, rock. Fish and chips to take-and-taste from around £1.40.
Fry:	Palm oil.
Side-lines:	Pickled onions. Other foods.
Wrapping:	Trays, white paper, greaseproof.

Somewhere over the Rainbow, you will find a fish and chip shop – probably just like this one in Brighton, serving fresh and wholesome fish plus heaps of chips! It's not very far from the Brighton race course. Get fed before you lose your shirt!

Fish meals eaten out increased by 25 per cent to reach a value of £13 million in the mid-1980s.

Eastbourne

HOLIDAY INN, 7 Carlisle Road. Tel: 0323 32481

Open:	11.30 a.m. – 2.30 p.m.; 5.00 p.m. – 9.00 p.m.
Facilities:	T/A & R (L); P near; T.
Fish finds:	Cod, haddock, plaice, skate. Fish and chips to take-and-taste from around £2.25; sit-and-savour around £2.75.
Fry:	Vegetable oil.
Side-lines:	Pickled gherkins, pickled onions. Other foods.
Wrapping:	Containers, paper.

This fine fish and chip restaurant is directly opposite the Congress Theatre, run by the Georgiou family, so try some freshly cooked fish and chips in their super sit-and-savour area, or walk along the Prom sharing a take-and-taste. Mind the seagulls! By the way, you can't sleep in at this Holiday Inn!

QUALISEA FISH RESTAURANT, 9 Pevensey Road. Tel: 0323 25203

Open:	Mon – Sat 11.30 a.m. – 8.00 p.m. (till 10.00 p.m. May – Oct).
Facilities:	T/A & R (L); P (limited); T.
Fish finds:	Cod, haddock, huss, plaice, scampi. Fish and chips to take-and-taste from around £1.40; sit-and-savour around £1.75.
Fry:	Groundnut oil.
Side-lines:	Pickled gherkins, pickled onions. Other foods.
Wrapping:	White wrap.

They've been frying at this traditonal chippy near the ABC cinema for nearly a quarter of a century. It's now run by Cosma Cosma (son of the founder Michael Cosma), who manages to serve up not only some of the tastiest but also the most reasonably-priced take-outs in the south. The decor is cream with green furniture and brown carpet. Speedy and pleasant service is aimed for in what could best be described as cosy conditions. Recommended by Mrs D. Mary Mullineux.

East Preston (Nr Littlehampton)

FRY INN, 127 North Lane. Tel: 0903 783395

Open:	Tue – Sat 11.45 a.m. – 1.45 p.m.; 5.00 p.m. – 8.00 p.m. (Fri till 8.30 p.m.).
Facilities:	T/A & R; P; T.
Fish finds:	Cod, haddock, huss, plaice, skate. Fish and chips to take-and-taste from around £1.45; sit-and-savour around £2.00.
Fry:	Palm oil.
Side-lines:	Mushy peas, pickled gherkins, pickled onions. Other foods.
Wrapping:	White paper, brown bag.

In 1931 the Duke of Norfolk sold much of the land in the area to the local authority. But it was not until thirty-five years later that W. Smerdon came along to open the first chippy. It's now run by Mr and Mrs Eed, and is situated on the corner of the main shopping street. Mr Smerdon always claimed humbly 'We are the best'! The Eeds work hard at living up to the claim. Certainly their many regulars think so, because they thoroughly recommend this busy fry-house with its 18-seater diner.

Horsham

DAY'S, Colletts Alley, 5 The Carfax. Tel: 0403 52246

Open: Mon, Tue, Wed 11.00 a.m. – 3.00 p.m. (R till 2.00 p.m.); Thu 11.00 a.m. – 7.00 p.m.; Fri 11.00 p.m. – 8.00 p.m.; Sat 11.00 a.m. – 6.00 p.m.

Facilities: T/A & R; P near; T; wheelchair friendly.

Fish finds: Cod, haddock, plaice, scampi, skate. Fish and chips to take-and-taste from around £1.50; sit-and-savour around £1.85.

Fry: Palm oil.

Side-lines: Pickled onions. Other foods.

Wrapping: Trays, paper, greaseproof, bags.

Mr and Mrs Critten oversee this pleasantly clean chippy, tucked away in Colletts Alley, serving Horsham folk with sizeable portions of fish and chips whether taking and tasting or sitting and savouring. The 45-seater diner has ample room for any size family. Horsham is an old market town, nearly half way to the Sussex coast. There's Smart's Pleasure Park in Littlehampton or the International Clown's Festival in Bognor Regis in April.

SEVEN SEAS FISH BUFFET, 44 East Street. Tel: 0403 53765

Open: Tue – Fri 11.30 a.m. – 2.00 p.m.; 5.00 p.m. – 10.00 p.m.; Sat 11.30 a.m. – 8.00 p.m.

Facilities: T/A & R; P near; wheelchair friendly.

Fish finds: Cod, haddock, huss, plaice, rock, skate. Fish and chips to take-and-taste from around £1.50; sit-and-savour around £1.85.

Fry: Palm oil.

Side-lines: Mushy peas, pickled gherkins, pickled onions.

Wrapping: Trays, white paper, greaseproof, bags, cartons.

Sail the Seven Seas, me hearties! Well, you won't get sea sick here, it's just the name the proprietors have given this town centre chippy serving succulent haddock and chips for as little as £1.50 for a take-and-taste. Or you can sit comfortably in the 60-seater diner and pay just £1.85.

Lancing

COD CAVE, 134 South Street. Tel: 0903 754996

Open:	Mon – Sat 11.45 a.m. – 2.00 p.m.; 5.00 p.m. – 9.00 p.m.; (Sat till 10.00 p.m.).
Facilities:	T/A; P near; wheelchair access.
Fish finds:	Cod, haddock, huss, plaice, scampi. Fish and chips to take-and-taste from around £1.30.
Fry:	Vegetable oil.
Side-lines:	Mushy peas, pickled gherkins, pickled onions. Other foods.
Wrapping:	Polystyrene trays, paper, bags.

J. Khokhar is still comparatively new to this extra clean outlet in a parade of shops near the seafront. He is very aware of his competition, which means the customer will always get the benefit. He is keen to build his trade and so offers a good selection, well cooked, with attentive service. If you want to try and fry at home, he'll also supply uncooked fish.

Newhaven

GALLEY, 6–7 Newhaven Square. Tel: 0273 514273

Open:	Mon – Sat 10.00 a.m. – 9.00 p.m.
Facilities:	T/A & R (L); P near; T.
Fish finds:	Clams, cod, haddock, huss, plaice, scampi, skate, whitebait. Fish and chips to take-and-taste from around £2.30; sit-and-savour around £2.95.
Fry:	Vegetable oil.

Side-lines:	Mushy peas, pickled onions. Other foods.
Speciality:	Delicious apple pie.
Wrapping:	Bags, paper.

The French may have been the originators of the chip, but it took the British to team it with fried fish. Why catch the boat from here to Dieppe when you can enjoy such fine fare by staying at home? Find this fish and chip galley in the pedestrian precinct of the town square, next to the Co-op. It's been open now for over eight years; Mr Coe and his team are doing a great job and his continental customers love it. Special prices for senior citizens and a £1.00 menu for children.

Polegate

POLEGATE FISHERIES, 31 High Street. Tel: 03212 3157

Open:	Tue – Sat T/A: 11.00 a.m. – 2.00 p.m.; 5.00 p.m. – 9.30 p.m.; R: 11.30 a.m. – 1.30 p.m.; 5.00 p.m. – 8.30 p.m.
Facilities:	T/A & R; P near; T; wheelchair access.
Fish finds:	Cod, cod's roe, haddock, huss, plaice, skate. Fish and chips to take-and-taste from around £1.70; sit-and-savour around £1.90.
Fry:	Groundnut oil.
Side-lines:	Marrowfat peas, pickled gherkins, pickled onions.
Wrapping:	Greaseproof bags, paper.

Nicky Charitou has been at this address for only five years, though he has been frying for over twenty-five. The chippy is just before the level crossing travelling south on the A22: turn left at the Polegate crossroads. The colour scheme of the shop is red and white with grained wood, formica topped tables, upholstered chairs and bench seats. Only fresh fish is fried, with mouth-watering results.

Rustington

THE STREET FISH BAR, 96 The Street. Tel: 0903 785318

Open:	Tue – Sat 11.30 a.m. – 2.00 p.m.; 5.00 p.m. – 9.00 p.m.
Facilities:	T/A; P near.
Fish finds:	Cod, haddock, huss, plaice, skate. Fish and chips to take-and-taste from around £1.60.
Fry:	Vegetable oil.
Side-lines:	Mushy peas, pickled gherkins, pickled onions. Other foods.
Wrapping:	White paper, bags.

Mr Tryfonos has been trading from this outlet for only a short while, but has built up a strong following of regulars. Among them is Mrs Val May who lives close by. The decor of this take-away is grey and white formica wall panels, divided by red strips, and a red and white tiled floor. The staff, who are always courteous, are decked out in red tabards. The nearest pub, the Lamb, is just 50 yd away.

Rye

KETTLE O' FISH, 25 Wish Street. Tel: 0797 223684

Open:	Daily 11.45 a.m. – 2.00 p.m.; 4.45 p.m. – 8.30 p.m. (summer till 10.30 p.m.).

Facilities: T/A & R; P; T.

Fish finds: Cod, huss, plaice, scampi. Fish and chips to take-and-taste from around £1.85.

Fry: FryMax vegetable fat.

Side-lines: Mushy peas, pickled gherkins, pickled onions.

Wrapping: Polystyrene boxes for fish, bags.

The proprietor, S. Tarrant, has been frying here for a few years. The shop is positioned nicely on the main A259, opposite the yacht moorings in this ancient cinque port. Mr Tarrant knows how important it is to give his customers only the best as they, more than most, not only know the difference but would not be backward in telling him. After all, many varieties of fish can almost jump from the sea into his 'Kettle'. For the tourist there are many interesting buildings to view, including the 12th-century Ypres tower, the Land Gate and the ancient Mermaid Inn. If you've had a bad day's fishing you can always console yourself with a good feed from the chippy – and imagine you caught it!

Seaford

TRAWLERS, 32–34 Church Street. Tel: 0323 892520

Open: Mon – Thu 11.30 a.m. – 2.00 p.m.; 5.00 p.m. – 9.00 p.m.; Fri & Sat 11.30 a.m. – 2.00 p.m.; 5.00 p.m. – 10.00 p.m.

Facilities: T/A & R (L); P near; T; wheelchair friendly.

Fish finds: Cod, huss, plaice, scampi, skate. Fish and chips to take-and-taste from around £1.40; sit-and-savour around £2.20.

Fry: Palm oil.

Side-lines: Pickled gherkins, pickled onions. Other foods.

Wrapping: Trays, white paper.

Apart from the seaside, there are several good golf courses round about, and the Old Clergy House belonging to the National Trust just a few miles away. When you've finished whatever you have to do, and worked up a worthwhile appetite, head for Mr and Mrs Berry's 66-seater outlet near the junction with the A259 in the town centre. With a well-earned reputation stretching farther than the immediate vicinity, this chippy has been written about and praised by the media consistently over the years. After your delicious fish meal try one of the super puds.

Southwick

**WINDMILL FISH BAR, 177 Windmill Parade, Old Shoreham Road.
Tel: 0273 596650**

Open: Tue – Sat 11.00 a.m. – 1.30 p.m.; 5.00 p.m. – 9.00 p.m.

Facilities: T/A & R; P near; T; wheelchair friendly.

Fish finds: Cod, Dover and lemon sole, haddock, halibut, plaice, rock, skate. Fish and chips to take-and-taste from around £1.55; sit-and-savour £3.25.

Fry: Palm oil.

Side-lines: Pickled gherkins, pickled onions. Other foods.

Wrapping: Greaseproof, bags.

Mr and Mrs Garlick have spent seven years knocking the Windmill Fish Bar into shape. They have a great selection of super fish, plenty of room in the 24-seater diner and a wide choice in the DIY for home cooking. The shop came third in the Daloon Foods 'Fish and Chip Shop of the Year Award 1989'. Keep on frying!

St-Leonards-on-Sea

HOLLINGTON FISH BAR, 171 Battle Road. Tel: 0424 423551

Open: Tue – Sat 11.30 a.m. – 2.00 p.m.; 5.00 p.m. – 10.00 p.m.

Facilities: T/A; P near; wheelchair friendly.

Fish finds: Cod, haddock, plaice, rock, skate. Fish and chips to take-and-taste from around £1.50.

Fry: Palm oil.

Side-lines: Mushy peas, pickled gherkins, pickled onions.

Wrapping: Trays, white paper, greaseproof.

Yet another traditional chippy serving good honest fare in clean and pleasant surroundings, with customer satisfaction first on the list – but be prepared to queue with everybody else. It's an interesting place with St Leonards, Hastings, 1066, and all that. Hastings, Bodiam and Pevensey castles are close by, and I bet you can't find Winkle Island . . . well it's at the bottom of East Hill, near the fishermen's quarter. Or take your son's pet mouse along to the Piece of Cheese House, All Saints Street.

Worthing

OLD NICK'S, Pavilion Road, Tel: 0903 200606

Open: Tue – Sat 11.30 a.m. – 2.00 p.m.; 5.00 p.m. – 10.00 p.m.

Facilities: T/A; P.

Fish finds: Cod, haddock, huss, plaice, skate. Fish and chips to take-and-taste from around £1.75.

Fry: FryMax vegetable oil.

Side-lines:	Mushy peas, pickled gherkins, pickled onions. Other foods.
Wrapping:	Bags, trays.

They've been frying on this site for over seventy years, though Nick John took over the range only in the early 1980s. The house specialty is a sea-food platter to take-away. All the fish is skinned, and they guarantee the oil is changed daily. Add the bright red decor – hence the devil as a logo – and you have a first-class chippy in every way. Perhaps that's why the celebrities flock to Old Nicks when they are in the area. Su Pollard and Bill Simpson are two to mention. When he's not afraid to cater for parties of up to 350 (yes 350), no wonder Mrs M.B. Clark, Mrs M. Wilson and Mrs C. Price all consider him to be the best. Nick also has a special menu for children at reduced prices, plus senior citizens' and vegetarians'. Home deliveries are also catered for.

TAISTY PLAICE, 63 Rowlands Road. Tel: 0903 38678

Open:	Mon – Sat midday – 2.00 p.m.; 5.00 p.m. – 9.00 p.m.; (Mon & Sat till 8.00 p.m.).
Facilities:	T/A & R; P near; wheelchair access.
Fish finds:	Cod, haddock, huss, plaice. Fish and chips to take-and-taste from around £1.85; sit-and-savour around £2.10.
Fry:	Palm oil.
Side-lines:	Mushy peas, pickled gherkins, pickled onions. Other foods.
Wrapping:	Greaseproof, white paper.

They are nearly all family-run shops in this parade, a couple of hundred yards from the main precinct. The Lamond family at the chippy are no exception. Father and son are in partnership with both their wives assisting, and they also have two cheerful part-time staff. The restaurant has wood-grain panels with just sixteen Windsor-style chairs and tables all nicely laid out. What's this I hear, Derek Jameson is a regular customer, both to sit-in and take-out? The grub is definitely good enough to have passed the Jameson test.

TYNE & WEAR
Blaydon

FRIER'S PLAICE, 5 Harriet Street. Tel: 091 4141340

Open:	Mon – Wed 11.30 a.m. – 1.30 p.m.; 7.00 p.m. – midnight; Thu 11.00 p.m. – 1.30 p.m.; 4.30 p.m. – midnight; Fri 11.30 a.m. – 1.30 p.m.; 4.00 p.m. – midnight; Sat 11.30 a.m. – 2.00 p.m.; 7.00 p.m. – midnight.
Facilities:	T/A; P.
Fish finds:	Cod, haddock, scampi, sole, squid rings. Fish and chips to take-and-taste from around £1.50.
Fry:	Oil.
Side-lines:	Mushy peas, pickled onions.
Wrapping:	Greaseproof, white off-cuts, carrier bags

Tom Fryer – yes, that is his name! – opened up in Burnopfield five years ago, and moved to this fifty year-old outlet last year. He has speedily built up a good reputation for fine fare, well cooked, and has brought many of his old clientele with him. The quality of fare is perhaps why – along with such names as Kirsty Wade and several soccer stars – he counts a number of doctors and dentists among his regulars. The shop is fully tiled in white and is particularly recommended for its cleanliness by Mrs Joan Jenson. More recent 'star' eaters include scrum-half Steve Bainbridge and goalkeeper Dave Besent.

Newcastle upon Tyne

BIMBIS, Odeon. Tel: 091 261 6334
Also at Fish & Boat. Tel: 091 232 4327; Haymarket. Tel: 091 261 5607;
Eldon Square Food Court. Tel: 091 232 3330

Open:	Daily 9.30 a.m. – 11.30 p.m.
Facilities:	T/ & R; P; T.
Fish finds:	Cod, haddock, plaice. Fish and chips to take-and-taste from around £1.70; sit-and-savour around £2.50.
Fry:	Oil with some fat.
Side-lines:	Mushy peas, pickled gherkins, pickled onions. Other foods.
Wrapping:	Cartons.

The Bimbi family has four excellent outlets in Newcastle. The Odeon shop was among the area finalists in the 1989 Sea Fish 'Fish and Chip Shop of the Year' contest.

SOUTH GOSFORTH FISHERIES, 11 Station Road, South Gosforth.
Tel: 091 2854896

Open:	Mon – Sat 11.30 a.m. – 2.00 p.m.; 5.00 p.m. – 11.45 p.m.; Sun 7.00 p.m. – 11.30 p.m.
Facilities:	T/A; P near.
Fish finds:	Cod, haddock. Fish and chips to take-and-taste from around £1.50.
Fry:	FryMax oil.
Side-lines:	Pickled onions. Other foods.
Specialities:	Black pudding, haggis.
Wrapping:	White paper.

Syd Appleby has been trading 'just down from the Metro' for over thirty years. The shop is smartly tiled throughout in red and white, with grey floor tiles. Business is brisk, not only because of the high standard of fare and friendly service, but also the position of the shop. There are several golf courses close at hand and it is near to the Great North Road, which carries all the traffic to the racecourse.

Spitaltongues

VILLAGE CHIPPY, 1 Cross Morpeth Street. Tel: 091 261 4330

Open:	Tue 7.30 p.m. – 11.30 p.m.; Thu – Sat 11.30 a.m. – 1.30 p.m.; 7.30 p.m. – 11.30 p.m.
Facilities:	T/A; P near.
Fish finds:	Cod, haddock. Fish and chips to take-and-taste from around £1.40.
Fry:	Palm oil.
Side-lines:	Fish cakes, mushy peas. Other foods.
Wrapping:	White paper bags, paper, newspaper.

Mrs Latimer runs a very friendly traditional village chip shop. She knows a thing or two about how to treat her many customers, with cod and haddock on offer, as well as tasty fish cakes, a favourite with the children, and chips of course! Spitaltongues is not far from Newcastle town moor.

Sunderland

BARNES FISHERIES, 6 Silksworth Lane, Barnes Roundabout. Tel: 091 5110022

Open:	Mon – Thu 11.30 a.m. – 1.30 p.m.; 5.30 p.m. – 11.30 p.m.; Fri 11.30 a.m. – 1.30 p.m.; 4.30 p.m. –

11.30 p.m.; Sat 11.30 a.m. – 1.30 p.m.; 5.30 p.m. –
11.30 p.m.

Facilities:	T/A; P.
Fish finds:	Cod, haddock, plaice, scampi. Fish and chips to take-and-taste from around £1.60.
Fry:	Beef dripping.
Side-lines:	Mushy peas, pickled onions.
Wrapping:	White paper.

*Frank and Pauline Bernard are now well settled into this friendly chippy,
tucked behind the Barnes Hotel. They've been here for about three years
and have built a strong following of regulars, with recommendations from
the likes of E.B. Smith. Find the shop off the B1286, which crosses the
Durham Road in the south-west of the city. It's half-tiled in green and has
an unusual red brick counter, topped with marble effect. Lots of plants,
and the paintings of local artists adorning the walls, make this both a
pleasant and interesting 'take-and-taste' experience. Only fresh fish is fried.*

FISH AND CHIPS

THE LAUGHING CAVALIER
BY
FRANS HALS

WALLACE COLLECTION

FRY-FRY, 33 Blackwood Road, Town End Farm. Tel: 091 536 9948

Open:	Mon – Sat 11.15 a.m. – 1.30 p.m.; 6.45 p.m. – midnight.
Facilities:	T/A; P near.
Fish finds:	Cod, haddock, lemon sole, plaice, scampi. Fish and chips to take-and-taste from around £1.35.
Fry:	Beef dripping.
Side-lines:	Mushy peas, pickled onions. Other foods.
Wrapping:	Cartons, white bags, white paper.

Mr John Downey, the Fry-Fry owner, has a large staff of girls working for him, all of whom he describes as 'very nice'. Lucky Mr Downey has them all geared out in smart overalls with name badges to encourage friendliness with the customers. In fact, you don't have to encourage friendliness, because that's the way everyone is in this westernmost part of town adjoining the A19. Perhaps it's the quality of the fry that makes people happy. The gourmet scampi and lemon sole are certainly worth travelling a few miles to indulge in. If you need to work up an appetite, why not have a look around the nearby aircraft museum?

SILVER GRID, 9 Sea Road, Seaburn. Tel: 091 548 6046

Open:	Mon – Sat 11.30 a.m. – 1.30 p.m.; 4.30 p.m. – 11.30 p.m.
Facilities:	T/A; P.
Fish finds:	Cod, haddock. Fish and chips to take-and-taste from around £1.35.
Fry:	Fat.
Side-lines:	Mushy peas. Other foods.
Wrapping:	Greaseproof, white paper.

You can change the name out-front and refurbish the place completely, but once a local chippy is known by a particular name, you'll never change it. This one, which has been frying for over forty years, is known throughout the area as Trembaths, although they have not owned it for over twenty years! Smartly done out in Silver Grid colours of dark brown walls and yellow ceiling, with pictures of Sunderland at the turn of the century all around, and plants surrounding the window area, it is a very pleasant, hygienic take-away. The Blue Bell is the nearest pub.

Walker

GUS'S CHIPPY, 109/111 Wharrior Street. Tel: 091 2657513

Open: Mon – Sat 11.30 a.m. – 1.30 p.m.; 8.00 p.m. – 11.30 p.m. (Fri & Sat till midnight).

Facilities: T/A; P; wheelchair access.

Fish finds: Cod, haddock. Fish and chips to take-and-taste from around £1.20.

Fry: Fat.

Side-lines: Mushy peas, pickled onions. Other foods.

Wrapping: White paper, newspaper.

Gurmel Singh Hyare (Gus) has been frying here for eight years, though it has been a chippy for around fifteen. Only in an emergency will he buy frozen fish; otherwise he buys daily direct from the quayside. You'll find this outlet next to the Lightfoot Stadium near Walker Park. Gus reports that trade has gradually picked up during his ownership, which must mean he is getting it right. Certainly the Spowart family think so: Kim, Victoria, Barrie and 'V.V.' recommend the shop.

Washington

RITZ FISH SHOP, 12 Eden Villas, Columbia. Tel: 091 4162329

Open: Mon – Sat 11.30 a.m. – 1.15 p.m.; 8.00 p.m. – 11.30 p.m.

Facilities: T/A; P.

Fish finds: Cod, haddock. Fish and chips to take-and-taste from around £1.30.

Fry: Fat.

Side-lines: Mushy peas. Other foods.

Wrapping: White paper.

A family of four can dine from the Ritz for less than a fiver. Though not exactly the Paris hotel of that name made famous by Blanche and Claude Auzello, or even the similar, equally prestigious, venue in London's Piccadilly, Jayne Thompson's fine chippy on the north of the Wear is making its mark with fryer Denise Bamburgh behind the range. Cleanliness and quality are their mottoes, always remembering that the only people who count are the customers. I'll add good value which many other establishments – let alone those other Ritzes – would find it difficult to equal. The walls are white, half-tiled, with a black and white trim. The floor is blue vinyl.

> *Ten million tons of salt is produced a year in the world, but not all goes on chips! Glass and explosives could not be produced without salt and its by-products.*

WARWICKSHIRE
Atherstone

DOLPHIN FISH & CHIP SHOP, 62 Long Street. Tel: 0827 716957

Open:	Mon – Thu 11.30 a.m. – 2.00 p.m.; 4.30 p.m. – 11.30 p.m.; Fri & Sat 11.30 a.m. – midnight.
Facilities:	T/A & R; P; T; wheelchair access.
Find finds:	Cod, haddock, plaice. Take-and-taste from around £1.25; sit-and-savour from around £1.75.
Fry:	Vegetable oil.
Side-lines:	Mushy peas, pickled onions. Other foods.
Wrapping:	White paper.

T. & M. Socratous are now well established at this very clean outlet opposite the Co-op supermarket: they've been here nearly eight years. Atherstone is on Watling Street, the old Roman road that ran from Dover to Wroxeter. The shop has seating for twenty with a white and cream decor, and photo-signs bordered with green and yellow.

Bidford on Avon

SEAFOOD, 84 High Street. Tel: 0789 773310

Open:	Mon – Sat 11.45 a.m. – 2.00 p.m.; 4.30 p.m. – 11.00 p.m.
Facilities:	T/A; P.
Fish finds:	Cod, haddock, plaice. Fish and chips to take-and-taste from around £1.60.

Fry: Vegetable oil.

Side-lines: Mushy peas, pickled onions. Other foods.

Wrapping: White paper.

Recently extended and redecorated throughout, this fine chippy stands in an idyllic spot on the northern bank of the River Avon, with the Frog and Bullrush opposite, just one of five pubs in the village just a chip's throw from the ancient bridge that was built by monks. On the opposite riverbank is a large car park, which plays host to thousands of tourists during the summer months. With Anne Hathaway's cottage just a short drive in Shottery village near Stratford upon Avon, Bidford forms an excellent base. Add the first class fare available at the Seafood, and what more could anyone want?

Henley-in-Arden

SEA SPRAY, 113 High Street. Tel: 05642 3461

Open: Mon – Wed 11.30 a.m. – 3.00 p.m.; 4.30 p.m. – 11.00 p.m.; Thu – Sat 11.30 a.m. – 3.00 p.m.; 4.30 p.m. – 11.30 p.m.

Facilities: T/A.

Fish finds: Cod, haddock, plaice. Fish and chips to take-and-taste from around £1.90.

Fry: Vegetable oil.

Side-lines: Mushy peas, pickled gherkins, pickled onions. Other foods.

Wrapping: White paper, trays.

This fish and chip shop has been trading for many years: it is a traditional outlet in every way. You'll find it on the main A34, in this lovely little market town mid-way between Stratford and Birmingham.

Kenilworth

CHIPS & FISHES, 82 Roseland Road. Tel: 0926 53782

Open:	Mon 5.00 p.m. – 10.00 p.m.; Tue – Thu midday – 1.30 p.m.; 5.00 p.m. – 10.30 p.m.; Fri midday – 1.30 p.m.; 4.30 p.m. – 11.00 p.m.; Sat midday – 2.00 p.m.; 5.00 p.m. – 11.00 p.m.
Facilities:	T/A; P.
Fish finds:	Cod, haddock, plaice, rainbow trout, scampi. Fish and chips to take-and-taste from around £1.60.
Fry:	Vegetable fat.
Side-lines:	Mushy peas, pickled onions. Other foods.
Wrapping:	White paper.

Mike and Maureen Passmore are, by now, past-masters of the art of fish-frying – their ever-increasing trade is verification of their high standards. You'll find the outlet on the corner of St Nicholas Avenue, opposite St John's School. I wonder if Queen Elizabeth I ever dined so well at Kenilworth Castle as you can at this fine chippy? The castle had bits built by John of Gaunt (the Strong Tower or Mervyn's Tower) and further additions by Henry VIII and the Earl of Leicester, to whom Queen Elizabeth I gave the castle in 1562. As most of the castle was dismantled during the Civil War, perhaps a visit to the chippy will prove more satisfying! Certainly we can confirm the recommendation of Mr D. McAll, who emphasizes the size of the portions and very reasonable prices.

Fish and chips make the perfect Wedding Breakfast – at home or at the chippy!

Leamington Spa

LANSDOWNE FISH SHOP, Lansdowne Street. Tel: 0926 423269

Open:	Tue – Thu & Sat 11.45 a.m. – 2.00 p.m.; 4.45 p.m. – 11.30 p.m.; Fri 11.30 a.m. – 2.00 p.m.; 4.30 p.m. – 11.45 p.m.;
Facilities:	T/A; P; T.
Fish finds:	Cod, haddock, plaice, scampi. Fish and chips to take-and-taste from around £1.75.
Fry:	Vegetable oil.
Side-lines:	Mushy peas, pickled onions. Other foods.
Wrapping:	White news off-cuts.

Andrew, your friendly fryer near Kennedy Square, tells me they've been satisfying customers in this part of the world for over fifty years. When he's not master of the range he enjoys both snooker and football. Not to offend his regulars, he names both the Greyhound and Builders Arms as the pubs nearest the chippy. After all, everyone likes to be friendly in this Royal Spa town, with its ancient pump rooms and their baths and gardens.

Lower Quinton

SEASPRAY FISH BAR, Main Road. Tel: 0789 720551

Open:	Mon 5.00 p.m. – 11.00 p.m.; Tue – Sat midday – 2.00 p.m.; 5.00 p.m. – 11.00 p.m.
Facilities:	T/A & R; P; T.
Fish finds:	Cod, haddock, plaice. Fish and chips to take-and-taste from around £1.45; sit-and-savour around £1.80.

Fry:	Vegetable fat.
Side-lines:	Mushy peas, pickled onions. Other foods.
Wrapping:	Greaseproof, paper, carriers.

Mr Wan has been frying at the large detatched building with the gallows sign for a few years now. He cooks fine fresh fish and is very friendly. The nearest pub, however, is half a mile away – the College Arms. But if you're out for the day in the foothills of the Cotswolds, you'll find this chippy just where the counties of Gloucester, Oxford and Warwick converge. Close by are the beautiful gardens of Kiftsgate Court and Hidcote Manor, the latter a National Trust property.

Rugby

PASCAL, 61 Wood Street. Tel: 0788 571205

Open:	Mon 11.30 a.m. – 2.00 p.m.; Tue, Thu & Fri 11.30 a.m. – 2.00 p.m.; 4.00 p.m. – 9.30 p.m.
Facilities:	T/A & R; P; T; wheelchair access.
Fish finds:	Cod, haddock, plaice (occasionally). Fish and chips to take-and-taste and sit-and-savour, both around £1.35.
Fry:	Vegetable fat.
Side-lines:	Mushy peas, pickled onions. Other foods.
Wrapping:	White paper.

Though it's been modernized to a very high standard, proprietors Jessie and Pascal de Rosa believe their chippy to be the oldest in the town – somewhere between seventy-five and eighty-five years old – and they've owned it for twenty-three years. The estate on which the shop stands was built in 1902; the property was probably converted from a butcher's shop a few years later. It's near the rail station and the cattle market, about five minutes' walk from the centre of the town: just long enough to work up a good appetite for Pascal's fine fare, sampled by many of the boys from the famous school over the years. As a member of the Grocers' Company, I am sure Lawrence Sheriff, who founded the school in 1567, would approve of pupils indulging themselves in nutritious fare such as that served by Pascal. He was awarded 'Best Chips' certificate in 1986 by St Matthew's Church Youth Fellowship.

Shipston on Stour

CHURCH STREET FISH & CHIP SHOP, 9 Church Street.
Tel: 0609 62830

Open:	Mon 5.00 p.m. – 11.30 p.m.; Tue – Sat midday – 2.00 p.m.; 5.00 p.m. – 11.30 p.m.
Facilities:	T/A; P near.

Fish finds:	Cod, haddock, plaice, scampi. Fish and chips to take-and-taste from around £1.70.
Fry:	Vegetable oil.
Side-lines:	Mushy peas, pickled onions. Other foods.
Wrapping:	Greaseproof, white off-cuts.

Shipston's ('sheep's town') roots are in the wool trade way back in pre-Saxon times. But it was only a handful of years ago that Sergios & Vasoulla Serghi set up shop in the shadow of the beautiful St Edmund's church, with its medieval tower. They have been fryers, however, for over twenty years. This unspoilt market town is a delightful place to explore, with its mellow stone houses. Just to the north, off the A34, is Honington Hall, which is also worth a visit.

Stratford-upon-Avon

KINGFISHER, 13 Ely Street. Tel: 0789 292513

Open:	Daily 11.30 a.m. – 2.00 p.m.; 5.00 p.m. – 11.00 p.m. (Oct to Mar: Mon closes 9.30 p.m.).
Facilities:	T/A & R; P near.
Fish finds:	Cod, haddock, plaice, scampi. Fish and chips to take-and-taste from around £1.80; sit-and-savour around £2.20.
Fry:	Vegetable oil.
Side-lines:	Mushy peas, pickled onions.
Wrapping:	Greaseproof, trays (extra), white wrap.

From the home of the Bard, you'd expect something rhyming . . . Aft' ten year o' cooking, all you'll get's: 'I'm fryin'!' Seriously, when you've parked in the nearby car park, done a few of the sites like the American Fountain,

Shakespeare's house and Harvard House, all within the block, you'll be ready for one of their fine frys. Only fresh fish is used and the place is kept immaculately clean. Restaurant seating for about twenty-eight.

Potatoes are known in Ireland as 'praties', in Scotland as 'tatties' and Wales and England as 'taters' or 'spuds.'

TAKE-AWAY TIFFIN, 2 Brookside Road. Tel: 0789 67340

Open: Mon – Sat 11.30 a.m. – 2.00 p.m.; 4.30 p.m. – 11.30 p.m.

Facilities: T/A; P (20 cars); T; wheelchair access.

Fish finds: Cod, haddock, plaice, scampi. Fish and chips to take-and-taste from around £1.60.

Fry: Vegetable oil.

Side-lines: Mushy peas, pickled gherkins, pickled onions. Other foods.

Wrapping: Greaseproof, white paper, newspaper. Cones for chips.

'Peace be at your labour, honest fishermen.'
William Shakespeare:
Pericles *Act II. 1.*

If chippies had been around in the Bard's day, I'm sure he would have written similarly about them! Certainly about Mrs Stavroula Gavriel's fine establishment, 300 yd off the Alcester Road (A422), close to Mason's Road Trading Estate. This outlet has been serving up fish delicacies for nearly twenty years, and Mrs Gavriel has been frying for well over a quarter of a century. She has her own recipe for fish cakes and also fried fish in breadcrumbs. The locals love her fries so it's well worth taking that detour and seeking her out.

Warwick

WEST GATE FISH & CHIP SHOP, West Street. Tel: 0926 92274

Open:	Mon – Sat 11.30 a.m. – 2.00 p.m.; 4.30 p.m. – 11.30 p.m.
Facilities:	T/A & R; T.
Fish finds:	Cod, haddock, plaice, scampi. Fish and chips to take-and-taste from around £1.55; sit-and-savour around £2.00.
Fry:	Vegetable oil.
Side-lines:	Mushy peas, pickled onions. Other foods.
Wrapping:	Greaseproof, white paper, news.

The name Warwick is an Anglo-Saxon translation (meaning a fortified or garrisoned town) of the ancient British name Caer Leon. Residents of the town have been fortifying themselves for over forty years with the fine fish and chips from this establishment. It is owned by Dimitris Gavriel. In fact, the fortification referred to by the town's name is the 14th-century castle, very near the shop. Warwick stands on the river Avon, 21 miles south-east of Birmingham. There is seating for thirty-six at this fine, well recommended chippy.

Wellesbourne

WELLESBOURNE FISH & CHIP SHOP, Bank House. Tel: 0789 840386

Open:	Tue – Thu 11.30 a.m. – 1.30 p.m.; 5.00 p.m. – 10.00 p.m.; Fri 11.30 a.m. – 2.00 p.m.; 4.30 p.m. – 10.00 p.m.; Sat 11.30 a.m. – 2.00 p.m.; 5.00 p.m. – 10.00 p.m.
Facilities:	T/A.

Fish finds:	Cod, haddock, plaice. Fish and chips to take-and-taste from around £1.60.
Fry:	Vegetable oil.
Side-lines:	Mushy peas, pickled onions. Other foods.

A very pleasant chippy, with friendly staff. They've been frying here for a very long time. It is easily found between Stratford and Leamington Spa, with the National Trust's Charlecote Park not far away. The fare is limited but the standard high and the portions plentiful.

WEST MIDLANDS

Birmingham

BEDDERS, 898 Coventry Road. Tel: 021 772 1532

Open:	Mon – Sat 11.30 a.m. – 2.00 p.m.; Fri 4.00 p.m. – 7.30 p.m.
Facilities:	T/A & café; P near.
Fish finds:	Cod, haddock. Fish and chips to take-and-taste from around £1.20; sit-and-savour from £1.75.
Fry:	Vegetable fat.
Side-lines:	Mushy peas, home-made pickled onions. Other foods.
Wrapping:	Brown paper, newspaper, trays.

John Bedder and his son Martyn are the second and third generations of fryers at this spot. It's a traditional corner-shop chippy that believes the best form of advertising is word of mouth – and that can only be achieved by a good product, well served. The queues and variety of vehicles parked about – from Rolls Royces to taxis, a builder's van and a rag and bone cart – prove

*that this policy has worked for them. The outlet has been trading since 1918
on the Heybard Circus roundabout opposite Asda superstore, off the A45
Birmingham to Coventry road. The café seats thirty and the decor is simple.
John's mother still pickles her own award-winning onions on the premises –
worth taking a jar home. Among their best customers – for fries – are the
local cabbies, 'Master Showman' Bobby Wilson and many other travelling
showmen: all discerning diners.*

NEEDLESS ALLEY FISH RESTAURANT, 10 Needless Alley, City Centre. Tel: 021 643 4775

Open:	Mon – Sat 11.00 a.m. – 7.00 p.m.
Facilities:	T/A & R; T.
Fish finds:	Cod, haddock, plaice. Fish and chips to take-and taste from around £1.90; sit-and-savour around £2.30.
Fry:	Vegetable oil.
Side-lines:	Mushy peas. Other foods.
Wrapping:	White news.

*'Chris' Christofi's spotless outlet has been trading less than four years, but
he's built up an excellent reputation for a city-centre chippy. It's not the
easiest place to find, probably the original reason for the name of the lane:
look out for the Midland Hotel in New Street (near the main railway
station) and you'll find Needless Alley opposite. The shop's decor is green
and beige which gives it a homely atmosphere. It's worth searching out –
particularly for families because of the special children's dishes Chris fries.*

PEARCE'S SHELLFISH, 209 Market Hall, Bull Ring. Tel: 021 643 3929

Open:	Mon – Sat 9.00 a.m. – 5.00 p.m.; (Wed till 1.30 p.m.).
Facilities:	T/A & Shellfish Bar; P near; T; wheelchair access.

Fish finds: All shellfish, plus jellied eels, smoked fish.

Wrapping: Paper.

Jeffrey Pearce's family have been trading in shellfish continuously for over a hundred years, which must be some kind of record! They were bombed out in the 1940s but this location was re-built in the 1960s, and they've never stopped trading. Jeffrey is the fifth generation in the family firm, and there's a sixth on the way (it must be all those oysters!). You'll find the fine food dispensary inside the main Market Hall, with refrigerated counters and display cases. If you fancy a drink to wash down your shellfish, there's the Matador in the same building.

Brierley Hill

CONCORD FISH BAR & RESTAURANT, 48 High Street.
Tel: 0384 262982

Open: Mon – Thu 11.00 a.m. – 11.30 p.m.; Fri & Sat 11.00 a.m. – midnight.

Facilities: T/A & R; P; T; wheelchair access.

Fish finds: Cod, haddock, plaice. Fish and chips to take-and-taste from around £1.70; sit-and-savour from £1.90.

Fry: Vegetable fat.

Side-lines: Mushy peas, pickled onions.

Wrapping: Greaseproof, white wrapping, paper bags.

This busy town-centre chippy is at the top end of the High Street, opposite the W.H. Smith Do-It-All store. Fryer Augustis Papantoniou not only cooks delicious fare, but also keeps a tight rein on the cleanliness and smartness of his outlet. The result: a Silver Salver Hygiene Award in 1985. And he maintains the same high standard today and every day. If you need to walk up an appetite, there's the extensive Saltwells Wood on the other side of the A4036 Pedmore Road.

Coventry

FISHY MOORE'S (Merryweathers), 10–12 Fairfax Street.
Tel: 0203 224938

Open:	Mon – Sat 11.30 a.m. – 10.30 p.m. (Wed till 8.30 p.m.; restaurant closes 8.30 p.m.).
Facilities:	T/A & R (L); T; P near (multi-storey); wheelchair access.
Fish finds:	Cod, cod's roe, haddock, plaice, scampi. Plus blackboard specials. Fish and chips to take-and-taste from around £1.55; sit-and-savour around £2.05.
Fry:	Oil.
Side-lines:	Mushy peas, pickled gherkins, pickled onions. Other foods.
Wrapping:	Stay-hot containers, greaseproof.

In 1990, Fishy Moore's celebrates its centenary of fish frying. Not quite old enough to have been around when Lady Godiva made her legendary streak through the town, though I'm sure she would have stopped for some fine fries had it been so. It's opposite the bus station, next to the De Vere Hotel, and backs on to St Michael's Cathedral. You won't need landmarks to direct you to this fine establishment, for it's famous throughout the area for its excellent standards of both food and service. Not so long ago it was added to the assets of that fast expanding, fish-frying company, Merryweathers, who are poised to take it into its next 100 years in fine style.

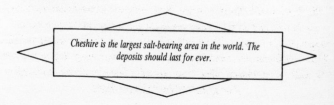

Cheshire is the largest salt-bearing area in the world. The deposits should last for ever.

J. KYRIAKOU, 262 Hipswell Highway, Wyken. Tel: 0203 453666

Open:	Mon – Thu 11.30 a.m. – 2.00 p.m.; 4.30 p.m. – 11.30 p.m.; Fri 11.30 a.m. – 2.00 p.m.; 4.00 p.m. – midnight; Sat 11.30 a.m. – 2.30 p.m.; 4.30 p.m. – midnight.
Facilities:	T/A; P near.
Fish finds:	Cod, cod's roe, fish cakes, haddock, plaice, scampi. Fish and chips to take-and-taste from around £1.60.
Fry:	Vegetable oil.
Side-lines:	Mushy peas, pickled gherkins, pickled onions.
Wrapping:	Paper, trays, white paper.

Mr Kyriakou's fine take-away was first established over thirty years ago. It's at the end of a row of shops in this suburb in the north-east of the city. They pride themselves on the quality and speed of their service, and I'll add that the fare is pretty good also! If your're heading towards the M6 on the A46, pop in and give it your verdict; I'm sure it will be favourable.

Halesowen

**TONY & GINA'S FISH & CHIP SHOP, 2 Howley Grange Road.
Tel: 021 422 2507**

Open:	Mon 4.30 p.m. – 11.30 p.m.; Tue – Sat midday – midnight.
Facilities:	T/A; P near.
Fish finds:	Cod, haddock, plaice. Fish and chips to take-and-taste from around £1.70.
Fry:	Groundnut oil.

Side-lines: Pickled onions.

Wrapping: White paper.

Tony and wife Gina have been frying beautifully crispy batter with golden brown, chunky chips at this location for over eighteen years. They take great pride in the quality of their products, the fish being delivered daily. The premises are exceptionally clean, with tiling from floor to ceiling. The portions are ample also. Find it near the Halesowen golf course.

Hall Green

CHEQUERS, 1545 Stratford Road. Tel: 021 744 40611

Open: Mon – Sat midday – 2.00 p.m.; 5.00 p.m. – 11.30 p.m.

Facilities: T/A & R; T.

Fish finds: Cod, haddock, plaice, scampi. Weekends only: skate and hake. Fish and chips to take-and-taste from around £1.65; sit-and-savour from around £1.85.

Fry: Vegetable oil.

Side-lines: Mushy peas, pickled gherkins, pickled onions. Other foods.

Wrapping: Paper, trays.

Peter Liperis is a keen golfer when he can get away from that other range. He's got several courses to choose from nearby, including the Robin Hood, Moseley and Cocks Moor Woods. Back at the fryer he'll cook to order if requested and can accommodate forty-eight in his restaurant. People travel for miles to this fine outlet on the Robin Hood Island off the Stratford Road. It's been there for over fifty years and has been commended by health inspectors for its high standard of cleanliness and hygiene.

Northfield

SOUTH SIDE FISH BAR, 1191 Bristol Road. Tel: 021 475 2557

Open: Mon 4.45 p.m. – 11.30 p.m.; Tue 11.45 a.m. – 2.00 p.m.; Wed – Sat 4.45 p.m..– 11.30 p.m.

Facilities: T/A; P.

Fish finds: Cod, haddock, plaice. Fish and chips to take-and-taste from around £1.75.

Fry: Vegetable fat.

Side-lines: Mushy peas, pickled onions. Other foods.

Wrapping: White paper, trays.

Perhaps the limited range of fish is necessary to cope with the queues of customers that form outside this busy outlet. It's spotlessly clean and, regardless of numbers, the service is both friendly and fast. It's opposite Kalamazoo Business Systems, a few miles down the road from the famous car and truck plant at Longbridge on this south-westerly tip of Britain's second city. They've been frying here for a quarter of a century, and Christos Solomon's family took over twenty years ago.

Solihull

SEASPRAY, 395 Stratford Road, Shirley.
Tel: 021 744 8987 (T/A); 745 5744 (R)
Also at 113 High Street, Henley (T/A only)

Open: T/A: Mon – Sat 11.00 a.m. – 2.30 p.m.; 4.00 p.m. – midnight; R: midday – 3.00 p.m.; 5.00 p.m. – 11.00 p.m.

Facilities: T/A & R (L); P near; T; wheelchair access.

Fish finds: Cod, Dover sole, haddock, lobster, plaice, shark, swordfish, tuna. Fish and chips to take-and-taste from around £2.00; sit-and-savour from £4.50.

Fry: Vegetable oil.

Side-lines: Mushy peas, pickled gherkins, pickled onions.

Wrapping: White paper, brown bags, plastic bags.

The take-away has been here for more than fifteen years, serving to a superb standard. Recently proprietor Hasan Hasan opened a smart restaurant next door at 393, still with the emphasis on fish. It has an open-style kitchen so that you can select and then watch your meal being prepared and cooked, either on a charcoal grill or more traditionally. There is also an element of Turkish cuisine available, with live Turkish guitar music to accompany your meal each Wednesday evening. Parties and weddings are also catered for in this luxurious and spacious dining hall, with its terrazzo-tiled floor and mahogany furnishings. Happily the opening of the restaurant has not detracted from the high standard and quality of the take-away. Recommended by BBC local radio, local Rotarians and many more customers.

Sutton Coldfield

CHESTERS TAKEAWAY, 19 Hollyfield Road South. Tel: 021 378 2623

Open: Mon – Sat midday – 2.00 p.m.; 5.00 p.m. – 11.00 p.m. (Sat till 11.30 p.m.).

Facilities: T/A; P; off-sales, wines & beers.

Fish finds: Calamari, cod, haddock, plaice, trout. Fish and chips to take-and-taste from around £2.20.

Fry: Vegetable oil.

Side-lines Pickled onions. Other foods.

Wrapping: White news off-cuts.

A definite Mediterranean flavour wafts through this magnificent take-away from the moment you cross the threshold. Not only does owner Michael Pili make his own taramosalata, but he will tempt you with calamari cooked in a wine sauce as an alternative to fried fish. While you are waiting for the fare to be freshly cooked, he will offer you a cup of piping hot coffee. If you prefer something stronger, there's the Reddicap pub opposite; however, this unique chippy is also licensed for wine and beer take-outs. Whetted your appetite? You'll find Chesters half a mile from the centre of the town.

Wednesbury

KEN MITCHELL'S, 144 Hydes Road. Tel: 021 556 4950

Open: Mon & Tue midday – 1.30 p.m.; 4.30 p.m. – 10.30 p.m;
Wed 4.30 p.m. – 8.00 p.m.; Thu 11.45 a.m. – 1.45 p.m.;
4.15 p.m. – 11.00 p.m.; Fri & Sat 11.30 a.m – 2.00 p.m.;
4.15 p.m. – midnight.

Facilities: T/A; P.

Fish finds: Cod, haddock, plaice (on or off the bone), roe (fresh or tinned). Fish and chips to take-and-taste from around £1.30.

Fry: Dripping.

Side-lines: Mushy peas. Other foods.

Wrapping: White paper.

Take the A461 off the M6 at junction 9 and you'll find Hydes road on your left. Ken's is a traditional chippy of the type more usually found in the north – particularly, because he fries in dripping. Delicious. Blindfold the only way you could tell you're not north of Sheffield is that proprietor Martin ('Mart') Phillips' most popular fish is cod, whereas they favour haddock in Yorkshire and thereabouts. His prices are somewhat a bargain in this part of the world. Incidentally, if you want something to think about while you enjoy his succulent food, the town's church of St Bartholomew is said to occupy the site of a temple of Woden (otherwise Odin) from whom the town, and the day Wednesday, get their name.

> *Heard in the queue at the time of the Icelandic Cod War: 'I hear things are getting worse. There's talk of sending tanks in!' Boing, boing!*

West Bromwich

DARBY'S, Wood Lane. Tel: 021553 4007

Open:	Mon – Fri midday – 2.00 p.m.; 5.30 p.m. – 11.30 p.m.; Sat 4.30 p.m. – 11.30 p.m.
Facilities:	T/A & R (L); P; T.
Fish finds:	Cod, haddock, halibut, lemon sole, plaice, shark, swordfish, tuna. Fish and chips to take-and-taste from around £1.50; sit-and-savour around £3.90.
Fry:	Vegetable oil.
Side-lines:	Mushy peas, pickled onions. Other foods.
Wrapping:	White paper.

Darby's is a pub with a fish restaurant and take-away shop alongside. My guess, and I may be completely wrong, is that it is named after a well-known hall porter at a certain hotel, in a now discontinued TV soap made in Birmingham! Not that it's important, because the venue stands out from the crowd on its own accord. Terry and Jackie Ewins (with a 'G' they could have called the place Dallas!) have gone out of their way to serve up exotic fish as well as the norm. Though the restaurant seats fifty, take my advice and book, particularly at weekends. Children are catered for.

WILTSHIRE
Highworth

HIGHWORTH CHIP SHOP, 13–14 Swindon Street. Tel: 0793 762352

Open:	Mon 11.30 a.m. – 2.00 p.m.; 5.00 p.m. – 11.30 p.m.; Tue – Thu 11.30 a.m. – 2.00 p.m.; 3.00 p.m. –

11.30 p.m.; Fri & Sat 11.30 a.m. – 2.00 p.m.; 5.00 p.m. – midnight; Sun 5.00 p.m. – 11.00 p.m.

Facilities:	T/A.
Fish finds:	Cod, haddock, plaice. Fish and chips to take-and-taste from around £1.90.
Fry:	Groundnut oil.
Side-lines:	Pea fritters, pickled onions. Other foods.
Wrapping:	Greaseproof, white paper, bags.

In times of yore, the derivation of surnames often followed the trade or calling of the holder. It is not surprising that this proprietor, M.M. Haddock (believe it!) returned to the noble art of fish frying, and has been well and truly 'plaiced' for many years. What is surprising, in the circumstances, is that he sells more cod than anything, dare I say it! Now that I've made enough jibes for everyone, we'll have a little respect for the fine fare served up in this delightful establishment a couple of miles north of Swindon. After a day out looking around the National Trust's Great Barn, Buscot Park or the Old Parsonage and Manor, all of which are close by, you'll do no better than the quality fries served up here.

Malmesbury

DYNASTY (Shoestrings), 3 Cross Hayes. Tel: 0666 823750

Open:	Mon – Sat 11.00 a.m. – 2.00 p.m.; 4.30 p.m. – 11.00 p.m. (later openings for night owls due soon).
Facilities:	T/A; P.
Fish finds:	Cod, fish cakes, haddock, plaice, scampi. Fish and chips to take-and-taste from around £1.60.
Fry:	Vegetable oil.

Side-lines: Mushy peas. Other foods.

Wrapping: Paper, trays.

Shoestrings is now Dynasty. Find it in the car park in the centre of Malmesbury, the most ancient borough in all England. The beautiful Abbey Church and the Market Cross are musts for visitors. The monastery was founded by an Irishman called Maildulf, Meildulf or Meldun. The chippy was founded about six years ago, and has a cheerful modern decor. William of Malmesbury was an eleventh-century author of chronicles. The proprietor is a twentieth-century fryer of good fish and chips.

Swindon

PARK FISH SHOP, 22 Cavendish Square. Tel: 0793 521302

Open: Mon – Thu & Sat 11.30 a.m. – 1.45 p.m.; 5.00 p.m. – 10.00 p.m.; Fri 11.30 a.m. – 1.45 p.m.; 5.00 p.m. – 11.00 p.m.

Facilities: T/A; P near.

Fish finds: Cod, haddock, plaice, rock salmon, skate. Fish and chips to take-and-taste from around £1.90.

Fry: Groundnut oil.

Side-lines: Pea fritters, pickled gherkins, pickled onions. Other foods.

Wrapping: Greaseproof, white paper, paper bags.

To avoid repeating the puns, we suggest you 'skate' your finger up the page to the Highworth fish shop, also owned by M.M. Haddock. When one used to talk about Swindon, it was always about the railway works set up by the old Great Western Railway company in 1841. But that's sadly a thing of the past. It's all M4 corridor industry, high-tech, computers, micro-chip and Mr Haddock's chips for the future. That's good, very good – and nourishing too!

Warminster

GOLDEN KITCHEN, 4 George Street. Tel: 0985 213268

Open:	Mon – Sat midday – 2.00 p.m.; 5.00 p.m. – 11.00 p.m.; Sun 5.00 p.m. – 10.00 p.m.
Facilities:	T/A; P.
Fish finds:	Cod, haddock, huss, plaice, scampi. Fish and chips to take-and-taste from around £1.45.
Fry:	Palm oil.
Side-lines:	Mushy peas, pickled onions. Other foods.
Wrapping:	White news off-cuts, bags.

For the 20th-century tourist, to talk about Warminster's 14th-century church is somewhat superflous. The most important information – apart from saying that the fare at the chippy is first-rate and the service pleasing – is to mention that the town is the nearest centre of civilization to Longleat House with its big game park. After the excitement of driving around the park with your windows closed and animals all around, it's relaxing to coast down into the main street of this market town to the spotless outlet run by the proprietor, a pleasant Mr Duff.

YORKSHIRE (NORTH)
Harrogate

ONE ARCH FISHERIES, 4 BOWER STREET. Tel: 0423 565654

Open:	Mon – Sat 11.30 a.m. – 2.00 p.m.; 4.30 p.m. – 6.30 p.m.

Facilities:	T/A & R; P near; T; wheelchair friendly.
Fish finds:	Haddock, plaice. Fish and chips to take-and-taste from around £1.35; sit-and-savour around £2.55.
Fry:	Dripping.
Side-lines:	Mushy peas. Other foods.
Wrapping:	White paper, cartons.

You may have come down from the Dales, or been on a visit to Ripley Castle or Fountains Abbey. More likely you're visiting the town as a delegate in one of its famed international conferences. Whatever the reason for working up an appetite, the place to satisfy those hunger pangs is One Arch Fisheries: you'll find it near the bus station. It has white tiled walls, after being recently refurbished. Note this busy chippy, run by Mr and Mrs Foxton, does not open in the evening after 6.30 p.m.

Hawes

J & M HOWARTH FISH & CHIP SHOP, Main Street. Tel: 096 97 663

Open:	Mon – Sat 6.00 p.m. – 10.00 p.m.; Tue, Wed, Fri & Sat 11.30 a.m. – 1.30 p.m.
Facilities:	T/A & R; P near; T near; wheelchair access.
Fish finds:	Cod, haddock, halibut, plaice, rainbow trout, scampi. Fish and chips to take-and-taste from around £1.25; sit-and-savour from £2.20.
Fry:	Fat.
Side-lines:	Mushy peas. Other foods.
Wrapping:	Greaseproof, white wrap, polystyrene trays.

Did you know that in 1964, the first automatic ticket barrier was installed on the London Underground? Also that Cassius Clay won his first world

*title that year; Prince Edward was born; James Bond creator Ian Fleming
died and Donald Campbell broke the land speed record? At the same time
as all this was going on, Joe Howarth and his wife Mary started serving
customers in their delightful little family concern on the cross-Pennine way.
The shop's got varnished pine walls and white paintwork, with tiled floor.
There's seating now for forty, all in pine, with individual cubicles and
brass light fittings. Mr and Mrs Howarth put their success down to their
efficient and friendly staff. I'd like to add that you don't get and keep good
staff if you are not nice people, both as employers and with the customers.
Add good, fresh fare, well prepared, cooked and served and that's the
complete recipe.*

Knaresborough

ARAGON FISHERIES, 14 Iles Lane. Tel: 0423 864022

Open: Wed 11.30 a.m. – 1.30 p.m.; Thu 4.30 p.m. –
7.30 p.m.; Fri 11.30 a.m. – 1.30 p.m.; 4.30 p.m.–
11.30 p.m.; Sat 11.30 a.m. – 1.30 p.m.; 4.30 p.m. –
7.30 p.m.

Facilities: T/A; P near.

Fish finds: Haddock and chips to take-and-taste from around £1.30.

Fry: Dripping and vegetable oil.

Side-lines: Mushy peas. Other foods.

Wrapping: Polystyrene trays, greaseproof bags, white paper.

*Piers Gaveston, Henry III and John of Gaunt each, at one time, lived at
the town's castle, which was dismantled in 1648. The stone pillaged from
the castle was used to build most of the buildings in the street where the
chippy stands. It is believed they have been frying haddock here for over a
hundred years. Proprietor David Toulson, here for the last twelve years,
believes in retaining the traditional fare, and gives this as the main reason*

for the success of the outlet. Even though it is hard to find, take the first left before the town centre – (the shop is sandwiched between York Road and Windsor Lane). Expect to queue: it is worth it. The fish is fresh, the chips are firm and the service friendly. Only what you would expect from one of the holders of a Certificate of Hygiene from the Royal Institute of Public Health and Hygiene. David believes in preaching what he practices; he regularly circulates cartoon posters to other fryers promoting the health aspects of our national dish.

**DRAKE'S FISH RESTAURANT, 3–5 Silver Street (off Market Place).
Tel: 0423 864864**

Open: Easter – October daily 11.30 a.m. – 11.00 p.m.; times vary in winter.

Facilities:	T/A & R (L); P adjacent; T; wheelchair access.
Fish finds:	Haddock, halibut, plaice, scampi. Fish and chips to take-and-taste from around £1.20; sit-and-savour around £3.00.
Fry:	Beef dripping.
Side-lines:	Mushy peas. Other foods.
Wrapping:	Polystyrene trays, paper, bags, cones.

Mr J.C. Drake has only recently finished refurbishing the restaurant section of this outlet, which he took over a couple of years ago. The building, like most in the market area, dates back around 250 years. The Drake family are no strangers to the trade, having been in business in Leeds since 1933; fryers at this outlet are Paul and Richard. Haddock is the favourite fry here, and to please those with a really hearty appetite, they prepare a special jumbo fry. When wandering around this interesting town, look out for the Dropping Well, the water from which, I'm told, has 'petrifying qualities'. I declined to enquire further.

Northallerton

RAMSDEN'S, 227 High Street. Tel: 0609 780272

Open:	Tue, Thu & Fri 11.30 a.m. – 1.30 p.m.; 4.30 p.m. – 7.30 p.m.; Wed 11.15 a.m. – 1.30 p.m.; 4.30 p.m. – 7.30 p.m.; Sat 11.15 a.m. – 2.00 p.m.; 4.30 p.m. – 7.30 p.m.
Facilities:	T/A & R; T.
Fish finds:	Cod, haddock. Fish and chips to take-and-taste from around £1.20; sit-and-savour around £1.90.
Fry:	Beef dripping.

Side-lines: Mushy peas. Other foods.

Wrapping: Bags, paper.

This outlet has one up on the famous Guiseley chippy – there still is an Alan and an Anna Ramsden frying here, summer and winter, at the north end of the High Street. While the Guiseley outlet changed hands again not so long ago, Mr and Mrs Ramsden have been the proprietors here for many years. They've built up a strong following, with party catering a speciality. The restaurant is very popular, particularly on Wednesday, market day. There are fifty-two seats in the very pleasing diner.

Scarborough

BAXTER'S FISHERIES, 86 Northway. Tel: 0723 375719

Open: Mon, Tue & Thu 8.00 p.m. – midnight; Wed & Fri
                11.30 a.m. – 1.30 p.m.; 4.30 p.m. – midnight; Sat
                11.30 a.m. – 1.30 p.m.; 8.00 p.m. – midnight; Sun
                6.00 p.m. – midnight.

Facilities: T/A & R; P; T; wheelchair access.

Fish finds: Cod, dabs, haddock, lemon sole, ling, plaice, queenies,
                fresh Whitby salmon (in season), skate, dogfish. Fish and
                chips to take-and-taste from around £1.30; sit-and-savour
                around £2.50.

Fry: Fat.

Side-lines: Mushy peas, pickled onions. Other foods.

Wrapping: Greaseproof, polystyrene trays, newspaper.

Mark Baxter's shop has been trading for over thirty years. They buy all their fish direct from the boats at nearby Whitby. Filleting is done on the premises. Not only does this result in the freshest of product always being available, as well as a good selection, but the prices are always kept keen

*to the benefit of his many regular customers. Both shop and restaurant –
which seats twenty – are decorated in two shades of green. Not only is
there a special children's menu, but there are seating arrangements
particularly for the young ones, plus a changing and nursing area. The
Northway pub is close at hand. Mrs Ann Reed reckons you'd be hard
pressed to find better fish and chips anywhere. Jill and David Pennock, the
daughter and son-in-law of the founder, are now running the range.*

DILTS, 2 Princess Square. Tel: 0723 500146

Open:	Oct – Mar: Wed – Sat midday – 2.00 p.m.; 8.00 p.m. – 11.30 p.m.; April – Sept: Mon – Sat 11.30 p.m. – 2.30 p.m.; 4.30 p.m. – 6.30 p.m.; 8.00 p.m. – 11.45 p.m.
Facilities:	T/A & R (L); P near; T.
Fish finds:	Cod, cod cheeks, dabs, haddock, lemon sole, monk, plaice, dogfish. Fish and chips to take-and-taste from around £1.40; sit-and-savour around £2.75.
Fry:	Dripping.
Side-lines:	Mushy peas, pickled onions.
Speciality:	Pieces of Eight (monk); Fisherman's Haul (selection of four fish).
Wrapping:	Greaseproof, white paper.

*The Smith family run the range near the Leeds Hotel and the Leeds Arms
pub. From the harbour, walk up Eastborough for 50 yd, turn left up West
Sandgate and left again at the Leeds Hotel. This 21-seater restaurant with
pine panels, carpet wall to wall and ceiling-slung fishing nets has been
known to play host to such cricketing notables as Mike Gatting, Paul
Downton, Wilf Slack and Basil Butcher. Showbusiness has taken a bow in
the form of Max Jaffa and the Grumbleweeds. This chippy has a
reputation for good quality.*

HANOVER FISHERIES, 14 Hanover Road. Tel: 0723 362062

Open: Mon 8.00 p.m. – 11.45 p.m.; Tue, Wed & Sat 11.30 a.m.
– 1.30 p.m.; 8.00 p.m. – 11.45 p.m.; Thu & Fri
11.30 a.m. – 1.30 p.m.; 4.30 p.m. – 11.45 p.m.

Facilities: T/A; P (limited); wheelchair access.

Fish finds: Cod, haddock, plaice, scampi. Fish and chips to take-
and-taste from around £1.35.

Fry: Beef dripping.

Side-lines: Mushy peas. Other foods.

Wrapping: White paper.

*Peter Haire is overseeing this 50-year-old establishment. It's immaculately
turned out with the walls panelled in red formica, suspended ceiling and
tiled floor, and has cheerful staff. Only fresh fish is fried and the standard
of fry and presentation is excellent. It's opposite the railway station and
behind the Odeon cinema. There are plenty of watering holes nearby – the
Naval Club just a minute away, the Working Men's Club and Victoria,
Alma and Spa pubs a couple of minutes each.*

ONE OF EACH, 118 Victoria Road. Tel: 0723 372536

Open: Winter: Mon, Wed – Sat 11.30 a.m. – 1.30 p.m.;
4.30 p.m. – 7.00 p.m.; in the summer, there's a time
explosion: open all hours!

Facilities: T/A; P near.

Fish finds: Cod, haddock, huss, lemon sole, plaice, rock, skate. Fish
and chips to take-and-taste from around £1.35.

Fry: Fat.

Side-lines: Mushy peas, pickled onions.

Wrapping: Polystyrene trays, greaseproof, wrapping paper, off-cuts.

288

K.J. Lockey, the proprietor, took over these premises, thought to be one of the longest trading in Scarborough, just over a year ago. Find it opposite the Ratcliffe shoe shop, 20 yd from the traffic lights and police station. There is always an abundance of fresh fish available, plus chips of course – all served by smartly-uniformed staff.

SMALL FRY, 52 North Street. Tel: 0723 367448

Open:	Tue – Sat 11.30 a.m. – 2.00 p.m.; Tue & Wed 4.15 p.m. – 7.15 p.m.; Thu & Fri 4.15 p.m. – 10.15 p.m.
Facilities:	T/A; P near; T; wheelchair access.
Fish finds:	Cod, haddock, plaice. Fish and chips to take-and-taste from around £1.30.
Fry:	Fat.
Side-lines:	Mushy peas. Other foods.
Wrapping:	Coloured wrap.

Sisters Karen and Jayne Holmes are now the equal owners of this fine chippy, which their father bought some years ago. They've built up quite a following by serving only fresh fish, delivered daily. Not so long ago a tourist walked in and calmly asked for fifteen large cod to be specially fried to take home – to Wakefield! A few days later came a letter of appreciation. The interior decor of this stone-clad building is tile throughout, with mahogany doors, window-frames and panels. The spotless presentation, quality product and friendly service are some of the reasons why many celebrities visiting the nearby Opera House are known to frequent this outlet. The Angel pub is two doors away.

The British eat over 244 lb of potatoes each per year – though the Russians eat more, around 265 lb.

Settle

WILSON'S FISH RESTAURANT, Church Street. Tel: 08292 3297

Open:	Daily 11.30 a.m. – 9.30 p.m.
Facilities:	T/A & R (L); P opposite; T.
Fish finds:	T/A: haddock; R: also halibut, plaice, scampi. Fish and chips to take-and-taste from around £1.40; sit-and-savour around £3.40.
Fry:	Fat.
Side-lines:	Mushy peas. Other foods.
Wrapping:	Polystyrene containers with/without lids, paper.

This market town on the Ribble, 11 miles from Skipton, boasts the 17th-century Folly Hall. A folly, as such, may have no use and be built just for vainglory. The same cannot be said about the ultra-smart chippy and restaurant which J. & M. Wilson have been running on the A65 main road to the Lake District for the last few years. It provides nourishment of the finest kind to tourists and locals alike. The decor is green and cream throughout, with pine furniture and indoor plants; the restaurant seats forty-two. The Royal Oak pub is not far away.

Skipton

BIZZIE LIZZIE'S, 36 Swadford Street. Tel: 0756 793189

Open:	Mon – Fri 11.30 a.m. – 2.30 p.m.; 4.00 p.m. – 11.30 p.m.; Sat 11.30 a.m. – midnight; Sun 4.00 p.m. – 11.30 p.m. (restaurant closes 10.00 p.m. daily).
Facilities:	T/A & R (L); T.
Fish finds:	Cod, haddock, plaice, scampi in restaurant. Fish and

chips to take-and-taste from around £1.20; sit-and-savour around £2.95.

Fry: Fat.

Side-lines: Mushy peas. Other foods.

Wrapping: Polystyrene boxes and trays.

I am cautious about including this fine outlet in the guide for one reason only – and it certainly isn't the fine quality of fare, the magnificent, spotless premises, service of staff or value for money. All these would be difficult to equal, let alone surpass. It is the fact that in the last fifteen years Philip and Jean Davison have owned four different shops – and I'm just a little nervous they may have moved on yet again by the time the print is dry on the pages of this book! If they have, they'll have left behind another fine outlet 'by build-up and blow', and the fact that they keep in touch with their previous premises' new owners must mean they are still proud of the standards maintained. Somehow I think they'll be at Skipton for a while yet, since they have already trebled the business in four years – and almost trebled the size of the premises to match! You'll have to go a long way to beat this outlet on all fronts. There's only one thing I will take Jean to task on – she does have a secret 'X' formula for her batter. It's the 'X' in eXperience that tells a Great Fryer when the batter is right, allowing for the wetness of the fish and the temperature of the day. Some have it, some haven't: Jean has!

Strensall (Nr York)

STRENSALL FISHERIES, 16 The Village. Tel: 0904 490370

Open: Mon & Thu 4.30 p.m. – 10.15 p.m.; Tue 4.30 p.m. – 6.30 p.m.; Wed 11.15 a.m. – 1.15 p.m.; 7.00 p.m. – 10.15 p.m.; Fri 11.15 a.m. – 1.15 p.m.; 4.30 p.m. – 10.15 p.m.; Sat 11.15 a.m. – 1.15 p.m.

Facilities:	T/A; P near; wheelchair access.
Fish finds:	Cod, haddock, scampi, 'Martyn's Specials' (large fish). Fish and chips to take-and-taste from around £1.30.
Fry:	Fat.
Side-lines:	Mushy peas, pickled onions. Other foods.
Speciality:	Fish cakes, Yorkshire style.
Wrapping:	Cartons.

Martyn Oldroyd, his wife Patricia and their son Philip are well settled in this outlet, which has been established for over forty years. Don't lose your way around these parts, as there's a military range near by and a golf range also. But it's the chippy range that we're most interested in, and what comes out of it. The Oldroyds have been in the fried fish trade for over a quarter of a century, so they should, and do, know their fish and chips by now. They're excellent. The shop is spotless, having been recently refurbished in oak, with marble counters, brass taps and a new Planit range. In case you think you know the name, but not the place, brother R.G. Oldroyd fries at Kirk Lane, Yeadon, near Leeds. Within a couple of miles of Strensall are four caravan camps and the Wildlife Nature Reserve is only a mile away.

Tadcaster

KIRKGATE FISHERIES, 6 Kirkgate. Tel: 0937 835686

Open:	Tue – Sat 11.30 a.m. – 1.30 p.m.; Tue, Thu, Sat 5.00 p.m. – 8.00 p.m.; (Wed & Fri till 10.00 p.m.).
Facilities:	T/A; P near; T near; wheelchair access.
Fish finds:	Cod, haddock. Fish and chips to take-and-taste from around £1.30.

Fry: Dripping.

Side-lines: Mushy peas. Other foods.

Speciality: Bradford Cakes (potato scallops, minced fish, battered).

Wrapping: CFC-free polystyrene trays.

Tadcaster, home of fine ale. Proprietor John Johnson comments: 'The three breweries in the town provide much benefit in ways other than employment!' In fact a major redevelopment of this conservation area is about to take place around Samuel Smith's old brewery. As well as being an excellent fryer of a fine product, well served, John is also something of a local historian. He tells me the Ark Museum, the town's oldest known house, is where the Pilgrim Fathers planned their trip to America (they missed John's fine fare!). Not only did the Vikings lose to King Harold at nearby Stamford Bridge (Chelsea don't always do so well there, either!) but Tadcaster was the last staging point for the Romans before they gained York from the south. The Royalists and Parliamentarians fought at nearby Marston Moor and the Yorkists gained victory over the Lancastrians at Towton, during a snowstorm on 29 March 1461. This was during the bloodiest conflict ever fought on British soil – the Wars of the Roses – in which it is said 28,000 died. Still enough left for their descendants to form a queue at the Kirkgate chippy quite regularly! However, this building has recently been completely rebuilt to a very high standard, following a major fire, so there's no chance of finding a piece of some ancient artefact among your chips.

Thirsk

WHITE HORSE CAFE, Market Place. Tel: 0388 815451

Open: Mon 8.00 a.m. – 6.00 p.m.; Tue & Wed 9.00 a.m. –
6.00 p.m.; Thu & Fri 9.00 a.m. – 7.00 p.m.; Sat
8.00 a.m. – 7.00 p.m.; Summer: open till 8.00 p.m.
Mon – Sat plus Sun 10.00 a.m. – 8.00 p.m.

Facilities:	T/A & R; P near; T; wheelchair friendly.
Fish finds:	Cod, fish cakes, haddock, scampi. Fish and chips to take-and-taste from around £1.40; sit-and-savour around £2.50.
Fry:	Jennings FatMix.
Side-lines:	Mushy peas, pickled onions. Other foods.
Wrapping:	Trays, white paper, greaseproof, bags.

Thirsk is a super little market town. Take the A168 off the A1 between Wetherby and Scotch Corner. The White Horse Café is just next to the clock in the market square. If you don't fancy fish, try the fish cakes or a plate of scampi. If you have time, relax in the 36-seater diner and try the special fish and chips, bread and butter, and a cup of tea or coffee for around £2.50.

Whitby

MAGPIE CAFE, 14 Pier Road. Tel: 0947 602058

Open: Daily 11.30 a.m. – 6.30 p.m. from 5 days before Easter to end Oct.

Facilities: R (L); P near; T; wheelchair friendly.

Fish finds: Cod, haddock, halibut, plaice. Fish and chips to sit-and-savour around £3.50.

Fry: Own recipe.

Side-lines: Mushy peas, pickled gherkins, pickled onions. Other foods.

Specialities: Yorkshire curd cheesecake and other delicious desserts.

Wrapping: Trays, paper, greaseproof, bags, cartons.

Not so much a fish and chip shop, more a seafood experience, delightfully placed not far from the water's edge. It's nigh on forty years since the McKenzie clan started to prepare the most delicious fishy feasts. Children are baited with a special menu complete with gooey pud.

SILVER STREET FISH & CHIP SHOP, 22 Silver Street. Tel: 0947 603087

Open: Tue 11.45 a.m. – 1.30 p.m.; 8.00 p.m. – 11.30 p.m.; Wed 11.45 a.m. – 1.30 p.m.; Thu 11.45 a.m. – 1.30 p.m.; 5.00 p.m. – 11.30 p.m.; Fri 11.30 a.m. – 1.30 p.m.; 4.45 p.m. – 5.45 p.m.; 8.00 p.m. – 11.30 p.m.; Sat 11.30 – 1.30 p.m.; 8.00 p.m. – 11.30 p.m.

Facilities: T/A; P near; wheelchair access.

Fish finds: Cod, haddock. Fish and chips to take-and-taste from around £1.40.

Fry: De-odorized fat.

Side-lines: Mushy peas. Other foods.

Wrapping: Polystyrene trays, paper.

Derek and Mary Webb insist that all food is cooked to order and only the freshest possible product is used. The outlet is coming up for its half-century, though the present proprietors have only been frying here for a few years. It has cream and green paintwork with attractive flower boxes outside. The Granby Hotel and Elsinore pub are close by, and of course there's the Albion Football Club opposite.

TRENCHER'S RESTAURANT, New Quay Road. Tel: 0947 603212

Open: Daily: Whitsun – Oct 11.00 a.m. – 9.00 p.m.; Winter: check by phone (closed Jan – March): April/May & Nov/Dec Sun – Thu 11.00 a.m. – 3.00 p.m.; Fri & Sat 11.00 a.m. – 8.00 p.m.

Facilities: R (L); P; T; wheelchair access.

Fish finds: Cod, local crab, haddock, halibut, lobster, plaice, Norwegian prawns, salmon, scampi, skate. Fish and chips to sit-and-savour from around £4.45.

Fry: Beef dripping.

Side-lines: Mushy peas. Other foods.

To state merely that the fish is bought fresh is, in this case, almost an insult to the good fishermen of Whitby! It seems almost as if a pan of piping hot dripping has been held out of the window and the fish have obligingly jumped in, via the batter! The list of recommendations proprietor Terry 'Fossie' Foster has received for his harbourside restaurant in the seven years he's owned it seems endless. The reasonably-priced menu, including 'Junior's Choice', is better perused in greater detail than I can give here. However, I was particularly drawn to one nattily-named item: a 'Torvil and Dean'. You've guessed it, double Whitby skate! The decor seems to manage the impossible: a feeling of intimacy and warmth at the same time as one of airiness and cleanliness, mainly achieved with cubicles of dark green, deep-buttoned banquette seating, low-hanging Tiffany-style lamps and light pine, parquet-effect flooring and ceiling, plus plenty of greenery. Accolades are given by David Goodswen, representatives of pensioners' groups, tour operators and even a photographic society from Swinton!

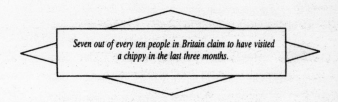

Seven out of every ten people in Britain claim to have visited a chippy in the last three months.

York

G & G FISHERIES, 64 Clarence Street. Tel: 0904 637886

Open:	Mon, Thu – Sat 11.30 a.m. – 1.30 p.m.; 5.00 p.m. – midnight; Tue 11.30 a.m. – 1.30 p.m.; 5.00 p.m. – 11.45 p.m.; Wed 5.00 p.m. – 11.45 p.m.; Sun 5.00 p.m. – 11.30 p.m.
Facilities:	T/A; R; P; T near.
Fish finds:	Cod, haddock. Fish and chips to take-and-taste from around £1.45; sit-and-savour around £2.05.
Fry:	Dripping.
Side-lines:	Mushy peas, pickled gherkins, pickled onions. Other foods.
Wrapping:	Polystyrene trays, greaseproof paper.

Most people who go to York want to visit the cathedral with its magnificent stained glass windows, thankfully saved in the terrible fire of a few years ago. Others want to know about the castle, the oldest part of which is

Clifford's Tower, dating back to Norman times, and is now the site of the Assize Court. But there's also the Hall of the Merchant Adventurers, which must include seamen, and in turn fishermen, which brings me nicely on to the business of fish frying carried out near the city hospital by George Papas and George Chrisou. The two 'G's have been trading here for around fifteen years, and have built up a keen following with locals as well as tourists. David Ropper and other mummers regularly facilitate themselves of their excellent fare when treading the boards locally. The outlet also does a good trade in party catering.

MILLERS, 77 Main Street, Fulford. Tel: 0904 633540

Open:	Mon 7.30 p.m. – 11.30 p.m.; Tue – Sat 11.30 a.m. – 1.30 p.m.; 5.00 p.m. – 11.30 p.m. (Sat till 11.45 p.m.).
Facilities:	T/A & R; P; T.
Fish finds:	Cod, haddock, plaice, scampi. Fish and chips to take-and-taste from around £1.40; sit-and-savour around £2.60.
Fry:	Beef dripping.
Side-lines:	Mushy peas. Other foods.
Wrapping:	Greaseproof, white wrap.

The Miller family have been frying in Yorkshire for over twenty years. They've currently three outlets – the others are at Haxby and Heslington Road. Steve Miller emphasizes their awareness of competition from other sectors of the fast food trade and knows that for fish and chips to remain at the fore, they must present a clean, bright and cheerful image. His own outlets are a good example and they serve up fine fare as well. The restaurant at Fulford is already reaping the rewards, after only a few years' trading, with some customers who use it as many as five times a week! They have special children's meals and also do a fully-inclusive meal, very reasonably priced, in the 28-seater diner. Find it opposite the Plough pub, not far from where Main Street joins the A64 outer ring road.

YORKSHIRE (SOUTH)
Balby
(Nr Doncaster)

BARNBY-DUN FISHERIES, Unit 4, Marlowe Road, Barnby Dun.
Tel: 0302 885237

Open:	Tue 5.00 p.m. – 10.00 p.m.; Wed 11.30 a.m. – 1.30 p.m.; 5.00 p.m. – 10.00 p.m.; Thu 4.15 p.m. – 10.00 p.m.; Fri 11.30 a.m. – 1.30 p.m.; 4.15 p.m. – 10.00 p.m.; Sat 11.30 a.m. – 1.45 p.m.; 4.15 p.m. – 10.00 p.m.
Facilities:	T/A; P (20 cars).
Fish finds:	Cod, haddock, plaice, scampi. Fish and chips to take-and-taste from around £1.35.
Fry:	Dripping.
Side-lines:	Mushy peas.
Speciality:	Grilled fish.
Wrapping:	Own special bags.

David Harrison, the proprietor, fries at this location right next door to the chemists in the middle of this village north of Doncaster. Sigebert, a monk of Gemblours in 1100, had a tale to tell about the history of the name Doncaster. He claimed it came from Thong-ceaster, the 'castle of the thong', and said that Hengist and Horsa purchased from the British king as much land as could be encircled by a piece of leather. They cut the leather into fine strips, which stretched around the city area! The name actually means 'city of the river Don' (Celtic for 'that which spreads') but I prefer Sigebert's tale. I'm also partial to Mr Harrison's fish and chips.

SCORAH'S FISHERIES, 8 St John's Road. Tel: 0302 852330

Open:	Mon & Thu 8.00 p.m. – 11.00 p.m.; Tue 11.30 a.m. – 1.30 p.m.; 4.15 p.m. – 6.15 p.m.; Fri 11.30 a.m. – 1.30 p.m.; 8.00 p.m. – 11.30 p.m.; Sat 11.30 a.m. – 1.30 p.m.
Facilities:	T/A; P near.
Fish finds:	Cod, haddock. Fish and chips to take-and-taste from around £1.30.
Fry:	Vegetable oil.
Side-lines:	Mushy peas.
Wrapping:	Greaseproof, white paper, plastic bags.

Betty Scorah and her husband have devoted nearly thirty years to their business on the racecourse side of Doncaster. The spotless decor is in black and white. The White Swan is the local pub and it is often told there how a limousine would be parked outside the chippy with a certain Mr Ronnie Barker, thespian, tucking into a take-away while filming 'Open All Hours' locally for the BBC. Remember the St Leger is run every September at the Town Moor racecourse, so the queues get particularly long around this time. But this delightful couple will always have enough fries to go round – particularly for Mrs Jean Eyne, who recommends them.

Barnsley

AGNES ROAD FISHERIES, 48 Agnes Road. Tel: 0226 245186

Open:	Tue 11.30 a.m. – 1.30 p.m.; 4.00 p.m. – 6.00 p.m.; 8.00 p.m. – midnight; Wed 11.30 a.m. – 1.30 p.m.; 4.00 p.m. – 6.00 p.m.; Thu 4.00 p.m. – 6.00 p.m.; 8.00 p.m. – midnight; Fri & Sat 11.30 a.m. – 1.30 p.m.; 8.00 p.m. – midnight.

Facilities:	T/A.
Fish finds:	Cod, haddock. Fish and chips to take-and-taste from around £1.30.
Fry:	Vegetable oil.
Side-lines:	Mushy peas. Other foods.
Wrapping:	Greaseproof, plain white wrap.

The Bourne family run one of the oldest chippies in Barnsley. Deeds date the building to around 1918 although it's actually thought to have existed at the turn of the century. In those far-off days much of the traffic was on the Barnsley Canal, which connects up with the Leeds–Wakefield canal. These days the country's main arterial road, the M1, runs close to the town. Take junction 37 to the first traffic lights towards Barnsley, then turn right. Take a left turn down Park Grove – a little over a mile away – then fifth on the right and the shop is in sight. If it is not, you've gone wrong somewhere, so start again! But it's worth it.

MORTON'S, 9/10 Wellington Street. Tel: 0226 203330

Open:	Mon & Wed 11.00 a.m. – 7.00 p.m.; Thu, Fri & Sat 11.00 a.m. – 11.30 p.m.; Sun 7.00 p.m. – 11.30 p.m.
Facilities:	T/A & R (L); P near; T; wheelchair friendly.
Fish finds:	Cod, haddock, plaice. Fish and chips to take-and-taste from around £1.30; sit-and-savour around £2.50.
Fry:	Vegetable oil.
Side-lines:	Mushy peas, pickled onions. Other foods.
Wrapping:	Trays, white paper, greaseproof, brown bags.

Mr Masie, the proprietor of this town centre chippy, is very proud of his reputation for first-class fish and chips. His staff believe in service with a smile at this 50-seater diner. Treat yourself to a special fish, chips, cup of tea and bread and butter for around £2.50: terrific value.

SCOTT'S FISHERIES, Highstone Lane, Ward Green. Tel: 0226 281362

Open:	Mon 8.00 p.m. – 11.30 p.m.; Tue 11.30 a.m. – 1.45 p.m.; 4.00 p.m. – 6.00 p.m.; Wed & Fri 11.30 a.m. – 1.45 p.m.; 8.00 p.m. – 11.30 p.m.; Thu 4.00 p.m. – 6.00 p.m.; Sat 11.30 a.m. – 1.45 p.m.
Facilities:	T/A; P near.
Fish finds:	Cod, haddock. Fish and chips to take-and-taste from around £1.15.
Fry:	Pure vegetable oil.
Side-lines:	Mushy peas, pickled onions. Other foods.
Wrapping:	Greaseproof, white paper, polystyrene trays.

Eric and Rosemary Scott have been serving their regulars from this mining community for over a decade. Their premises are beside the Working Men's Club in this town on the river Dearne about 16 miles north of Sheffield. They are particular folk, their regulars, and will soon tell you if there is owt wrong. There've been no complaints about their seasoned specialities, Yorkshire scallop fish cakes, which form as much a part of the locals' diet as the best bitter served up next door!

Mexborough

ANGIE'S PLAICE, 47 Harlington Road. Tel: 0709 570200

Open:	Tue & Thu 8.00 p.m. – midnight; Wed & Sat 11.45 a.m. – 1.45 p.m.; 8.00 p.m. – midnight; Fri 11.45 a.m. – 1.45 p.m.; 4.30 p.m. – midnight.
Facilities:	T/A; P; T; wheelchair access.
Fish finds:	Cod, haddock, scampi. Fish and chips to take-and-taste from around £1.20.

Fry: Bibby's P.100 oil.

Side-lines: Mushy peas, pickled onions. Other foods.

Wrapping: Greaseproof, white paper.

'Any fish fresher than ours is still in the sea' is the impressive motto of this shop on the corner of Auckland Road, opposite the Star pub. Proprietor Angela Worley has been here for five years. The decor is one that would make even the fish feel at home: fishermen's nets, shells, animated fishermen, crabs, lobsters, paintings hang all around. In the window is a cold-water fish tank for those who, fish included, haven't yet got the message as to the trade carried on at this fine establishment. Andrea Newby cannot recommend the 'plaice' highly enough!

Rotherham

TANYARD FISHERIES, 224 Bawtry Road, Wickersley. Tel: 0709 525967

Open: Mon – Sat 11.30 a.m. – 1.30 p.m.; Tue 7.30 p.m. – 11.15 p.m.; Wed 5.00 p.m. – 10.00 p.m.; Thu & Fri 4.30 p.m. – 11.30 p.m.; Sat 7.00 p.m. – 11.30 p.m.

Facilities: T/A; P; T adjacent.

Fish finds: Cod, haddock, scampi. Fish and chips to take-and-taste from about £1.30.

Fry: Vegetable oil.

Side-lines: Mushy peas. Other foods.

Wrapping: White paper.

Wickersley nestles between the M1 and M18, a couple of miles east of Rotherham. There's a golf course near by, and just over the M18 is Roche Abbey. The Tanyard can be found in the shopping centre of the same name, with the Three Horse Shoes pub close by. John Gilding has been the proprietor for more than twenty years. It's funny how ex-patriots of an area savour the flavour of their favourite fry. John Whiturham, who hails from Ilkley Moor 'baht 'at', but now lives in Portsmouth, raves about this outlet.

MRS SIDDONS
EATING
FISH AND CHIPS
BY
GAINSBOROUGH

YORKSHIRE (WEST)
Batley

HEALEY FISH BAR, 71 Healey Lane. Tel: 0924 478573

Open: Tue – Fri 8.00 p.m. – midnight; Sat 11.30 a.m. – 1.30 p.m.; 8.00 p.m. – midnight.

Facilities: T/A; P; T.

Fish finds: Haddock and chips from around £1.00.

Fry: Fat.

Side-lines: Mushy peas. Other foods.

Wrapping: Pink paper and newspaper.

Apart from the excellent value and fresh quality product, I wonder why proprietor F. Hodgeson is in the pink about his 3-year-old haddock-only business? Because that's the colour of his wrapping paper! The Financial Times *is printed on this colour paper because they use re-pulped newspaper left over from other publications. It's a sure thing this fish paper has never seen vinegar in a previous life! Curious? Pop along to the shopping precinct at the bottom of Healey Lane and ask Mr Hodgeson the reason. It used to be the heavy woollen trade Batley was known for, then along came the famous Variety Club opened by the late, great, fabulous, Louis Armstrong; now it's the pink paper at the chippy!*

KIRKGATE FISHERIES, 68 Kirkgate, Hanging Heaton. Tel: 0924 463013

Open: Mon & Tue 11.30 a.m. – 1.15 p.m.; 8.00 p.m. – midnight; Thu 4.15 p.m. – 6.15 p.m.; 8.00 p.m. – midnight; Fri 11.30 a.m. – 1.15 p.m.; 4.15 p.m. – 6.00 p.m.; 8.00 p.m. – midnight; Sat 11.30 a.m. – 1.30 p.m.

Facilities: T/A; P near.

Fish finds: Cod, haddock. Fish and chips to take-and-taste from around £1.00.

Fry: Beef dripping.

Side-lines: Mushy peas.

Wrapping: Greaseproof, white paper, chip-bags.

One of the seven wonders of the world are the Hanging Gardens of

Babylon. Hanging Heaton of Batley may not quite measure up to these heights, though they do have a nice golf course! They've also had an excellent chippy sandwiched between the parish church and the Fox and Hounds pub. Another wonder must be how they can produce such fine haddock and good chips at such moderate prices (they've been practising for over half a century, though!). The Family Robinson run this pleasant-looking, stone-fronted outlet with its turquoise-tiled serving area, which gives the place its light and airy appearance.

Bradford

HOLME LANE FISHERIES, 443 Tong Street. Tel: 0274 6822549

Open:	Tue 4.30 p.m. – 6.15 p.m.; Wed 11.30 a.m. – 1.15 p.m.; 8.15 p.m. – 11.15 p.m.; Thu 11.15 a.m. – 1.15 p.m.; 4.30 p.m. – 6.15 p.m.; 8.15 p.m. – 11.15 p.m.; Fri 11.30 a.m. – 1.15 p.m.; 8.15 p.m. – midnight; Sat 11.15 a.m. – 1.15 p.m.
Facilities:	T/A; P (limited).
Fish finds:	Haddock and chips from around £1.00.
Fry:	Beef fat.
Side-lines:	Mushy peas. Other foods.
Speciality:	Yorkshire bread cakes.
Wrapping:	White paper.

They erected a statue to Richard Cobden, the man mainly responsible for the 1846 repeal of the Corn Laws, in the Exchange Building in Bradford, which was opened in 1867. Perhaps the man who was MP for this and several other areas would have preferred the fine, light batter produced from good flour, served up on the haddock in this well-established outlet. The husband and wife team of Spurley and Maureen Stansfield serve up the fare with Yorkshire bread cakes – a side-line speciality. No messing, straight-from-the-shoulder good food, well served, and excellent value. Maureen was brought up in the trade – peeling potatoes at five years old, and serving from thirteen! They've been at this outlet for over twenty years.

MERRYWEATHERS MOTHER HUBBARDS, Ingleby Road.
Tel: 0274 541694

Open:	Daily 11.30 a.m. – 10.00 p.m. (Fri & Sat 11.00 p.m.).
Facilities:	T/A & R (L); P (250 cars); T.
Fish finds:	Cod, haddock, halibut, plaice, scampi. Fish and chips to take-and-taste from around £1.40; sit-and-savour 'king-size special' from around £3.55.
Fry:	Dripping.
Side-lines:	Mushy peas, pickled onions. Other foods.
Wrapping:	White wrapping.

Old Mother Hubbard, so the nursery-rhyme goes, devoted all her time to her dog. But it's more likely you will be asking for a 'pet-bag' to take what's left home to your favourite feline, should you plump for one of this outlet's 'king-size specials'. They really are a meal and a half! The outlet is well packaged to suit all tastes, with the emphasis on families, children's parties and coach parties. With a car park this size on hand, there's even room for the businessman to enjoy a good lunch.

OLD ROAD FISH SHOP, 138 Old Road, Great Horton. Tel: 0274 578902

Open:	Tue, Wed & Thu 11.30 a.m. – 1.15 p.m.; 4.15 p.m. – 6.30 p.m.; Fri 11.30 a.m. – 1.30 p.m.; 4.15 p.m. – 6.30 p.m.; 8.00 p.m. – midnight; Sat 11.30 a.m. – 1.30 p.m.
Facilities:	T/A; P; wheelchair access (mornings).

Fish finds:	Haddock and chips to take-and-taste from around £1.05.
Fry:	Dripping.
Side-lines:	Mushy peas. Other foods.
Wrapping:	White-wrap, newspaper.

Mr and Mrs Ingham ran a very successful chip shop in Halifax before taking over this half-century-old outlet. Since then a lot of people have started to sit up and take notice of this typical single-storey cottage with its black and white decor inside and out, and red terrazzo tiled floor. It has already been mentioned in several other general food guides for the quality, of its fish and fry, which is pleasantly dished up at all times. Find the outlet off the A647 Great Horton Road, behind the Crown pub, half-way down on the left.

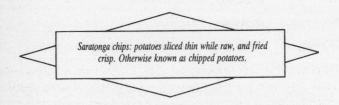

Saratonga chips: potatoes sliced thin while raw, and fried crisp. Otherwise known as chipped potatoes.

PARRY LANE FISHERIES, 236 Sticker Lane. Tel: 0274 668154

Open:	Mon – Sat 11.00 a.m. – 1.30 p.m.; Mon, Thu & Fri 4.15 p.m. – 6.15 p.m.
Facilities:	T/A; P; wheelchair friendly.
Fish finds:	Haddock and chips to take-and-taste from around £1.00.
Fry:	Beef dripping.
Wrapping:	White paper.

Brian Thornton has been running this haddock-house for nearly twenty years. However, they've been frying at this address for over forty. I was first told about this fine fryer by Jim Casey – who was angling to make every day a pensioner's FRYDAY – for himself at least!

Bingley

BECKSIDE FISHERIES, 1a Main Street, Cottingley. Tel: 0274 566354

Open: Mon 4.30 p.m. – 6.00 p.m.; 8.00 p.m. – 11.30 p.m.; Wed 11.30 a.m. – 1.00 p.m.; 8.00 p.m. – 11.30 p.m.; Thu 11.30 a.m. – 1.00 p.m.; Fri 11.30 a.m. – 1.00 p.m.; 4.30 p.m. – 6.00 p.m.; 8.30 p.m. – 11.45 p.m.; Sat 11.30 a.m. – 1.00 p.m.; 8.30 p.m. – 11.45 p.m.

Facilities: T/A; P; T; wheelchair access.

Fish finds: Cod, haddock. Fish and chips to take-and-taste from around £1.00.

Fry: Dripping.

Side-lines: Mushy peas. Other foods.

Wrapping: White wrap.

Until a few years ago they really did believe in these parts that there were fairies at the bottom of their gardens! Then it came to light that the photos of the famous Cottingley fairies, taken just a short walk from the chippy, were a hoax by two little girls in Victorian times. Never mind, what you can believe is that Peter Wilson and his team keep an immaculate shop with mahogany grain panelling and white melamine around the food area. Peter installed himself here about two years ago, and he is only the fifth owner since the shop started trading just after the First World War. It's opposite the Sun pub, a quarter of a mile up the B6269 from its junction with the A650. It's worth a detour.

PARK ROAD FISHERIES, Park Road. Tel: 0274 566931

Open: Mon 11.30 a.m. – 1.15 p.m.; 4.15 p.m. – 6.00 p.m.; 8.00 p.m. – 11.30 p.m.; Wed & Thu 11.30 a.m. – 1.15 p.m.; 8.00 p.m. – 11.30 p.m.; Fri 11.30 a.m. – 1.15 p.m.; 4.15 p.m. – 6.15 p.m.; 8.00 p.m. – 11.30pm; Sat 11.30 a.m. – 1.30 p.m.; 8.00 p.m. – 11.30 p.m.

Facilities:	T/A; P.
Fish finds:	Fish cakes, haddock. Fish and chips to take-and-taste from around £1.00.
Fry:	Beef dripping.
Side-lines:	Mushy peas. Other foods.
Wrapping:	White paper.

There's been a chippy here for many a long year – probably well before the famous Damart thermal wear company set up business near by. However, Peter Norfolk, no relation to the Duke, is the present incumbent. Many of his older customers remember when the range was coal-fired, though they all claim the fare now on offer is as good as it has ever been, if not better. For those needing to work up an appetite, there's the St Ives golf course a little way away.

Cleckheaton

PARK FISHERIES, 19–27 Dewsbury Road. Tel: 0274 872675

Open:	Mon – Thu 11.30 a.m. – 2.00 p.m.; 4.00 p.m. – 11.30 p.m.; Fri & Sat 11.00 a.m. – 2.00 p.m.; 4.00 p.m. – midnight; Sun 3.00 p.m. – 11.30 p.m.
Facilities:	T/A & R; P; T.
Fish finds:	Cod, haddock. Fish and chips to take-and-taste from around £1.10; sit-and-savour around £3.00.
Fry:	Dripping.
Side-lines:	Mushy peas. Other foods.
Wrapping:	Greaseproof, white news.

There has been a 'Clecky Fryer' at this site for over forty years. The

*premises were once an undertaker's in a 'previous life': the laying-out slabs
in the cellar have come in handy as the resting place for sacks of flour and
peas! Refurbished throughout to a very high standard, with the very latest
equipment, the facilities ensure an hygienically prepared meal – and it's
cooked the traditional way: in dripping. The diner seats fifty people; mind
you, if it's a bit slack business-wise the diner might be closed, so 'phone
first. Find them opposite the park, near the bus station, about a mile from
the M62/M606 Chain Bar roundabout.*

Fitzwilliam
(Nr Pontefract)

THORNTON'S CENTRAL FISHERIES, 13 Wakefield Road.
Tel: 0977 615706

Open:	Mon 4.00 p.m. – 6.00 p.m.; 8.00 p.m. – 11.15 p.m.; Wed 11.00 a.m. – 1.30 p.m.; 4.00 p.m. – 6.00 p.m.; Fri & Sat 11.00 a.m. – 1.30 p.m.; 4.00 p.m. – 6.00 p.m.; 8.00 p.m. – 11.15 p.m. (Sat till 11.45 p.m.).
Facilities:	T/A.
Fish finds:	Cod and chips to take-and-taste from around £1.00.
Fry:	Beef dripping.
Side-lines:	Mushy peas, pickled onions. Other foods.
Wrapping:	White wrap, outer wrap.

*No doubt Geoff Boycott, one of Yorkshire's favourite sons, has many fond
memories of popping into the blue and grey shop opposite the Fitzwilliam
Hotel in the centre of the village for his boyhood fish and chips. The
famous cricketer was born in the village and the shop was trading long
before he was born. The Thornton family are in charge. Although the*

prices we quote throughout this book are only a guide, it is fair to say that, to our knowledge, the prices here are among the most reasonable anywhere in the country. So, if you've had a day out at Nostell Priory or the National Trust's Ackworth School, why not pop down the B6428 to round off a good day with a fine meal?

Gildersome

TRIUMPH FISHERIES, The Green. Tel: 0532 533101

Open:	Mon, Fri & Sat 10.45 a.m. – 2.00 p.m.; 7.30 p.m. – 11.30 p.m.; Wed 10.45 p.m. – 2.00 p.m.; Thu 10.45 a.m. – 2.00 p.m.; 3.30 p.m. – 7.00 p.m.
Facilities:	T/A.
Fish finds:	Haddock and chips to take-and-taste from around £1.05.
Fry:	Beef dripping.
Side-lines:	Mushy peas, pickled onions. Other foods.
Wrapping:	Newspaper outer wrapping.

Though this is a new, purpose-built shop that is fully tiled throughout with an Island range, Roger Taylor has been frying in the town for over twenty years. He fries only fresh haddock, which come in two sizes. The outlet is opposite the Junction Inn in Gildersome, which is north of Batley off the A62. Well worth a visit.

Remember – though fast food outlets may sprout up in town centres, your local chippy has probably been part of the community for generations.

Guiseley

**HARRY RAMSDEN'S PLC, White Cross, Guiseley, Nr Leeds.
Tel: 0943 74641**

Open:	Sun – Thu 11.30 a.m. – 10.30 p.m.; Fri & Sat 11.30 a.m. – 11.30 p.m.
Facilities:	T/A & R (L); P (200 cars); T; wheelchair access.
Fish finds:	Fish cakes, haddock, halibut, plaice, scampi, seafood platter. Fish and chips to take-and-taste from around £1.45; sit-and-savour around £4.15.
Fry:	Dripping.
Side-lines:	Mushy peas. Other foods.
Wrapping:	Trays, bags, brown wrap, newsprint.

In 1928 one Mr Harry Ramsden borrowed £150 to open a modest wooden hut selling fish and chips on a site adjacent to the tramway station at White Cross. Three years later he built on the present site, a venture everyone claimed to be a sure recipe for disaster: the largest fish and chip shop in the country. In the half-century or more since, Harry Ramsden's has not only made the critics eat their words, but most of them eat his fish as well! Business has grown at a pace that would make Topsy look like a snail, to become reputedly, not just the largest, but also the most famous fish and chip shop in the world! The statistics are staggering: 1.5 million customers each year; 230,000 lb dripping to fry their own special batter; 120,000 pints of milk; 10,000 lb of tea . . .

In 1965 the business was acquired by Associated Fisheries who have ensured the tradition and reputation of the past have been maintained, up-dating where needed while retaining the image and atmosphere of the past. They developed the take-away, tea-bar, toilet facilities and basement areas in 1988. Then the famous restaurant changed hands again, as part of a £7 million deal, to begin the next chapter in its celebrated life as part of the Merryweather Group, and late in 1989 Harry Ramsden's became the first fish and chip PLC. I have every confidence that the future of this outlet is in more than capable hands. Eating here is more of an experience than just a fish and chip shop, and it is one everyone should try again and again. May I wish Merryweathers continued success with this fine fish-eating emporium.

Halifax

ILLINGWORTH FISHERIES, 108 Keighley Road, Illingworth.
Tel: 0422 244343

Open:	Mon 8.00 p.m. – midnight; Thu 4.30 p.m. – 6.00 p.m.; 8.00 p.m. – midnight; Fri 11.00 a.m. – 1.00 p.m.; Sat 11.30 a.m. – 1.30 p.m.
Facilities:	T/A; P (street).
Fish finds:	Haddock and chips to take-and-taste from around £1.10.
Fry:	Dripping.
Side-lines:	Mushy peas. Other foods.
Wrapping:	White paper and newspaper.

Colin Foulds and family run this typical no-nonsense fish and chip shop. The speciality is super haddock which is the only type of fish sold, but the best. Mr Foulds has been chipping away here for the last eight years. No fuss or bother, take it or leave it. This outlet is on the Halifax to Keighley road near Morrison's supermarket.

The word 'chip' is said to originate from the north of England.

Headingley (Leeds)

BRETT'S FISH RESTAURANT, 12–14 North Lane. Tel: 0532 755228

Open: Mon – Thu 10.15 a.m. – 2.45 p.m.; 4.00 p.m. – 7.30 p.m.; Fri – Sun 10.15 a.m. – 2.15 p.m.

Facilities: T/A & R; P opposite; T.

Fish finds: Cod, haddock, plaice, scampi. Fish and chips to take-and-taste from around £1.15; sit-and-savour around £2.65.

Fry: Beef dripping.

Side-lines: Mushy peas, pickled onions. Other foods.

Wrapping: Greaseproof bags, white paper.

Charlie Brett's family business was first established just after the First World War, though the building dates back to the last century. With the famous Test Cricket ground close by and the Leeds Building Society opposite, it is no wonder he scores with many 'great savers' like Bob Willis, Ted Dexter, Don Mosey and Bill Bowes, plus followers like John Arlott, Michael Parkinson, John Alderton, Bill Pertwee and Peter West. If you've room after the generous portions of fish served, try one of his home-made pudding specialities. The nearest off-licence is opposite, but the Skyrack and Original Oak pubs are both a couple of boundaries away. To compensate, a prize-winning garden can be viewed through the windows of the restaurant, which seats around fifty. A definite 'catch' for the people of Headingley, and for those just visiting.

BRYAN'S OF HEADINGLEY, 9 Weetwood Lane. Tel: 0532 785679

Open: Mon – Sat 11.30 a.m. – 11.30 p.m.

Facilities: T/A & R; P (50 cars); T; wheelchair access.

Fish finds:	Haddock, halibut, hake, plaice, prawns, sole. Fish and chips to take-and-taste from around £1.20.
Fry:	Dripping.
Side-lines:	Mushy peas, pickled onions.
Wrapping:	Paper, bags.

As in any business there are bad and good examples, then special places. Bryan's is definitely a very special place, and has proved so consistently since it first started trading nearly fifty-five years ago. John Bryan, a boy soldier in the 1914–18 war, opened a terraced house that now forms part of the restaurant. The business was passed down to his son, Albert, and grandson John, before changing hands – but not quality – in 1985. It is now run by Mrs Jan Fletcher and Alan Germaine. Leaving Leeds on the Otley Road, turn right opposite the Teacher Training College at a pub called the Three Horse Shoes. Bryan's is 50 yd down on the left. Don't be surprised to find the large carpark filled with Jags, Mercs and Rolls Royces. High recommendations came from Jack Braithwaite, who savoured the flavours all the way back to Oxford, and Christine Lee, closer at hand at Collingham.

Holmfirth

**COMPO'S FAMILY RESTAURANT & TAKE-AWAY, Greenfield Road.
Tel: 0484 686040**

Open:	Mon – Fri 11.30 a.m. – 1.30 p.m.; 4.00 p.m. – 11.00 p.m.; Sat & Sun 11.30 a.m. – 11.30 p.m.
Facilities:	T/A & R (L); P; T; wheelchair access.
Fish finds:	Cod, haddock, plaice, scampi. Fish and chips to take-and-taste from around £1.20; sit-and-savour from £2.60.
Fry:	Beef fat.

Side-lines:	Mushy peas, pickled onions. Other foods.
Wrapping:	White wrap, newspaper.

With the town now known as the place where BBC TV filmed 'Last of the Summer Wine', it was natural for proprietor Neil Pickles to trade on its popularity. I'm not sure if look-alikes to actor Bill Owen's scruffy character – wellies, knitted cap, string-held trousers – would be welcome in this attractive, purpose-built fish restaurant. Anyway, there's always the take-away with similar fare, and then you can sit outside on the wall and make faces at everyone else – just like the man himself did recently! Find this fine fry-house a quarter of a mile along Greenfield Road from the A635 Manchester Road. Mr Pickles has been trading here for seventeen years, in an outlet that has been frying for over half a century.

HOLLOWGATE CHIP SHOP, 1 Hollowgate. Tel: 0484 686842

Open:	Daily 11.30 a.m. – 11.30 p.m. (Fri & Sat till 11.45 p.m.; restaurant till 10.00 p.m.).
Facilities:	T/A & R (L); T.
Fish finds:	Cod, haddock, scampi, and also plaice in the restaurant. Fish and chips to take-and-taste from around £1.10; sit-and-savour from around £1.75.
Fry:	Dripping.
Side-lines:	Mushy peas, pickled onions. Other foods.
Wrapping:	Greaseproof, white paper.

Another 'Last of the Summer Wine'-country outlet. This one they describe as being situated 'betwixt Norah Batty's cottage and Sid's Café.' Because it is located in a listed building and has existed for more than sixty-five years as a chippy – eighteen years under the present ownership of Rodney Chapman and David Senior – it is not surprising it was once viewed on the award-winning television programme. Spot one or more of these local watering holes when next viewing, as they are all close by: Elephant and

Castle, Rose and Crown (known locally as the Nook), Shoulder of Mutton, White Hart and Bridge Hotel. Incidentally, the fare is fine and the service friendly: so much so they came second in the Sea Fish 'Fish and Chip Shop of the Year' contest, North East region, and first in Yorkshire. The restaurant has recently become fully licensed.

Huddersfield

WOODEN HUT, 29a Quarmby Road, Paddock. Tel: 0484 655903

Open:	Mon & Thu 4.30 p.m. – 6.30 p.m.; 8.30 p.m. – 11.30 p.m.; Fri 11.30 a.m. – 1.30 p.m.; 4.30 p.m. – 5.30 p.m.; 8.30 p.m. – 11.00 p.m.; Sat 11.30 a.m. – 1.30 p.m.; 8.30 p.m. – midnight.
Facilities:	T/A.
Fish finds:	Cod, haddock. Fish and chips to take-and-taste from around £1.00.
Fry:	Dripping.
Side-lines:	Mushy peas, pickled onions. Other foods.
Wrapping:	Greaseproof, white paper.

The Shackleton family took over these premises in July 1989. The Wooden Hut takes its name from the shack that once stood on the site, which burned down. It was replaced by a fine, free-standing, pebble-dash building that now houses the chippy, though the space is still confined. It's a bright and cheerful place, however, with flowers and amusing wall posters. This bright approach bubbles over into the service, which is always friendly, and the fry first class with only fresh fish used. You'll find the Hut by taking a right fork at Paddock Head roundabout, near the Angel and Royal Oak pubs, and follow the road for 200 yd. It gets top marks for quality, hygiene, efficiency and sociability from Frank Sykes of Longwood.

Keighley

INGROW LANE FISHERIES, 104 Ingrow Lane. Tel: 0535 665484

Open: Tue 11.15 a.m. – 1.00 p.m.; 4.00 p.m. – 6.00 p.m.;
             8.00 p.m. – midnight; Wed 11.15 a.m. – 1.00 p.m.;
             8.00 p.m. – midnight; Thu 11.15 a.m. – 1.00 p.m.;
             4.00 p.m. – 6.00 p.m.; Fri 11.15 a.m. – 1.00 p.m.;
             4.00 p.m. – 6.30 p.m.; Sat 11.15 a.m. – 1.00 p.m.

Facilities: T/A; P near.

Fish finds: Cod and chips to take-and-taste from around 90p.

Fry: Dripping.

Side-lines: Mushy peas. Other foods.

Wrapping: Greaseproof, white paper.

I've no doubt the locals are well used to quips and jibes about this address, but every time I read it I can't help thinking about toe-nails! Which, I promise you, has nothing to do with Kevin Scanlan's 'plaice' near the bottom gates of Oakbank School, opposite Ingrow Lane Potteries. Then there's the Ingrow Lane Stores close at hand with their off-licence. The building – believed to have been a Mill Cottage – is over 100 years old. Although Kevin (a fryer of some fifteen years' experience) has only been producing his quite superb product here for a few years, the site has housed a chippy for over sixty-five.

Alongside the British pub, it is the fish and chip shop that tax exiles like Tom Jones and Rod Stewart claim to miss most from Britain.

Leeds

AMAZON FISHERIES, 100 Dixon Lane. Tel: 0532 638149

Open: Mon – Sat 11.30 a.m. – 1.30 p.m.; Thu & Fri 11.30 a.m. – 1.30 p.m.; 4.30 p.m. – 6.30 p.m.

Facilities: T/A; P; T; wheelchair access.

Fish finds: Haddock and chips to take-and-taste from around £1.15.

Fry: Beef dripping.

Side-lines: Mushy peas. Other foods.

Wrapping: Greaseproof bags, white paper and pink wrapping.

A beige tiled floor with green ceramic tiles on the walls – that's the decor at this extra-clean and tidy outlet. They've got beige marble-effect panels on the range and green window strip lights as well. Alan & Mary Granger are in their eleventh year as proprietors of the 30-year-old outlet; they've built up a strong regular clientele at the shop off Whitehall Road in a parade of shops at the end of Dixon Lane. It's worth noting they sell wet fish also – but at these prices and quality, who wants to cook their own?

BARKLY FISHERIES, 149 Barkly Road, Beeston. Tel: 0532 716119

Open:	Mon, Tue, Thu, Fri 11.30 a.m. – 1.30 p.m. 4.30 p.m. – 6.30 p.m.; Sat 11.30 a.m. – 1.30 p.m.; 8.30 p.m. – 11.30 p.m.
Facilities:	T/A.
Fish finds:	Cod and chips to take-and-taste from around 90p.
Fry:	Dripping.
Side-lines:	Mushy peas. Other foods.
Wrapping:	White paper, newspaper.

Unusual to find in Yorkshire, where the haddock-house reigns supreme: a chippy that only serves cod! He must be from the south or somewhere! In fact Yan Yan Ng runs a first-rate outlet in the south of the city, which you can reach by taking exit 1 off the M621. His home-made fish cakes are particularly recommended by Mrs Jill Robinson, who also remarks on the pleasant service and the spotless shop.

COE'S FISHERIES, 124 Crossgates Road. Tel: 0532 664431

Open:	Mon – Wed 11.30 a.m. – 1.30 p.m.; 4.00 p.m. – 11.30 p.m.; Thu & Fri 11.30 a.m. – 1.30 p.m.; 4.00 p.m. – 10.30 p.m.; Sat 11.00 a.m. – 2.00 p.m.
Facilities:	T/A; P near.

Fish finds:	Haddock and chips to take-and-taste from around £1.20.
Fry:	Fat.
Side-lines:	Mushy peas.
Wrapping:	Greaseproof, white paper, brown bags.

There's been a chippy at this site, near the Crossgates roundabout on the A6120 ring road, for well over sixty-five years. Present proprietor Robin Jaques' family have been in charge of the range for the last three generations. The road network and many other things may have changed in that time – though the Seacroft Hospital has been down the road for a good few years – but one thing has remained constant: the high standard of fry to be had from Coe's. The service is equally good whether you are a regular popping in for the usual, or a casual in transit looking for a tasty bite to eat.

MOORTOWN FISHERIES, 75 Lingfield Drive. Tel: 0532 687206

Open:	Mon & Thu 4.30 p.m. – 9.30 p.m.; Tue 4.30 p.m. – 6.30 p.m.; Wed & Fri 11.30 a.m. – 1.30 p.m.; 4.30 p.m. – 6.30 p.m.; Sat 11.30 a.m. – 1.30 p.m.
Facilities:	T/A; P near; T.
Fish finds:	Haddock and chips to take-and-taste from around £1.20.
Fry:	Fat.
Side-lines:	Mushy peas, pickled onions. Other foods.
Wrapping:	White paper, newspaper.

When a local couple take over the chippy, ten-to-one the product will be good: they don't want their friends talking about soggy chips and greasy fish. So it is with Susan and Alfred Durrant who, after twenty years frying, took over here a few years ago. Their quality control ensures that only the very best of fare is served to their customers at any time. After all, they had a reputation to keep up – that of Walt and Lily Moss who kept the place at a remarkably high standard for nearly thirty years. A hard act to follow, but Susan and Alfred are really working at it! You'll find this happy couple opposite the Lingfield pub. The shop has been redecorated with peach and white paintwork inside and red outside. It's in the north-east corner of the city, near the ring road.

NASH'S FISH BAR & RESTAURANT, 102 Harrogate Road, Chapel Allerton. Tel: 0532 622015

Open:	Mon 4.30 p.m. – 10.00 p.m.; Wed 11.30 a.m. – 1.30 p.m.; 6.00 p.m. – 10.00 p.m.; Thu 4.30 p.m. – 7.00 p.m.; Fri 11.30 a.m. – 1.30 p.m.; 4.30 p.m. – 10.00 p.m.; Sat 11.30 a.m. – 1.30 p.m.; 6.00 p.m. – 10.00 p.m.
Facilities:	T/A & R (L) ; P near; T.
Fish finds:	Cod, cod's roe, haddock, halibut, plaice, scampi, shark, skate, swordfish, tuna. Fish and chips to take-and-taste from around £1.20; sit-and-savour from £3.75.
Fry:	Beef dripping.
Side-lines:	Mushy peas, pickled onions. Other foods.
Speciality:	Frogs' legs.
Wrapping:	White paper, newspaper.

This is one of the few Yorkshire outlets still alive and well today that was listed in my first fish and chip guide. It was a winner then, and is a winner now. Their prices have stood the test of time – not that then or now they'd stand much chance of rooking the public even if they wanted to: they are situated right beside Chapeltown Police Station! Funny how chippies beside the nick always have a good standard! The Nag's Head pub is close by too but that's not why Annis Marshall recommends them – she just loves the traditional taste served up by the Bellhouse family. They'll fry fish in breadcrumbs, too, by special request.

PEPPERS, 70 High Street, Kippax. Tel: 0532 864216

Open:	Mon 4.00 p.m. – 10.00 p.m.; Tue 4.00 p.m. – 11.00 p.m.; Wed – Fri 11.00 a.m. – 1.30 p.m.; 4.00 p.m. – 11.30 p.m.; Sat 11.00 a.m. – 1.30 p.m.; 4.00 p.m. – 6.30 p.m.; Sun 7.00 p.m. – 11.30 p.m.
Facilities:	T/A; P.
Fish finds:	Haddock, plaice. Fish and chips to take-and-taste from around £1.00.
Fry:	Beef dripping.
Side-lines:	Mushy peas. Other foods.
Speciality:	Scallop fish cakes.
Wrapping:	White paper.

Tim Perkins refurbished this fine haddock-house a couple of years ago. It now sports a smart five-pan Island range and very attractive and clean decor. The building is over a century old, and he reckons they've been frying here for almost as long. Tim is a friendly sort with many colleagues in the trade. You'll find the shop at the end of the High Street, with the Commercial Hotel nearby. Kippax is just outside the eastern boundary of Leeds, about 2 miles from Castleford on the B6137, which leads to historic Ledston Hall. The Steeton Hall Gateway, another interesting place to visit, is just the other side of the nearby A1.

SEAFARER, North Parkway, Seacroft. Tel: 0532 735731

Open:	Mon – Sat 11.30 a.m. – 11.00 p.m.; Sun 6.00 p.m. – 11.00 p.m.
Facilities:	T/A & R; P near.
Fish finds:	Cod, haddock, plaice, scampi. Fish and chips to take-and-taste from around £1.10; sit-and-savour around £1.60.
Fry:	Dripping.
Side-lines:	Mushy peas. Other foods.
Wrapping:	Greaseproof, paper.

Frying started from this address around a decade ago. They have an excellent reputation for fresh fish served in hygienic surroundings by pleasant staff. I note the building was opened by the Queen, but as it forms part of the main entrance to the shopping centre, I presume it was the complex for which she performed the ceremony. Not that there is anything wrong with HRH enjoying a meal of Britain's favourite national food in the 82-seater diner, with all its nutritious, health-giving ingredients. The shopping centre is just off the A6120 ring road at the main Leeds to York roundabout. Both the City and Roundhay Park golf courses are quite close, with Bramham Park historic house a few miles up the A64.

SKYLINER RESTAURANT, 15 Austhorpe View. Tel: 0532 646853

Open:	Mon & Wed 11.30 a.m. – 2.00 p.m.; 8.00 p.m. – 11.30 p.m.; Tue 11.30 a.m. – 2.00 p.m.; Thu 11.30 a.m. – 2.00 p.m.; 4.00 p.m. – 11.30 p.m.; Fri 11.30 a.m. – 2.00 p.m.; 4.00 p.m. – midnight; Sat 11.30 a.m. – 2.00 p.m.; 8.00 p.m. – midnight; Sun 8.00 p.m. – 11.30 p.m.
Facilities:	T/A & R; P; T.
Fish finds:	Haddock, halibut, plaice, scampi. Fish and chips to take-and-taste from around £1.25; sit-and-savour around £1.85.
Fry:	Dripping.
Side-lines:	Mushy peas.
Wrapping:	Paper, trays.

Does it have something to do with being the nearest point east of Leeds to Hull and the fishing fleet, that there are so many good outlets around this side of town? David and Elaine Meeham have now taken over this family business, which was run for over a quarter of a century by David's parents. It's on the main A63 ring road junction with Selby Road. Lilian Whitehead recommends this outlet, particularly because it gives such good value for money.

STATION FISHERIES, 18 Station Road, Crossgates. Tel: 0532 649612

Open:	Tue – Thu 11.30 a.m. – 1.30 p.m.; 4.30 p.m. – 8.00 p.m.; Fri & Sat 11.30 a.m. – 1.30 p.m.; 4.30 p.m. – midnight.
Facilities:	T/A; P.
Fish finds:	Haddock and chips to take-and-taste from around £1.15.
Fry:	Fat.

326

Side-lines: Mushy peas, pickled onions. Other foods.

Wrapping: Greaseproof paper, own-name bags.

Find this quality outlet on the eastern edge of the city, opposite Crossgates's British Rail station and the Comet warehouse. It's also close to the A6120 ring road and a short drive from the historic Temple Newsam House and golf course. The shop, now run by the Pearce family, has been trading in the area for many years and is recognized for the high standard of hygiene and friendly staff. The fresh fish fried is consistently first-rate.

WOODHOUSE FISHERIES, 5–7 Johnston Street. Tel: 0532 420031

Open: Tue 11.30 a.m. – 1.45 p.m.; 4.30 p.m. – 6.00 p.m.; Wed 11.30 a.m. – 1.15 p.m.; 4.30 p.m. – 6.00 p.m.; 8.00 p.m. – 11.30 p.m.; Thu 11.30 a.m. – 1.15 p.m.; 4.30 p.m. – 10.00 p.m.; Fri 11.30 a.m. – 1.15 p.m.; 4.30 p.m. – 6.00 p.m.; 8.00 p.m. – 11.45 p.m.; Sat 11.30 a.m. – 1.15 p.m.

Facilities: T/A; P near.

Fish finds: Cod and chips to take-and-taste from around £1.25.

Fry: Beef dripping.

Side-lines: Mushy peas.

Wrapping: White paper.

Proprietor P. Ruane can trace the origins of this building back to the 'gay nineties', before even Leeds University was founded (1904). The wool, leather and clothing trades were still the occupations of many of the first customers when the chippy opened here in the 1920s, and tradition is something the owners are proud of and want to keep alive. Although the shop was completely refurbished a few years ago – 'investing in the future of fish and chips', they call it – the proprietors still keep faithfully to the staple diet of chippies. How green can you get? Another environment-friendly fryer. They feel many outlets are losing their identities and becoming nothing more than hot food take-outs. There's no chance of that happening here, for the qualilty of fare and standard of service are quite superb.

Morley

MERMAID FISH RESTAURANT, 123 Britannia Road.
Tel: 0532 535376/523017
Also at Crackenedge Lane, Dewsbury; Burlington Arcade, Barnsley; and Vernon Road, Scarborough

Open:	Mon – Sat 11.30 a.m. – 11.00 p.m.; Sun midday – 11.00 p.m.
Facilities:	T/A & R (L); P; T.
Fish finds:	Cod, haddock, halibut, plaice, scampi. Fish and chips to take-and-taste from aorund £1.15; sit-and-savour from £4.00.
Fry:	Fat.
Side-lines:	Mushy peas. Other foods.
Wrapping:	Boxes, paper.

For more than fifteen years they have been frying at the junction of Britannia and Howley Park roads, the last nine under the captaincy of Norman Lodge. You can count on fresh fish being served whenever possible, in a friendly atmosphere and very clean surroundings. Britannia Road runs parallel to the M62 with the Howley Hall golf club on the other side of the motorway. Morley is another of the famous old Yorkshire woollen market towns. Yorkshire folk in these parts know a thing or two about good chippies and bad. Judging by the queues that regularly form at this fine establishment, they have awarded it five stars.

Ossett

BARRACUDA FISHERIES, 5 Horbury Road. Tel: 0924 276326

Open:	Mon 8.00 p.m. – midnight; Tue & Sat 11.15 a.m. – 1.15 p.m.; Wed & Fri 11.15 a.m. – 1.15 p.m.; 8.00 p.m. – midnight; Thu 4.30 p.m. – 6.30 p.m.; 8.00 p.m. – midnight.
Facilities:	T/A; P.
Fish finds:	Cod, haddock. Fish and chips to take-and-taste from around £1.05.
Fry:	Fat.
Side-lines:	Mushy peas, pickled onions. Other foods.
Wrapping:	Greaseproof paper, white paper, carrier bags.

I like it when a proprietor describes an outlet as 'traditional'. It usually means they are interested in maintaining the good things in life like qualilty, standard and service at reasonable prices. So speaks Mrs Maureen Dickinson, who has been trading here for around six years, though she's been frying for seventeen. Add to this that she refuses to sell other fried products so as to avoid tainting the fats, and so always maintains a high standard. If you want to fry your own, she sells wet fish also on the mornings that she is open. Find the Barracuda on the corner of Storrs Hill and Horbury Road, nearly opposite the Crown Hotel. The Weavers Arms pub is also close by. The chippy's interior is attractively tiled throughout in primrose and blue.

QUEEN'S DRIVE FISHERIES, 123 Queen's Drive. Tel: 0924 275474

Open:	Mon – Sat 11.30 a.m. – 1.30 p.m.; 4.30 p.m. – 11.45 p.m.; Sun 8.00 p.m. – 11.45 p.m.
Facilities:	T/A; P; wheelchair access (side door).

Fish finds:	Cod, haddock. Fish and chips to take-and-taste from around £1.05.
Fry:	Beef dripping.
Side-lines:	Mushy peas, pickled onions. Other foods.
Wrapping:	Greaseproof chip bags, white paper.

The Ward family are 'reet proud' of their chippy, next door to the Post Office on the main road through Ossett, and so they should be. After eleven years of frying they proclaim the old adage: 'You've tried the rest; come try the best', and afterwards swill it down with a glass of ale at the nearby Two Brewers, no doubt! The shop is nicely tiled in white and blue ceramic, with the preparation areas in grey. Ossett stands mid-way twixt Wakefield and Dewsbury, three miles from each. Alternately, take exit 40 from the M1, and look out for the red and white shop front.

Pudsey (Nr Leeds)

CRAVENS, 32 Lowtown, Pudsey. Tel: 0532 551396

Open:	Tue – Fri 11.30 a.m. – 2.00 p.m.; 4.30 p.m. – 11.00 p.m.; (Thu & Fri till 11.30 p.m.); Sat 11.30 a.m. – 11.30 p.m.; Sun midday – 11.30 p.m.
Facilities:	T/A & R (L); P; T; wheelchair access.
Fish finds:	Haddock, halibut, plaice, prawns, scampi, sole. Fish and chips to take-and-taste from around £1.50; sit-and-savour around £3.00.
Fry:	Beef dripping.
Side-lines:	Other foods.
Wrapping:	White paper.

Mrs Jan Fletcher and Mr David Mitchell only took over this five-year-old outlet in 1989, though they've been frying for what seems like a lifetime! They've certainly practised long enough to get near-perfect: Leeds folk would be quick enough to criticize the quality of fry if it were not right! My guess is they'll be here for many a long fry yet.

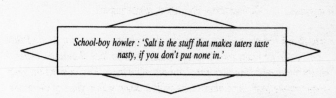

School-boy howler : 'Salt is the stuff that makes taters taste nasty, if you don't put none in.'

Rothwell (Nr Leeds)

BLAMIRES FISH BAR, 92 Commercial Street. Tel: 0532 823832

Open: Mon 11.15 a.m. – 2.00 p.m.; 4.00 p.m. – 6.30 p.m.; Fri 11.15 a.m. – 6.30 p.m.; Sat 11.15 a.m. – 2.30 p.m.

Facilities: T/A; P near.

Fish finds: Haddock and chips to take-and-taste from around £1.20.

Fry: Beef dripping.

Side-lines: Mushy peas. Other foods.

Wrapping: Wet-strength paper, white wrap, polystyrene trays, plastic knives and forks.

Ian Blamires has been frying at this prime-position outlet near Morrison's supermarket since 1978, though the outlet has traded for over twenty years. The shop is fully tiled in blue and has a large following among shoppers, and shop, office and factory workers – hence the opening hours to coincide with shopping times. The nearest pub is the Hare and Hounds, also in Commercial Street. Rothwell is close by the River Aire and the Leeds and Liverpool canal on one side, and on the other are the A61 and M1. There are two golf courses at Middleton Park just over the M1.

Wakefield

ROBIN HOOD FISHERIES, 500 Leeds Road. Tel: 0532 822292

Open:	Tue, Wed, Fri & Sat 11.30 a.m. – 1.30 p.m.; 8.00 p.m. – 11.45 p.m.; Thu 4.30 p.m. – 6.30 p.m.; 8.00 p.m. – 11.45 p.m.
Facilities:	T/A; P near; wheelchair access.
Fish finds:	Cod, haddock. Fish and chips to take-and-taste from around £1.20.
Fry:	Fat.
Side-lines:	Mushy peas, pickled onions. Other foods.
Speciality:	Yorkshire fish cakes.
Wrapping:	Greaseproof, white paper, outer-wrap.

In 1988 Wakefield celebrated the centenary of becoming the county town of the West Riding and the seat of a bishop. In 1990, Paul and Adele Mason celebrate their seventh anniversary of frying at this address. You may consider the connection tenuous, but to the Masons, the ongoing success of the city is a barometer of their own achievements! They are champions for the little man aiming for recognition – and have gone about it in the right way, with quality product, clean surroundings and pleasing service. Find them between the Halfway House pub and the Angel Inn – making them three-quarters of the way to Paradise!

MERRYWEATHERS, 597 Denby Road, Calder Grove. Tel: 0924 274994

Open:	Mon – Fri 11.30 a.m. – 11.30 p.m.; Sat 11.30 a.m. – 12.15 a.m.; Sun midday – 11.30 p.m.
Facilities:	T/A & R (L); P; T.

Fish finds: Cod, haddock, halibut, plaice, scampi. Fish and chips to take-and-taste from around £1.25; sit-and-savour around £3.70.

Fry: Dripping.

Side-lines: Mushy peas, pickled onions. Other foods.

Wrapping: Cartons, paper bags.

Don't tell Fergie, but it was at the battle of Wakefield, between the Yorkists and the Lancastrians, on 30 December 1460, that Richard, Duke of York was slain. By whom? A lady, no less: Margaret of Anjou! Still, you'll certainly live to fight another day if you dine out at this fine eatery in the south of the city, close to junction 39 of the M1, about half a mile down the A636 Denby Dale Road. It's now part of the Merryweathers chain and they have a pleasant, efficient team on hand. They specialize in arranging birthday parties for children in the 60-plus-seater diner, but you can come too!

SPRING LANE FISHERIES, 7 Spring Lane, New Crofton.
Tel: 0924 861014

Open: Mon 8.00 p.m. – 11.30 p.m.; Thu 4.15 p.m. – 5.45 p.m.; 8.00 p.m. – 11.30 p.m.; Fri & Sat 11.30 a.m. – 1.30 p.m.; 8.00 p.m. – 11.30 p.m.; Sun 9.00 p.m. – 11.00 p.m.

Facilities: T/A; P; T; wheelchair access.

Fish finds: Cod or haddock and chips to take-and-taste from around £1.00.

Fry: James Jennings fat.

Side-lines: Mushy peas, pickled onions. Other foods.

Wrapping: Greaseproof and newsprint.

Now the leaning tower of Pisa is about to close, New Crofton take up the

*reins with the going-to-be-famous 'LEANING CHIPPY'! Word has spread
to such an extent they have even built a pub near by and called it The
Slipper (they are all trying to get in on the act – lean, slip . . .).
Presumably the hostelry is needed to cope with the overflow of tourists
scheduled to visit what used to be known simply as Freddie Palmer's
Chippy until a few years ago. What with autographs and posing for upright
photographs, will they have time to continue to fry their fine fare, I ask
myself? No wonder it's a cod and haddock-only house. James Lee with his
son and daughter-in-law took over the century-old outlet recently, though
he's been in the trade since 1980.*

WOODCOCK FISHERIES, 14 Woodcock Street, Sandal. Tel: 0924 377998

Open:	Tue 4.30 p.m. – 8.00 p.m.; Wed 11.30 a.m. – 1.15 p.m.; 4.30 p.m. – 7.00 p.m.; Thu 4.30 p.m. – 8.00 p.m.; Fri 11.30 a.m. – 1.15 p.m.; 4.30 p.m. – 8.00 p.m.; Sat 11.30 a.m. – 1.30 p.m.
Facilities:	T/A; P.
Fish finds:	Cod, haddock. Specials to order. Fish and chips to take-and-taste from around £1.00.
Fry:	Dripping.
Side-lines:	Mushy peas, pickled gherkins, pickled onions. Other foods.
Wrapping:	White news.

*Wakefield is described in the 1906 edition of Pannell's Reference Book as
'a handsome town on the Calder . . . in 1888 its handsome parish church
became a cathedral and was afterwards restored and enlarged as a
memorial to Bishop Walsham How'. I'll add a few more handsomes:
there's a handsome castle (Sandal) and battlefield, with the more recently
handsome Wakefield Leisure Park, and of course there's the ever-
handsome Wakefield Trinity Rugby League Football Club. All these, and
more, are situated close to the extremely handsome chippy opposite*

334

Manygates Maternity Hospital at the top of the hill that runs parallel to the main A61 Wakefield to Barnsley road. Mrs B. Dale has only been keeping up the outlet's 70-year-old tradition for a few years, but I'm happy to report the fish and chips are, you've guessed it, just handsome.

Wetherby

WETHERBY WHALER, 18 Market Place. Tel: 0397 62968

Open:	Mon – Wed 11.30 a.m. – 1.30 p.m.; 4.30 p.m. – 11.30 p.m.; Thu – Sat 11.30 a.m. – 11.30 p.m.; Sun 4.00 p.m. – 11.30 p.m. (restaurant till 9.30 p.m. daily).
Facilities:	T/A & R; P; T.
Fish finds:	Cod, haddock, plaice. Fish and chips to take-and-taste from around £1.20; sit-and-savour from £2.25.
Fry:	Dripping.
Side-lines:	Mushy peas.
Wrapping:	White paper, newspaper.

Peter Idle certainly puts the lie to his name at this busy outlet opposite West York Bus Station. He's been trading here, under the name of Better Fish Ltd., for well over a dozen years. The pleasant market town 15 miles from Leeds is perhaps best known for its horse-racing, though there are several interesting sites close at hand, including Spofforth Castle and the historic house at Stockeld Park. It's certainly a convenient place to break your journey on the A1. Win or lose on the horses, it's a sure thing you'll have to go a long way to better the fare laid on by Peter Idle, but if you're looking to sit down, remember the upstairs restaurant closes at 9.30 p.m.

Yeadon

FOUNTAIN, 152 Harrogate Road. Tel: 0532 506070

Open:	Tue – Fri midday – 2.00 p.m.; 5.00 p.m. – 11.00 p.m.; Sat & Sun midday – 11.00 p.m. (Sat till 11.30). (Restaurant closes 10.30 p.m. daily.)
Facilities:	T/A & R (L); P; T (R only); wheelchair access.
Fish finds:	Haddock, halibut, plaice, scampi. Fish and chips to take-and-taste from around £1.25; sit-and-savour (special haddock meal) about £4.50. Pensioners: three courses for £3.00.
Fry:	Dripping.
Side-lines:	Mushy peas. Other foods.
Wrapping:	Newsprint over personalized greaseproof wrap, own label bags.

If there are more chippies in Yorkshire than the rest of the country, it can only be that the customers know what they want, and the good fryers know how to give it 'em. Fresh fish, mainly haddock, served in clean, pleasant surroundings by pleasant people – Don and Glennis Aykroyd – at reasonable prices. You can't ask fairer than that – and that's what you get at the Fountain, which has been a chippy for forty years, although less than three under the present ownership. It's not just those whose plane has been delayed at the nearby Leeds/Bradford Airport who come here, but you do see them rushing from the planes after a couple of weeks on the Costas: 'I've been dying to get back to good old fish and chips – blow that paella and pasta!' It's 8 miles north west of Leeds on the A65/A658. They specialize in children's parties in the restaurant.

SCOTLAND

ANGUS
Letham

S. & I. PORTERFIELD CHIP SHOP, 18a The Square. Tel: 030 781 591

Open:	Tue – Sun 4.30 p.m. – 11.00 p.m.
Facilities:	T/A & R; P; T; wheelchair access.
Fish finds:	Fish cakes, haddock, scampi. Fish and chips to take-and-taste from around £1.50; sit-and-savour from £2.30.
Fry:	Palm oil.
Side-lines:	Pickled onions.
Wrapping:	Insulated boxes, paper.

By now everyone will have heard about the recent bicentenary. No, not of Australia, but of Letham! Just how they figure this out, when the building that houses the chippy dates back to the early 1700s, will take a Scotsman to explain. Perhaps they started again after the first inhabitants left for the Antipodes? Anyway, it's a pleasant shop decorated inside in peach. Irene Porterfield and her husband have been frying there for just about three years, though the business has been there, we're told, for a century or more. Sit-and-savour facilities have recently been added for eighteen people, no doubt to cater for the mass influx of Aussie tourists expected to explore their family trees! They'll want to know that the nearest pub is the Commercial across The Square. Whether the 'Amber nectar' is called Scotch or lager rather depends on your tipple.

FIFE
Anstruther

ANSTRUTHER'S, 17 Shore Street. Tel: 0333 310518

Open:	Mon – Thu midday – 2.00 p.m.; 5.00 p.m. – 11.00 p.m.; Fri – Sun 5.00 p.m. – midnight (restaurant open summer only).
Facilities:	T/A & R (L); P near; T.
Fish finds:	Haddock and chips to take-and-taste from around £1.90; sit-and-savour about £3.00.
Fry:	Fat.
Side-lines:	Pickled onions.
Wrapping:	Paper, trays optional in summer.

If you want to know more about the history of the fishing industry, go to Anstruther (pronounced Anster), where they've a superb museum specializing in the subject. If you want to eat good fish to to Anstruther's (pronounced Mmmm . . .) where Ian Shyte has been in charge of this century-old outlet for the last nine years. Ian's a trained chef and often welcomes some of the world's top golfers and members of the showbusiness fraternity to his 40-seater restaurant. It's just a long drive (by ball) or a short drive (by car) from St Andrews Golf Club. Kellie Castle and Gardens are even closer to this seaport and market town on the Firth of Forth. Its fine harbour is the reason why it became the centre of the Fife fishing industry.

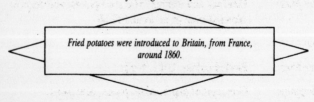

Fried potatoes were introduced to Britain, from France, around 1860.

Kirkaldy

VALENTE & PANETTA, 73 Overton Road. Tel: 0592 51991

Open:	Mon, Tue, Thu – Sat 11.30 a.m. – 1.30 p.m.; 4.00 p.m. – 11.00 p.m.
Facilities:	T/A.
Fish finds:	Haddock and whiting. Fish (two pieces) and chips to take-and-taste from around £2.00.
Fry:	Oil.
Side-lines:	Pickled onions. Other foods.
Wrapping:	Greaseproof paper, white paper, newspaper.

I know this book is intended to highlight the best in fish and chips – and both the standard and the amount served up at this 60-year-old establishment are excellent. But I would be doing the readers a disservice if I were not to mention the delicious home-made ice-cream, which rounds off the fish supper a treat. John Valente is to be congratulated.

GRAMPIAN
Aberdeen

ASHVALE FISH RESTAURANT, 44–48 Great Western Road.
Tel: 0224 596981

Open:	Daily midday – 1.00 a.m.
Facilities:	T/A & R (L); P (32 cars); T.
Fish finds:	Cod, haddock, lemon sole, plaice, scampi, skate, turbot. Fish and chips to take-and-taste from around £1.80.
Fry:	Fat.
Side-lines:	Mushy peas, pickled onions. Other foods – proprietor describes as '157 items to take-away'.
Wrapping:	Greaseproof bags, news off-cuts.

Mr John Low junior has been trading from this spot, near the cemetery at the junction of Holburn Street, for five years. He admits his prices are not the cheapest in Scotland, but emphasizes, modestly, that the accent is on quality and 'we're Number 1 in Scotland'. To state this in this home of fisheries and fish-curing takes some living up to. Maybe the oil business has replaced fishing in this chief seaport on the North Sea in northern Scotland, but they still know a good fry when they taste it. The queues at the Ashvale must stand for something . . . And to be judged among the best in Scotland by your peers, is something else! In 1989 John's outlet was a regional and national finalist in the Sea Fish Authority contest.

LANARKSHIRE
Airdrie

CAFE LA FIESTA, South Bridge Street. Tel: 0236 63564.

Open:	Mon, Tue, Thu 11.00 a.m. – 1.30 p.m.; 3.30 p.m. – 11.00 p.m.; Wed 11.00 a.m. – 1.30 p.m.; 4.30 p.m. – 11.00 p.m.; Fri & Sat 11.00 a.m. – midnight; Sun 4.30 p.m. – 11.00 p.m.
Facilities:	Haddock, scampi. Fish and chips to take-and-taste from around £2.20; sit-and-savour around £2.30.
Fry:	Groundnut oil.
Side-lines:	Mushy peas, pickled gherkins, pickled onions. Other foods.
Wrapping:	White and brown paper wrap, cartons.

If you're on the road between Glasgow and Edinburgh, stop off at Airdrie and meet the Zambonini family at the Café la Fiesta for a feast of beautifully cooked haddock and chips, or scampi and chips, followed by a portion of delicious home-made ice-cream. There's ample room in the 38-seater diner for the largest of parties. The family have a right to be proud of their reputation: they came a very close second in the Sea Fish Industry Authority's 'Fish Shop of the Year Award 1989' for Scotland.

> *To popularize potatoes in France during the late 18th century, Monsieur Parmentier gave a dinner with potatoes, of one kind or another, used in each course. It is said Marie Antoinette, who attended, wore potato flowers in her hair!*

LOTHIAN
Edinburgh

L'ALBA D'ORO, 5 Henderson Row. Tel: 031 557 2580

Open:	Mon – Thu 11.30 a.m. – 1.30 p.m.; 4.30 p.m. – midnight; Fri 11.30 a.m. – 1.30 p.m.; 4.30 p.m. – 1.00 a.m.; Sat 4.30 p.m. – 1.00 a.m.; Sun 4.30 p.m. – midnight.
Facilities:	T/A; P near.
Fish finds:	Fish cakes, haddock, scampi, squid. Fish and chips to take-and-taste from around £1.75.
Fry:	Oil.
Side-lines:	Pickled onions. Other foods.
Wrapping:	Greaseproof paper, brown paper, newspaper.

Filippo Crolls has been frying for nearly twenty years, and at this address for not much less. It's just down the road from the main TSB in Dundas Street. The walls are panelled in pine, with brown tiled floor. The range also is in shades of brown and cream with coloured trims. Various celebrities have been known to pop in when recording for Scottish Television. Before moving south, that irascible, talented performer Robbie Coltrane devoured many a morsel of Filippo's fine fare. If it's good enough for him, I'm not sure who it is good enough for, but I enjoyed their fries.

Penicuik

TRIDENT FISH BAR, 155 John Street. Tel: 0968 72731

Open:	Mon, Wed & Thu 11.30 a.m. – 1.30 p.m.; 5.00 p.m. –

1.00 a.m.; Tue 11.30 a.m. – 1.30 p.m.; Fri 11.30 a.m. –
1.30 p.m.; Sat 11.30 a.m. – 1.30 p.m.; 5.00 p.m. –
1.30 a.m.; Sun 5.00 p.m. – 1.00 a.m.

Facilities:	T/A; P near; wheelchair access.
Fish finds:	Haddock, scampi, shark, trout. Fish and chips to take-and-taste from around £1.70.
Fry:	FryMax oil.
Side-lines:	Pickled gherkins, pickled onions. Other foods.
Wrapping:	Greaseproof paper, trays, white news.

Whether you spell it the above way or Pennycuik, the name still means Cuckoo's Hill. It's on the North Esk river, ten miles from Edinburgh, close to Roslyn Castle in one direction and Castlelaw Hill Fort in another. They have been frying regularly on the corner with Carnethy Avenue – under the clock tower and across from the Carnethy Inn – for over twenty years.

STRATHCLYDE
Ardrossan

EUGENE'S RESTAURANT, 57 Prince's Street. Tel: 0294 63696

Open:	Daily 10.00 a.m. – 10.00 p.m.
Facilities:	T/A & R (L); P near; T; wheelchair access.
Fish finds:	Haddock, whiting (filleted). Fish and chips to take-and-taste from around £1.85; sit-and-savour around £2.35.
Fry:	Soya oil.
Side-lines:	Mushy peas, pickled onions. Other foods.

Wrapping: Cartons, greaseproof.

The town owes its rise to the harbour, which was begun in 1806 by the 12th Earl of Eglinton. The restaurant owes its current popularity to John Gilmour, the 'Number One Fryer'. It's been trading for over forty years, close to the Harbour. The decor is in red, white and green, and is always spotless – and the standard of fare is first rate. There is seating for around forty, so take a friend.

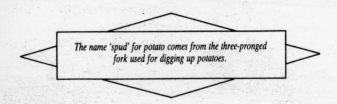

The name 'spud' for potato comes from the three-pronged fork used for digging up potatoes.

Faslane

NEPTUNE FISH BAR, HMS *NEPTUNE*, FASLANE. Tel: 030 12301

Open: Sun – Fri 9.00 p.m. – midnight.

Facilities: T/A; P – boats only!

Fish finds: Haddock, cod, whiting. Fish and chips to take-and-taste from around £1.80.

Fry: 'Secret' recipe.

Side-lines: Pickled onions.

Wrapping: White paper.

The most exclusive fish and chip shop in the world! Who says so? John 'Soapy' Watson, who's been running this 'fission chips' outlet (his pronunciation) for seven years. And I'm not about to argue with him, even if I could. Why? It's the only fry-house where the customers need a high security check to buy their fries! In fact the only secret I'm about to unfold is its location – on the nuclear submarine base in Loch Lomond.

Glasgow

BLUE LAGOON, 10 Renfield Street. Tel: 041 221 5561

Open:	Mon – Thu 9.00 a.m. – midnight; Fri & Sat 9.00 a.m. – 4.00 p.m.; Sun 9.00 a.m. – midnight.
Facilities:	T/A & R; T.
Fish finds:	Cod, haddock, prawn dumplings, scampi. Haddock and chips to take-and-taste from around £1.90; sit-and-savour around £2.85.
Fry:	Beef dripping.
Side-lines:	Pickled onions. Other foods.
Wrapping:	Paper.

Part of the Scottish-Italian connection of father and son, Ersilio and Angelo Varese. The Renfield Street outlet has seating for eighty as well as take-away. This one's near the Central Station, with another five (three take-away only) also in the midst of Scotland's largest city. With over 100 staff they are certainly the largest fryers in Glasgow, if not the west of Scotland. However Ersilio (who has himself thirty years' experience riding the range) insists only highly experienced fryers are employed in each outlet. I can't see many others wanting to challenge for another title claimed by the Varese outlets that they keep the latest hours. They're open till four in the morning at weekends! But you don't have to be an insomniac to enjoy their fare – it's consistently good at all times.

DEEP SEA FISH & CHICKEN BAR, 828 Mosspark Drive, Cardonald.
Tel: 041 882 4338

Open:	Mon – Fri 12.45 p.m. – 1.30 p.m.; 4.30 p.m. – 11.00 p.m.; Sat 4.30 p.m. – 11.00 p.m.
Facilities:	T/A; P near.
Fish finds:	Haddock and chips to take-and-taste from around £1.55. Scampi and specials also served.
Fry:	Oil and fat.
Side-lines:	Pickled onions. Other foods including black pudding.
Wrapping:	Greaseproof, Pure Kraft.

Peter Rossi has been dipping-the-fat for nearly forty years, twenty-five of them at this fine outlet 100 yd from the main Cardonald library. There's an off-licence next door. The decor is yellow and grey with mosaic flooring. Like most true fish-fryers who have been in the trade for some time, he prefers to fillet all his own fish on the premises. He only uses fresh fish. The end product lives up to the care and attention he gives his work. Friendly service rounds off the pleasurable experience of dining out from this outlet.

Largs

P. NARDINI & SONS LTD, Esplande. Tel: 0475 674555

Open:	Daily 9.00 a.m. – 10.30 p.m.
Facilities:	R (L); P; T; wheelchair access.
Fish finds:	Crayfish, Dover sole, haddock, halibut, lobsters, salmon, sea bass, sea trout, trout. Fish and chips to sit-and-savour from around £4.40.
Fry:	Groundnut oil.

While the Forte family were building ice-cream parlours and Lyons were establishing corner-houses in the south of England, the Nardini family were busy carving a name in catering in the west of Scotland. It was way back in 1890 that Pietro and Rosa Nardini set out from their native Barga in northern Italy to seek their livelihood in Paisley. From humble café beginnings the business expanded, and in 1931 the first outlet in Largs was opened. Fish suppers sold then for the princely sum of 6d (2½p). Three years later they purchased the present site and within a year were trading from the magnificent and imposing single-storey building on the corner of Nelson Street and Greenock Road. With an exterior as white as the ice cream for which the family was to become famous, the fruits of their endeavours were not long in the reaping. The huge 'café' signs belie a true description of the fare (to the degree of calling Buckingham Palace a detached London home). From a menu of at least 100 dishes, changing several times daily, items like crayfish and lobster, freshly landed by local fishermen, can form the basis of five-course banquets. Other tomes may describe the quality of their confectionery and ice-cream, which has been enjoyed by Royalty and the Prime Minister. We'll just remind you they still know how to fry fish to a turn. Director Peter Nardini considers their reputation has been built on quality throughout the business. 'People trust our name and know they are paying for the best,' he says.

Oban

ONORIO'S FISH BAR, 86 George Street. Tel: 0631 63736

Open:	Mon – Sat midday – 2.00 p.m.; 4.00 p.m. – 11.30 p.m. (and Sun in summer).
Facilities:	T/A; P near.
Fish finds:	Haddock, scampi, whiting. Fish and chips to take-and-taste from around £1.00.
Fry:	Fat.
Side-lines:	Pickled gherkins, pickled onions. Other foods.
Specialities:	Black puddings, bridies, haggis, oatmeal puddings, Scotch pies.
Wrapping:	Cardboard trays, brown paper.

Vera and Onario ('Norrie') Di Ciacca have been trading from this location for some seventeen years, though they've been in the trade for over thirty. Oban is a seaport and tourist centre 113 miles from Glasgow. The George Street building was constructed by the McCaig family, who also built the tower in the town that carries their name. This dates the building at over 100 years old. The shop's interior has grey, marble-effect, formica walls. The family's reputation for fine fare, nicely presented and politely served, has led to an expansion to further premises, called Mario's Fast Food, also in George Street, at No. 64. The fare comes consumer-recommended by Mrs Irene MacDougall.

> *It was strongly believed, in government circles at the time, that Britain only survived the critical U-Boat period of the First World War because we had a good stock of potatoes.*

Paisley

ALLAN'S SNACK BAR & FISH RESTAURANT, 6 Storie Street.
Tel: 041 889 4915

Open:	Mon – Thu 11.00 a.m. – 7.00 p.m.; Fri & Sat 11.00 a.m. – 8.00 p.m.
Facilities:	T/A & R; P; T.
Fish finds:	Haddock, whiting. Fish and chips to take-and-taste from around £1.50; sit-and-savour from about £1.75.
Fry:	Oil and lard mix.
Side-lines:	Mushy peas, pickled onions. Other foods.
Wrapping:	Paper.

Mr Allan Toti's family have been selling fish and chips from this address for over forty years, though they've been established in the trade for half as long again. He calmly informs me that before this the premises were known as Sloan's Fish Restaurant and had been trading since 1879. I must calmly tell you, Mr Toti, if you can establish documentary evidence to this effect, your outlet is certainly a contender for the title of Oldest Fish and Chip Shop in the World! Paisley was once famous for the manufacture of thread, being the base for the Coats mills. It's been a manufacturing centre since about 1700 and, of course, the shawls are known world-wide. Now they may become famous for something else! Mr Toti prides himself on running an old-fashioned traditional outlet without gimmicks. Facts are not gimmicks, Mr Toti: your shop's history is worth shouting about. This apart, the standard of the fare from succulent fresh fish to secret family recipe batter, spotless premises and generous portions brings queues to the door.

TAYSIDE
Arbroath

PEPPO'S HARBOUR CHIP BAR, 51 Ladybridge Street. Tel: 0241 72373

Open:	Sun – Fri 4.00 p.m. – 11.00 p.m. (Fri till 10.00 p.m.).
Facilities:	T/A; P near.
Fish finds:	Haddock, skate. Fish and chips to take-and-taste from around £1.55.
Fry:	Fat.
Side-lines:	Pickled onions.
Speciality:	Haggis.
Wrapping:	Greaseproof, brown paper, newspaper.

The old name for Arbroath is Aberbrothick, because this seaport sits on the river Brothick near its mouth, 17 miles north-east of Dundee. The shorter name was already well established when the Orsi family started frying opposite the harbour in 1951 – the same year the steel industry was nationalized. Readers of the Scottish Daily Record *recently voted this outlet one of the best north of the border. Its decor is now fawn and cream with a blue-backed range. The Smugglers Inn is nearby. The founder of the chippy was Peppo Orsi (that's why the locals still call it Peppo's) though it is now in the capable hands of his two sons, John and Frank. Expect to queue, especially on Sundays. You may meet Mrs Greta McVeigh in the queue – she recommends the outlet highly.*

Nearly £70 million worth of cod and £68 million of haddock was landed in the UK in 1985.

Auchterarder

THE FISH AND CHIP COMPANY, 98–102 High Street. Tel: 0764 62530

Open:	Mon – Sat midday – 1.30 p.m.; 4.00 p.m. – 11.00 p.m.; Sun 4.00 p.m. – 11.00 p.m.
Facilities:	T/A & R (L); P; T.
Fish finds:	Haddock, scampi. Fish and chips to take-and-taste from around £1.75; sit-and-savour around £2.00.
Fry:	Oil.
Side-lines:	Mushy peas, pickled gherkins, pickled onions.
Wrapping:	White paper.

A visit to the Fish and Chip Company is a must if you are passing through the Auchterarder Tayside region. The outlet's slap bang in the middle of town next to the main car park. Michael Giannandrea and his staff will give you a warm welcome, whether you eat in or take out. Second in the 'Fish and Chip Shop of the Year' Contest for Scotland. Speciality fresh haddock, not haggis.

Dundee

DORA'S, 61 Dura Street. Tel: 0382 462121

Open:	Mon – Fri 11.30 a.m. – 1.00 p.m.; 4.30 p.m. – 11.30p.m; Sat 11.30 a.m. – 1.00 p.m.; 4.00 p.m. – 8.00 p.m.
Facilities:	T/A & R; P; T.
Fish finds:	Haddock, scampi. Fish and chips to take-and-taste from around £1.40; sit-and-savour around £1.65; Reduced prices for senior citizens.
Fry:	Beef fat.

Side-lines:	Mushy peas, pickled onions. Other foods.
Specialities:	Black/white puddings, 'busters', haggis.
Wrapping:	Greaseproof, brown paper, newspaper.

Others may claim their premises to be among the longest established, but you'd have to search hard to find a family with a longer unbroken line in the frying trade than that of Guilio Dora. He took over the business from his father less than ten years ago, who had been trading from this site on the corner of Eliza Street opposite Wallace's since 1954. However, the family started frying in this country in 1895! The shop, decorated both inside and out in summer blue and lemon, has been featured on a local television comedy show. There's waitress service in the restaurant section, which seats twenty. Mrs Ina Cameron speaks highly of the establishment, especially the fritters. Bulk deliveries made.

LUIGI'S SNACK BAR, 17–21 Strathmartine Road. Tel: 0382 814041

Open:	Mon – Sat 9.30 a.m. – 8.00 p.m.
Facilities:	T/A & R; P; T; wheelchair access.
Fish finds:	Cod, haddock, lemon sole. Fish and chips to take-and-taste from around £1.50; sit-and-savour around £2.00.
Fry:	Dripping.
Side-lines:	Mushy peas, pickled onions. Other foods.
Wrapping:	Paper.

Since Luigi Esporito took over the business in 1976 the trade, and then the premises, have been growing apace. He has expanded into next door and now offers an even greater menu for the sixty sit-down diners. Very continental in appearance, with awnings over the brown mosaic fronting and wood-panelled walls inside the restaurant: you'll find it at the top of Hilltown, with the famous Dundlee Law hill rising up not far away.

WALES
CLWYD
Mold

WES EDWARDS, 17 Elm Drive. Tel: 0352 3201

Open: Mon, Tue, Thu – Sat midday – 2.00 p.m.; 4.30 p.m. –
                 midnight.

Facilities: T/A; P near; T.

Fish finds: Cod, haddock, plaice, scampi. Fish and chips to take-
                 and-taste from around £1.35.

Fry: Vegetable fat.

Side-lines: Mushy peas.

Wrapping: Greaseproof, trays, white news.

Apart from being an important lead and coal-mining centre, Mold has
been known for the manufacture of bricks, tiles and nails. Thirty years ago
the Edwards family opened their chippy on the housing estate near the new
Community Hospital. Margaret Navarro is part of the second generation of
family fryers now running the outlet with her husband Emilio. The shop
was completely modernized a couple of years ago, and now sports Italian
floor and shaded wall tiles in cream, to match the cream and brown range.
The service is friendly and the fare always piping hot.

Rhyl

**STUART'S FISH AND CHIP SHOP, 69/71 Foryd Road, Kinmel Bay.
Tel: 0745 334331**

Open:	Mon – Sat 11.45 a.m. – 2.00 p.m.; 5.00 p.m. – 11.45 p.m.
Facilities:	T/A; P; T.
Fish finds:	Cod, haddock, plaice, roe. Fish and chips to take-and-taste from around £1.35.
Fry:	Vegetable oil.
Side-lines:	Mushy peas, pickled onions. Other foods.
Wrapping:	Greaseproof, trays, white news.

Stuart Jaap does not claim his to be anything modern like a fast food take-away, but what he may lack in speed he makes up with friendly banter which his customers enjoy almost as much as the fare. After a decade at the range, he prides himself not only in his friendly service in this seaside resort on the mouth of the Clywd, 30 miles from Chester, but also his freshly cooked product. The spotless premises, opposite Asda and Comet, are traditional in decor, with the emphasis on the light and airy, with plenty of room for both customers and staff to move. The Square pub is close at hand.

Wrexham

HIGH STREET CHIP SHOP, High Street, Johnston. Tel: 0978 841659

Open:	Mon 8.00 p.m. – 11.30. p.m.; Tue – Fri 5.30 p.m. – 11.30 p.m.; Sat 11.30 a.m. – 2.00 p.m.; 5.30 p.m. – 11.30 p.m.

Facilities:	T/A; P near; T opposite.
Fish finds:	Cod, haddock. Fish and chips to take-and-taste from around £.125.
Fry:	Vegetable oil.
Side-lines:	Home-soaked mushy peas. Other foods.
Wrapping:	Greaseproof, white paper, trays.

The Green family are not far off celebrating the diamond anniversary of the opening of their eat-out emporium opposite the village memorial in Johnston. The current generation of fryers are Ioan Green and his wife, Marie. The large queueing area means no one need get soggy if it's raining outside – and the chips inside are firm and crisp, with fresh fish cooked in light, dry batter. The shop itself is tiled throughout in green and is always found to be immaculately clean. There's one item constantly on offer in this outlet, gratis, which doesn't appear on the menu – Welsh hospitality by the sack-load.

G.G. & M. ROBERTS, 43 St George's Crescent. Tel: 0978 361169

Open:	Mon 11.30 a.m. – 7.30 p.m.; Tue 11.00 a.m. – 1.30 p.m.; Wed & Thu 11.00 a.m. – 1.30 p.m.; 3.30 p.m. – 7.30 p.m. Fri 11.00 a.m. – 7.30 p.m.; Sat 11.00 a.m. – 11.00 p.m.
Facilities:	T/A; P.
Fish finds:	Haddock and chips to take-and-taste from around 90p.
Fry:	Palm oil.
Side-lines:	None.
Wrapping:	Greaseproof, white paper.

Since the early 1930s this shop has successfully sold two products: haddock and chips. They've also given service par excellence and plenty of satisfaction – with more than a sprinkling of smiles along the way. While you're pondering on the delights of what's to come at this marvellous chippy, why not take a wander (minus chips, please!) around the 15th-century St Giles church, with its magnificent west tower, said to be one of the Seven Wonders of Wales (don't ask me what the other six are!)

DYFED
Aberystwyth

V. CAFFARELLI & SON, Bridgend Fish Restaurant, 40 Bridge Street. Tel: 0970 612095

Open: Mon – Sat 11.00 a.m. – 2.00 p.m.; 4.00 p.m. – 11.00 p.m.

Facilities: T/A & R; T (on request); wheelchair access.

Fish finds: Cod, cod's roe, haddock, plaice, scampi. Fish and chips to take-and-taste from around £1.50; sit-and-savour around £2.20.

Fry: Fat.

Side-lines: Mushy peas. Other foods.

Wrapping: White paper.

Good all-year-round trade has been experienced under the same ownership for twenty-five years, although the outlet has existed since 1946. In summer there are the tourists who flock to this popular resort on Cardigan Bay, at the mouth of the rivers Ystwith and Rheidol. The rest of the year the local population is swollen by students attending the University of Wales. It's worth going out of your way to find this fine fry-house, where they usually fry fresh fish. They work hard at pleasing their customers and making a success of their trade.

> *Polyunsaturates, in which fish are rich, are good for the brain – just what my old Granny used to tell me! They're also good for arthritis.*

Carmarthen

**MORGAN'S TRADITIONAL FISH AND CHIP SHOP, 80 Water Street.
Tel: 0267 230813**

Open: Mon – Sat 10.30 a.m. – 10.00 p.m. (closes 15 Jan for 2 weeks annual holiday).

Facilities: T/A & R; P near; T; wheelchair friendly.

Fish finds: Cod, hake, plaice. Fish and chips to take-and-taste from around £1.35; sit-and-savour around £1.65.

Fry: Vegetable oil.

Side-lines: Mushy peas, pickled onions. Other foods.

Speciality: Apple pie.

Wrapping: Paper.

This is one of the most famous fish and chip shops nestling in the heart of celtic Carmarthen, winner of awards for fine foods, fresh and tasty white fish, accompanied by generous helpings of chunky chips. There's plenty of room for your coming-out party, your wedding or junior's birthday, with enough seating in the diner for all three together. Bring your own booze.
Cheers!

Letterston

SOMETHING'S COOKING, The Square, Tel: 0548 840621

Open: Mon – Sat 11.00 a.m. – 2.00 p.m.; 5.30 p.m. – 10.30 p.m. (and Sun May – Sept).

Facilities: T/A & R (L); P; T.

Fish finds: Cod, haddock, halibut, plaice, scampi, seafood platter, shark steaks, skate, squid rings, whitebait. Fish and chips to take-and-taste from around £1.50; sit-and-savour around £2.00.

Fry: Palm oil.

Side-lines: Mushy peas, pickled onions. Other foods.

Wrapping: White news off-cuts.

My guess is Mr and Mrs T. Rands are either true Welsh people, or real lovers of what is sometimes referred to as 'Little England Beyond Wales'. The reason: on their letterhead, they describe themselves as being in Pembrokeshire – the correct address until a few bureaucrats decided otherwise. True locals still call it Pembrokeshire and even fly their own flag! The flags have been flying at Letterston Square for other reasons of late – the outlet was not only a regional finalist in the 'Fish and Chip Shop of the Year' contest run by Sea Fish, but also came in the top ten of the Daloon contest. It has also been recognized by other guides. Find it on the main A40.

Llandovery

POP IN FISH BAR, 36 High Street. Tel: 0550 21283

Open: Mon – Sat 11.30 a.m. – 2.00 p.m.; 5.00 p.m. – 11.00 p.m. (till 10.00 p.m. Oct – April).

Facilities: T/A & R; P; T.

Fish finds: Cod, fish cake, haddock, plaice, scampi. Fish and chips to take-and-taste from around £1.35; sit-and-savour around £1.85.

Fry: Fat.

Side-lines: Mushy peas, pickled onions. Other foods.

Wrapping: Trays, white paper.

Proprietors Viv and Avril Nicholson are in charge of the range. The shop is opposite the antique emporium towards the end of the High Street in this pleasant mid-Wales market town, with its cobbled square and fishing centre. The restaurant, tastefully decorated with fresh flowers and country paintings, seats around forty. A focal point on the menu is the extensive variety of sweets available. The service is always bright and cheerful, and the premises immaculately clean at all times. When visiting this delightful area Mrs M. Lewis of nearby Llanwrda recommends you can do no better than to dine here.

Tenby

D. FECCI & SONS, Oxford House, Lower Frog Street. Tel: 0834 2424

Open:	Mon – Sat 11.30 a.m. – 11.30 p.m. (Sat till midnight); Sun May–Sept.
Facilities:	T/A & R; T; wheelchair access.
Fish finds:	Cod, haddock, hake, lemon sole, mackerel, plaice, rock salmon, squid. Fish and chips to take-and-taste from around £2.00; sit-and-savour around £2.50.
Fry:	Groundnut oil.
Side-lines:	Mushy peas, pickled onions. Many other foods.
Wrapping:	White news.

Delmon Fecci and his family have been serving the town and tourists from their spotless premises within the old town walls for almost as long as the walls have been there! Well not quite, as they were repaired by Henry VIII and Mr Fecci actually started frying at the chippy over fifty-five years ago – it just seems almost as long! He is now ably aided by his three sons. They cater for many tastes, with baked potatoes, rice and vegetarian items on the menu. Very nice business motto: 'To serve is our duty; to serve well is our pleasure.' May you do so for many more years, Mr Fecci.

GWENT
Newport

M. VACARA & CO., 39 Llanarth Street. Tel: 0633 264150

Open:	Mon – Sat 11.00 a.m. – 7.00 p.m. (Fri till 7.30 p.m.).
Facilities:	T/A & R; P near; T; wheelchair access.
Fish finds:	Cod, hake, plaice. Fish and chips to take-and-taste from around £1.55; sit-and-savour around £2.65.
Fry:	Vegetable oil.
Wrapping:	White bags, white news.

One hundred and one years ago, when Margaret Vacara opened this first chip shop in the Newport area, the town was a fast expanding coal port. In recent years the coal export trade has declined, though business at the chippy has gone from strength to strength. The fry-house was first handed down to three of Margaret Vacara's children, then to her grandchildren and it is currently run by her great-grandchildren. Their pride has always been to maintain the tradition of fine fish fare, fried in home-made batter. However, Alan Edwards, one of the present partners, with Eric Vacara, says current eating trends have resulted in several expansions into other lines – but he insists this will never be done at the expense of quality in their original product. Here's to the next hundred years of a fine family business!

> *From the 17th century potatoes have been known not only for producing wind, but also as an aphrodisiac ('exciting Venus' as many, including Clusius, commented).*

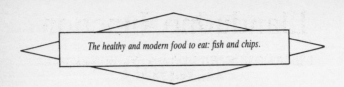

The healthy and modern food to eat: fish and chips.

GWYNEDD
Bala

Y BADELL-AUR, High Street. Tel: 0678 520310

Open:	Mon – Thu 8.00 a.m. – 7.30 p.m.; Fri 8.00 a.m. – 8.30 p.m.; Sat 8.00 a.m. – 9.00 p.m.; Sun 9.00 a.m. – 8.30 p.m.
Facilities:	T/A & R; P; T.
Fish finds:	Haddock, plaice and more. Fish and chips to take-and-taste from around £1.50; sit-and-savour around £2.55.
Fry:	Vegetable fat.
Side-lines:	Mushy peas, pickled onions. Other foods.
Wrapping:	Polystyrene trays, white news.

The town's famous theological college and grammar school were founded in 1712; for the first two and a half centuries the students had to do without the services of this fine Welsh fry-house. It's now firmly established (probably on Bala Series rocks, which, for those geologically inclined, is the uppermost division of the Ordovician system) at the centre of the High Street, opposite the National Westminster Bank. Proprietor John Williams reckons it to be the most well-known in Wales. It certainly turns out excellent fare from spotless surroundings, and comes highly recommended from numerous residents of Denbigh and around. As you can see, the shop opens early in case you need a good breakfast, but fish frying starts from around 11.00 a.m.

Llandudno Junction

ENOCH'S FISH & CHIP RESTAURANT, 146 Conway Road.
Tel: 0492 581145

Open: Mon – Sat 11.00 a.m. – 11.30 p.m.; Sun 11.00 a.m. –
              11.00 p.m.

Facilities: T/A & R (L); P (street); T; wheelchair access.

Fish finds: Cod, haddock, hake, halibut, plaice, salmon, skate, sole,
              trout. Fish and chips to take-and-taste from around
              £1.65; sit-and-savour around £2.70.

Fry: Vegetable fat.

Side-lines: Mushy peas. Other foods.

Wrapping: Polystyrene containers or unprinted paper.

*John and Linda Norcliffe took over this 30-year-old frying outlet in 1988.
It's opposite the National Westminster Bank and, with the Midland next
door, they must be banking on continuing the success of the previous
owners! They are certainly able to cater for most tastes. They supply an
excellent selection of fish, with specials like salmon or pink trout to tempt
the more adventurous. With the new A55 motorway forging its way
through to Angelsey, the whole of the North Wales coastline is easily
accessible from here. There are plenty of sites to visit within a few miles,
including Aberconwy House and Bodnant Gardens run by the National
Trust and Conwy Castle and Plas Mawr House on the west bank of the
Conwy.*

*Up to £500,000 worth of elvers, or baby eels, are fished from
the banks of the river Severn around Gloucester each year.
They are transported by tanker to fish farms in Germany,
Poland and Scandinavia to be grown into eels.*

MID GLAMORGAN
Pontypridd

JOHN'S FISH BAR, 22–23 Park Street, Treforest. Tel: 0443 404482

Open:	Mon – Fri 11.00 a.m. – 2.00 p.m.; 5.00 p.m. – 11.00 p.m.; Sat 11.00 a.m. – 11.00 p.m.
Facilities:	T/A; P near; T.
Fish finds:	Cod, fish bites, fish burgers, fish cakes, hake, plaice, scampi, trout. Fish and chips to take-and-taste from around £2.00 with salad.
Fry:	Oil.
Side-lines:	Pickled gherkins, pickled onions. Other foods.
Wrapping:	Cartons, greaseproof lidded trays.

Pierre Luigi Spagna has been running this outlet, on Park Street near the railway station, for over twenty years. With the Polytechnic of Wales on the doorstep and a vast trading estate just down the road, business is brisk all year round. But standards are always maintained, as vouched for by Miss S.M. Nurse.

POWYS
Llanidloes

FISH SHOP, 24 China Street. Tel: 055 122734

Open:	Tue & Thu midday – 2.00 p.m.; 7.00 p.m. – 10.00 p.m.; Fri midday – 2.00 p.m.; 7.00 p.m. – 9.15 p.m.; Sat 11.45 a.m. – 2.00 p.m.; 5.30 p.m. – 9.00 p.m.

Facilities:	T/A & R; P near; wheelchair access.
Fish finds:	Cod, haddock. Fish and chips to take-and-taste from around £1.30; sit-and-savour around £1.55.
Fry:	Beef dripping.
Side-lines:	Mushy peas, pickled onions. Other foods.
Wrapping:	Trays, white news.

On the A470 between Builth Wells and Newtown, Llanidloes, lies near the head of the River Severn. In the middle of China Street, between the National Westminster Bank and the Mount Inn stands the chippy – where Henry Noe Benbow has traded successfully for over a decade. Just outside the town, near the Llyn Clwedog reservoir, you'll find the Bryn Tail Lead Mine buildings. Inside the chippy you'll find not only good fare but friendly service and spotless surroundings.

SOUTH GLAMORGAN
Cardiff

CLARE ROAD FISH & CHIPS, 118 Clare Road, Grangetown.
Tel: 0222 342217

Open:	Mon – Sat midday – 2.00 p.m.; 5.00 p.m. – 11.00 p.m.
Facilities:	T/A; P (street: no restrictions); wheelchairs welcome.
Fish finds:	Cod, plaice. Fish and chips to take-and-taste from around £1.45; mini cod and chips around £1.10.
Fry:	FryMax vegetable fat.

Side-lines: Various foods.

Wrapping: White news, carrier.

Tony Pattas bought this edge-of-the-Welsh-capital outlet in 1974, though it has been trading since at least 1948, and possibly well before the war. Mr Pattas and his wife Barbara have maintained consistently high standards and despite considerable take-away competition, have been rewarded by regular customers travelling quite long distances to buy their fare. The future development of nearby Cardiff Bay, plus the new athletics stadium a few blocks away, are bound to bring even greater support to this traditional chippy, which was recommended by Mr Neil Sprinks of Dinas Powis.

M.L. & J.W. DICKSON, DEVONIA, 179 Whitchurch Road.
Tel: 0222 619478

Open: Tue – Sat 11.45 a.m. – 1.30 p.m.; Mon & Fri 5.00 p.m. – 10.45 p.m.; Wed & Sat 6.00 p.m. – 10.45 p.m.

Facilities: T/A.

Fish finds: Cod, Dover sole (when available), haddock, hake, halibut, lemon sole, monkfish, plaice, scampi, skate, trout. Fish and chips to take-and-taste from around £1.60.

Fry: Groundnut oil.

Side-lines: Various foods.

Wrapping: Greaseproof bags, trays, white paper, plastic carrier.

Mr and Mrs Dickson's highly respected outlet to the north of the city has been frying since 1930, with this second generation in occupation for nearly forty years. They're just 100 yd from the Gabalfa interchange – where the busy North Road and Eastern Avenue cross, meaning that many a weary traveller takes a detour to pick up some of the best fries in the Principality.

For those on a fat-free diet, fish is cooked in the microwave – without batter, of course. The interior decor is black and white glassed walls with similarly chequered floor in ceramic tiles. The impressive range of fish – all but whitebait served from fresh – is sufficient to illustrate the standard attained and demanded by their discriminating clientele. It has previously drawn recommendations from more general guides for its standard of fare and service, which have been confirmed by T. Alexander of Cardiff.

F. RABAIOTTI & SONS, 200 Cowbridge Road East. Tel: 0222 221950

Open: Mon – Sat midday – 2.00 p.m.; 5.00 p.m. – 11.00 p.m.

Facilities: T/A; P near.

Fish finds:	Cod, hake, plaice. Fish and chips to take-and-taste from around £1.75.
Fry:	Groundnut oil.
Side-lines:	Mushy peas. Other foods.
Wrapping:	White paper.

Rabaiottis have been trading from this address for over a dozen years. The name is synonymous with catering in all its forms and levels throughout south-east Wales, and has been for several generations. Whether they all stem from the same stock I have yet to discover. The outlet is to be found between Peacock's store in Canton, and the Police Station, on this main thoroughfare and busy suburban shopping centre out of the capital to the west. The decor is plush, with tiling in various shades of brown on the walls and floor. Overall, the outlet is quite immaculate, and the fare is recommended by many, including Helen Huzzey.

Cowbridge

MULLIGAN'S FISH & CHIP RESTAURANT & OYSTER BAR,
A48 Stalling Down. Tel: 04463 2221

Open:	Mon – Sat midday – 2.15 p.m.; 6.30 p.m. – 10.30 p.m.
Facilities:	T/A (drive-in); R (L); P; T; wheelchair access.
Fish finds:	Cod, hake, plaice, skate (T/A); much larger sit-and-savour menu, including lobster from own pool. Fish and chips to take-and-taste from around £1.55; sit-and-savour around £5.00.
Fry:	FryMax.
Side-lines:	Mushy peas, pickled gherkins. Other foods.
Wrapping:	Trays, greaseproof, own-name paper carrier bags.

This site is 1 mile from a Welsh market town with a population of around 7,000. It's set on a patch of bare land on the bleak, windswept Roman road which has been usurped as the main artery by the nearby M4. When Beppe and Chris Villa announced their intention to build a new drive-in chippy and 70-seater designer-Victoriana fish restaurant at this forsaken spot, the local response was 'They must be twp!' (Twp: quaint Welsh word meaning daft – to be polite.) . . . But then, Beppe and Chris Villa are not most people. They have a reputation stretching back a number of years as enterprising caterers, with several other long-shot success stories to their credit. This high-rolling gamble has paid off and is considered one of the success stories of the '80s catering trade. Mulligan's became recognized as the 'in plaice' to eat between Swansea and Bristol – where a second, even bigger outlet was opened in Park Street. In late 1989, the Villas sold out to Whitbread. Other than Mondays (when no fish outlet that opens is at its best) it is advisable to book to eat in, and to be prepared to wait for a take-out. The lay-out consists of mock-marble cast-iron tables and former chapel pew seating.

Dinas Powis

THE IN PLAICE, 3 The Parade, Castle Drive, The Murch.
Tel: 0222 513131

Open:	Mon – Sat 11.45 a.m. – 2.30 p.m.; 4.45 p.m. – 10.30 p.m.
Facilities:	T/A; P (30 cars); wheelchair access.
Fish finds:	Cod, haddock, plaice, scampi. Fish and chips to take-and-taste from around £1.60.
Fry:	Groundnut oil
Side-lines:	Garlic mushrooms in batter. Other foods.
Wrapping:	White paper, trays.

For over twenty years, since Mr Leaver gave up his shop in the 'old village', this dormitory village to Cardiff has been without a chippy. During this time the population has trebled, to over 10,000. Now, after only a few months during the last year, it can boast the existence of two shining new fish-fry establishments. Who says the number of outlets are on the wane? They are merely relocating! There's one customer more than pleased at the re-emergence of the frying art in this locale – this book's editor, Rod Harrod, who was born in Dinas Powis. This latest of the two outlets (the other, owned by Robert Berni, flies under the flag of Pandora and is situated on the Cardiff Road) is owned by 31-year-old Paul Conti, a former civil engineer. A strange change of occupation – but not so when you discover his family have been in the catering business for sixty years in Newport, Gwent, with Conti's Restaurant in the town centre. He still has an uncle who's a chippy in Nelson. As a newly created outlet Paul's In Plaice is immaculate, with a gleaming Preston and Thomas range and tiled walls and floors. He takes a pride in his product and uses only fresh fish, cooked to perfection, in light, crispy batter. The editor expects a discount!

WEST GLAMORGAN
Swansea

DICK BARTON'S FISH & CHIPS, 16 Alderwood Road, West Cross, Mumbles. Tel: 0792 404793

Open:	Mon – Sat midday – 2.00 p.m.; 5.00 p.m. – 9.30 p.m.; Sun 5.00 p.m. – 9.00 p.m.
Facilities:	T/A; P; T.
Fish finds:	Calamari, cod, plaice, scampi. Fish and chips to take-and-taste from around £1.60.
Fry:	Oil.

Side-lines:	Mushy peas, pickled onions. Other foods.
Wrapping:	EPS boxes, tubs, paper, news.

Anyone remembering the old steam radio Special Agent Dick Barton will be able to date the opening of this outlet to 1949. Quite what he had to do with Mumbles, its lighthouse, lifeboat station, pier and miniature golf course opposite the chippy has probably been lost in the mists of time over Swansea Bay! However, it's a traditional chippy of exceptionally high standard fare, fast service, good value and clean and airy premises. It also has one of the best marine views possible.

MACARI'S RESTAURANT, 8 Dillywn Street. Tel: 0792 654482

Open:	Mon – Sat 11.00 a.m. – 10.45 p.m.
Facilities:	T/A & R; P near; T; wheelchair friendly.
Fish finds:	Cod, plaice. Fish and chips to take-and-taste from around £1.50; sit-and-savour around £1.95.
Fry:	Oil.
Side-lines:	Mushy peas, pickled gherkins, pickled onions. Other foods.
Wrapping:	Trays, white paper, greaseproof, bags.

Macari's have just celebrated fifty years of trading since Mother Macari opened the doors for the first time in 1939. You can imagine how many portions of fish and chips have been served to all their loyal customers in this spotlessly clean, 90-seater diner.

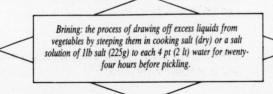

Brining: the process of drawing off excess liquids from vegetables by steeping them in cooking salt (dry) or a salt solution of 1lb salt (225g) to each 4 pt (2 lt) water for twenty-four hours before pickling.

CHANNEL ISLANDS

GUERNSEY
St Peter Port

KINGFISHER CHIP INN, 45 Longstore, St Peter Port. Tel: 0481 23120

Open:	Daily 11.45 a.m. – 1.30 p.m.; 4.45 p.m. – 11.30 p.m.
Facilities:	T/A; P; T.
Fish finds:	Cod and chips to take-and-taste from around £1.65.
Fry:	Palm oil.
Side-lines:	Mushy peas, pickled gherkins, pickled onions. Other foods.
Wrapping:	White paper.

Jean Crouchley's cod-corner has been trading for over twenty-one years. You'll find it just before you reach the Co-op supermarket, going out of St Peter Port. Guernsey is the second largest of the Channel Isles, 9 miles long, 5 miles broad and covering 24½ square miles. The cattle breed is world famous, the tomatoes and other salad vegetables very tasty, and the fare served up at the Kingfisher equal to any you'll find on the island.

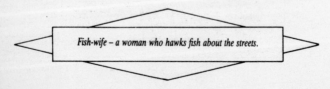

Fish-wife – a woman who hawks fish about the streets.

GUERNSEY

JERSEY
St Helier

ALBERT J. RAMSBOTTOM, 90 Halkett Place. Tel: 0534 78772

Open:	Mon – Sat 11.30 a.m. – 2.00 p.m.; 5.00 p.m. – 10.00 p.m.; Sun (April – Sept only) 5.00 p.m. – 10.00 p.m.
Facilities:	R (L); P; T.
Fish finds:	Clams, cod, fisherman's platter, king prawns, plaice, scampi. Fish and chips to sit-and-savour from around £4.00.
Fry:	Vegetable oil.
Side-lines:	Mushy peas. Other foods.

Colin Chaffe has been welcoming diners to his establishment for a half-dozen years or so. Find it in the small streets behind Queen Street, between Bath Street and New Street, St Helier. Decorated with nautical paraphernalia, it's definitely a worthwhile home-from-home for the floundering holiday-maker. They do half-price children's portions and seat 125, so there's plenty of room to take your friends! The fish portions are large with crisp, dry batter. The chips have to be good with Jersey potatoes on hand, plus the island is only 12 miles from France – and the French introduced us to the chip originally. Elizabeth Castle, off the beach of St Helier, was the home in exile of Charles II and the later Earl Clarendon. It may now house a casino and one kind of chip, but they don't taste as good as those at Ramsbottom's!

NORTHERN IRELAND

COUNTY ANTRIM

Ballymena

DOLPHIN HOUSE, Larne Road. Tel: 0266 656254
Also at 114 Broughslane Street. Tel: 0266 40922

Open: Mon – Sat midday – midnight.

Facilities: T/A; P near; wheelchair friendly.

Fish finds: Cod, haddock. Fish and chips to take-and-taste from around £1.45.

Fry: Vegetable oil.

Wrapping: White paper.

The name Ballymena is Gaelic for middle town. But there's nothing middle of the road about this fine chippy. Mr A.J. Dyball's family have been trading from this address for going on thirty years. They're now into their fourth generation in the fish business – having started in the 1920s, selling wet fish from a horse and cart in the Croydon area. A few years ago they opened another take-away in the town – at 114 Broughshane Street. Both outlets are modern in decor and well ventilated, with wall tiles and panelling. Their motto is: 'We cook to please the customer, not ourselves.' They've always operated a guaranteed total satisfaction or money back policy, honoured at all times, though rarely called upon. The shop comes recommended by William S. Neill.

Belfast

THE BELMONT, 79 Belmont Road. Tel: 0232 657823

Open:	Mon – Sat midday – 2.00 p.m.; 4.00 p.m. – 11.00 p.m. (Thu – Sat till midnight).
Facilities:	T/A.
Fish finds:	Whiting (battered or breaded) to take-and-taste from around £1.50.
Fry:	Fat.
Side-lines:	Mushy peas, garlic bites.
Wrapping:	Bags, white paper, brown bag.

Just to prove you do not need to have been long established, have a wide range of fare or serve it on silver platters to be judged by your peers: John Bickerstaffe took on this outlet a little over a year ago, serves only whiting with few alternative side-lines, and wraps in the traditional way. In fact, it is my guess it was the traditional approach that drew the judges in the 1989 'Fish and Chip Shop of the Year' contest to choose his outlet as a regional finalist. Not only this, but they awarded him a special enterprise award. If you can do this after one year, what does the future hold, John?

CAFÉ MONTMARTRE, 102 Stranmillis Road. Tel: 0232 668032

Open:	Mon – Sat 11.00 a.m. – 11.00 p.m.
Facilities:	T/A & R; P; T.
Fish finds:	Cod, plaice, scampi, whiting. Fish and chips to take-and-taste from around £1.35; sit-and-savour around £1.50.
Fry:	Vegetable oil
Side-lines:	Mushy peas, omelettes. Other foods.

Speciality: Ulster fry.

Wrapping: White paper, brown bags.

Vincent D'Agostino and his wife have been frying for a whole generation in this University sector establishment, and lending more than an occasional ear to students away from home. Actors galore, treading the boards at the nearby Lyric Theatre, satisfy their inner desires on the fine fare served up here. With clientele such as this, no wonder the outlet goes under the name Montmartre: for Left Bank of the Seine read Lagin; for onion soup and snails read best fried fish and chips! They've received several recommendations for quality and cleanliness, including one from Colin D. McClure.

COPPER KETTLE TAKE AWAY, Unit 11, Town and Country Shopping Centre, Carryduff. Tel: 0232 813505

Open: Mon – Sat 11.00 a.m. – 9.00 p.m.

Facilities: T/A; P.

Fish finds: Cod, plaice, scampi, whiting. Fish and chips to take-and-taste from around £1.50.

Fry: Beef dripping.

Side-lines: Mushy peas. Other foods.

Wrapping: Bags, polystyrene trays, newsprint, specialized containers.

Proprietor John Manley took over the range at this outlet only last year, though he's been frying for nearly six. It is busy all day, particularly with shoppers from the Spar supermarket next door, and only fresh fish is used. The chippy has beige tiles with burgundy trim, and pine display units. The name is smartly designed on the windows, again in burgundy with tones of brown. There's a Wine Lodge off-licence in the shopping centre, but you'll have to go half a mile for a drink at the Royal Ascot pub.

FRYAR TUCK, 89 Bloomfield Road. Tel: 0232 471921

Open:	Mon, Wed, Thu 4.30 p.m. – 11.30 p.m.; Fri 4.00 p.m. – 11.30 p.m.; Sat 4.00 p.m. – 8.00 p.m.
Facilities:	T/A; P; wheelchair access.
Fish finds:	Cod, haddock (occasionally), whiting. Fish and chips to take-and-taste from about £1.60.
Fry:	Fat.
Side-lines:	Other foods including spiced potato and onion pastie.
Wrapping:	Plain newsprint, sulphite bags.

They've been frying and tucking in here for around a quarter of a century. The Keown family have been looking after the business since it opened in 1962. As Gavin Keown says, 'Every fish has been fried by a member of the family.' Part of a small suburban shopping centre, the shop has recently been completely refurbished and is now sparklingly clean in white and stainless steel. There's plenty of foliage around, with geometric prints in primary colours adorning the walls. The fish batter is crisp and excellent, the chips firm and dry. The result: the outlet is very popular – expect to queue. Recommendations come from Henry Hull and Mrs E. Getty.

MISTER J.D.'S FISH RESTAURANT OF BELFAST, 222 Newtownards Road. Tel: 0232 458383

Open:	Mon – Sat 11.30 a.m. – 7.00 p.m.
Facilities:	T/A & R; T; P; wheelchair access.
Fish finds:	Cod, smoked cod, haddock, hake, plaice, whiting (battered, breaded or char-grilled), and many more. Fish and chips to take-and-taste from around £1.60; sit-and-savour from around £1.85. Children's from £1.00.
Fry:	Vegetable oil.
Side-lines:	Other foods.

Speciality:	Cod Kiev.
Wrapping:	Trays, white paper.

John Duncan O'Hara (J.D.) claims his fish are out of the sea and on to the plate within 24 hours – lucky he has such an excellent choice, landed locally. Behind the brightly tiled shop-front lurks not only fine fare, but also a trip down memory lane, with the emphasis on old railway memorabilia. The walls are littered (nicely) with anything and everything to do with the days of the puffin' billy – including pictures, signs and an old station clock. Then there's a stuffed Royal Sturgeon mounted above the counter. The restaurant holds forty-four, but that's often not enough since John won the Sea Fish 'Fish and Chip Shop of the Year' award for Northern Ireland, not only in 1988, but again in 1989. Here's one chippy who, with wife Phyliss and mother Lily, will be providing food for the brain in more ways than one, for many years to come. 'It's not a business; it's a way of life,' he says.

SILVER LEAF CAFE, 15 Belmont Road. Tel: 0232 471164

Open:	Mon – Sat midday – 2.00 p.m.; 4.00 p.m. – 10.30 p.m.; Sat midday – 2.00 p.m.; 4.00 p.m. – 8.30 p.m.
Facilities:	T/A & R; P; T; wheelchair access.
Fish finds:	Whiting and chips to take-and-taste from around £1.50; sit-and-savour around £1.65.
Fry:	Beef dripping.
Side-lines:	Mushy peas. Other foods.
Wrapping:	Newspaper, white off-cuts.

Hazel and Steven Patterson's quaint olde worlde shop first opened for business in 1946. Complete with bowed Georgian-style windows, window boxes and shutters, it really is a picture. There's seating downstairs for a dozen with room for a further thirty upstairs – which is also used for private functions. The outlet has been recognized locally for the standard of the building, and nationally for the quality of fare (coming second runner-up in TV'S 'Cod War' competition). Actor James Ellis, astrologer Russel Grant and game show host Gordon Burns have dined out from here, as have many US Air Force and Philippine Airline crews when visiting to collect aircraft from the Short Bros. factory. With a simple motto of 'good food and friendly service', they will always have queues outside, even when there aren't at the nearby Strand cinema.

Holywood

BERTIE'S HOT FOOD BAR, 91 High Street. Tel: 023 17 6785

Open:	Tue – Sat 11.30 a.m. – 1.45 p.m.; 4.30 p.m. – 9.30 p.m.
Facilities:	T/A; P near; T near.
Fish finds:	Cod, whiting. Fish and chips to take-and-taste from around £1.60.
Fry:	Beef dripping.
Side-lines:	Other foods.
Wrapping:	White paper, brown bags.

Although proprietor R. Crutchley is a relatively new 'star' on the Holywood horizon, the business has been trading for over a quarter of a century. They've earned quite a reputation for their 'secret batter' mix. Their pasties are made fresh daily and customers are asked to wait, for not only is the fresh fish fried to order but chips are as well! You'll find them opposite the Presbyterian church. They offer a sound motto: 'Taste and try, we're sure you'll buy!' Myra Shannon certainly does – and recommends not only the high standard of fare but also the consistently spotless surroundings in which it is served.

COUNTY LONDONDERRY
Castledawson

PICKERING'S TAKE-OUT, 7 Main Street. Tel: 0648 68201

Open:	Wed – Sat 4.45 p.m. – midnight.
Facilities:	T/A; P near.
Fish finds:	Plaice, whiting. Fish and chips to take-and-taste from around £1.30.
Fry:	Beef fat.
Side-lines:	Other foods.
Wrapping:	Bags.

The county took the prefix 'London' when, in 1609, much of the land was made over to the corporation of London. That's the history of the county; the history of Annie Pickering's fine outlet is that she's been trading from this location for over a quarter of a century. It's right opposite Moyola Football Club, so expect to queue on match days. Though the quality of Annie's fine fries means you often have to queue, whatever the day.

The Irish have different potato lifting days according to area, many relating to religion and saints' days.

EIRE

Dublin

BESHOFF OCEAN FOODS, 14 Westmoreland Street. Tel: 0001 778026

Open:	Sun – Thu 11.30 a.m. – midnight; Fri & Sat 11.30 a.m. – 1.00 a.m.
Facilities:	T/A & R; P; T.
Fish finds:	Black sole, cod, haddock, mackerel, ray (skate), rock, salmon, shark. Fish and chips to take-and-taste from around £2.90 (Irish punts).
Fry:	Groundnut oil.
Side-lines:	Range of sauces.
Wrapping:	Boxes, double bags.

The story goes that grandfather Ivan Beshoff emigrated to Ireland from Odessa, Russia in 1913, to open up his fish business. The family had been in the business for generations, always promoting the health aspect of the food. Grandfather Beshoff lived to the fine old age of 104 years – just to prove the point! Whether or not, as is claimed, his father lived to 108 and his grandfather to 115 seem fishy Irish stories to me, but never mind. The point is made that this fine fish restaurant and take-out is a compliment not only to their reputation and tradition but the product it serves direct from the quayside. The selection is terrific, with ray and chips (we call it skate) the most popular. The style of decor is that of an Edwardian oyster bar with tradition being emphasized. Even the potatoes are grown on their own 300-acre farm in North Tipperary and chipped only moments before they are cooked. An outlet that deserves its success – pointing the way forward by remembering the best things of the past. Recommended by Mary Fay. If you can't get in try the other branch at 7–8 Upper O'Connell St, Dublin 2 – or fly over to London, where they've just opened in London's West End at the Trocadero Centre.

LEO BURDOCK'S, 2 Werburgh Street. Tel: 0001 540306

Open: Mon & Wed – Sat 5.00 p.m. – 10.45 p.m.; Thu & Sat 5.30 p.m. – 10.45 p.m.

Facilities: T/A; P.

Fish finds: Cod, smoked cod, haddock, ray (skate), whiting. Fish and chips to take-and-taste from around £1.75.

Fry: Cooking fat.

Wrapping: Greaseproof bags, brown paper bags, white wrap.

It was over seventy-five years ago that Brian Burdock's predecesors did their first fry on these premises in the shadow of Christchurch Cathedral. Since then this family-run concern has established itself firmly at the fore of Irish chip shops. In the last few years they have been applauded for their consistent high standard and were even featured on television. Ray (skate) and chips is the most popular dish in Dublin, and Brian's just radiate freshness and good cooking. Henry Anderson of Mitchell's Wine Bar recommends this outlet for quality and super service.

Fat absorption of chips is usually around 5–6 per cent, meaning 10 lb of potatoes will pick up about half a pound of fat.

Newtownards

EDIT SMYTH'S CAFE, 134 Frances Street. Tel: 0247 810655

Open: Mon – Thu midday – 2.00 p.m.; 4.00 p.m. – midnight; Fri midday – 2.00 p.m.; 4.00 p.m. – 12.30 a.m.; Sat 11.30 a.m – 12.30 a.m.

Facilities: T/A & R; P near; T; wheelchair friendly.

Fish finds: Scampi, whiting. Fresh fish and chips to take-and-taste from around £1.40; sit-and-savour a little more.

Fry: Fat.

Side-lines: Mushy peas, home-made pasties. Other foods.

Wrapping: Paper and bags.

Edit Smyth has been frying from the shop on the Bangor Road side of town for over thirty years. The trade is considered a life's work, and pride is taken in it as such. The outlet's success – which is considerable – is put down to remaining faithful to the 'good old-fashioned home-cooking style and personal supervision'. The ground floor decor is wood-panelled walls, with arched mirrors inset. Upstairs, there's seating for seventy in clean and smart surroundings. High recommendation comes from Doris Coffey, who pens these lines:

Ode to a fish fryer

The chips are crisp perfection,
The fish is battered bliss,
I'll bet no matter where you go,
You'll find none so good as this.

EPILOGUE

Into the Frying Pan . . .

The world of the chippy is at last changing. Sometimes for the better, often slowly, sometimes quickly. Keeping track of the fashions, fads, frys and even locations of the nation's fryers is rather like trying to watch a particular chip throughout the fry.

There are those who enter and leave the industry quicker than you can say 'fresh-fried-fish'. We hope few of these 'quick-friers' have crept into these pages – though, inevitably, one or two may have been caught in our net.

Then there are those enterprising, entrepreneurial fryers who use their talents not only at the range, but also in the way they buy and build up their fry-house. Then, almost before you've added the salt and vinegar, they're doing it all over again!

Lastly, there is the new breed of fast-expanding multiples. Unlike their predecessors, the new chains now take on board many of the marketing skills of their franchised fast food cousins. They have set out to create a total slick package, counting decor, ambiance and service as important as the product and packaging.

Not every outlet has been in the financial position of the Big Boys, able to lavish tens of thousands on shop re-fits and fancy fascias. However, many have tried to keep up with changing demands in other, smaller yet equally significant ways. The number of outlets that go out of their way, not only to supply nourishing, good-value food for the older generation, but who search continually for interesting ways to present children's fare, is increasing daily.

Then there are those who try to keep abreast of our times by offering the facility to use Luncheon Vouchers, and even more who are prepared to accept credit cards for reasonable sized orders. Telephone ordering and home delivery are also on the increase – though we would urge proprietors to spare a little time to teach their staff some telephone technique . . . many leave a lot to be desired!

We were pleased to discover, since our last edition, the growing number of outlets that are prepared to experiment with other methods of cooking fish. Many chippies now offer non-battered fish, either micro-cooked or grilled. There are even those who have made a conscious effort to contribute to the growing green movement, as more ozone-friendly packaging material comes on to the market.

Although it is not always practicable, it is nice to see some who are seeking to accommodate those less fortunate, or disabled. Even if some premises are unsuited for wheelchair access, it was pleasing to hear from a number of fryers who said they always did all they could to accommodate disabled people, and very wheelchair friendly they are too.

All in all there has been a definite move over the past couple of years to brighten up the industry and push it forward into the 21st century as Britain's original fast food to be proud of!

CONSUMER FEEDBACK

Chip in your Comments

If you'd like to register your comments on a chippy where you have eaten recently, return this form to:

The Gourmet's Guide to Fish and Chips, Alan Sutton Publishing Limited, Far Thrupp, Stroud, Gloucestershire, GL5 2BU

Chippy's Name ....

Address ....

....

....Telephone ....

Date ....

Facilities (please tick if available):

Take-away
Restaurant
Licensed for alcohol (specify if off-sales)
Parking
Toilets
Wheelchair access
Other (specify)

What is the decor like inside?

Approximate cost of fish and chips:

To take-and-taste ....
To sit-and-savour ....

What fish did you eat?

Did you have any side-lines? (specify)

General comments on food, service, hygiene, value and selection:

Why do you feel this outlet particularly deserves mention/should not be mentioned in the next edition of the *Gourmet's Guide to Fish and Chips?*

I am in no way associated with the management.

Signed ....

Do you think that gift vouchers for fish and chip shops are a good idea?

Name ....
Address ....
....
....
Telephone ....

(All replies will be treated in confidence)

CONSUMER FEEDBACK
Chip in your Comments

If you'd like to register your comments on a chippy where you have eaten recently, return this form to:

The Gourmet's Guide to Fish and Chips, Alan Sutton Publishing Limited, Far Thrupp, Stroud, Gloucestershire, GL5 2BU

Chippy's Name ....

Address ....

....

....Telephone ....

Date ....

Facilities (please tick if available):

Take-away
Restaurant
Licensed for alcohol (specify if off-sales)
Parking
Toilets
Wheelchair access
Other (specify)

What is the decor like inside?

Approximate cost of fish and chips:

To take-and-taste ....

To sit-and-savour ....

What fish did you eat?

Did you have any side-lines? (specify)

General comments on food, service, hygiene, value and selection:

Why do you feel this outlet particularly deserves mention/should not be mentioned in the next edition of the *Gourmet's Guide to Fish and Chips?*

I am in no way associated with the management.

Signed ....

Do you think that gift vouchers for fish and chip shops are a good idea?

Name ....
Address ....
....
....
Telephone ....

(All replies will be treated in confidence)

CONSUMER FEEDBACK
Chip in your Comments

If you'd like to register your comments on a chippy where you have eaten recently, return this form to:

The Gourmet's Guide to Fish and Chips, Alan Sutton Publishing Limited, Far Thrupp, Stroud, Gloucestershire, GL5 2BU

Chippy's Name ....

Address ....

....

....Telephone ....

Date ....

Facilities (please tick if available):

Take-away
Restaurant
Licensed for alcohol (specify if off-sales)
Parking
Toilets
Wheelchair access
Other (specify)

What is the decor like inside?

Approximate cost of fish and chips:

To take-and-taste ....

To sit-and-savour ....

What fish did you eat?

Did you have any side-lines? (specify)

General comments on food, service, hygiene, value and selection:

Why do you feel this outlet particularly deserves mention/should not be mentioned in the next edition of the *Gourmet's Guide to Fish and Chips?*

I am in no way associated with the management.

Signed ....

Do you think that gift vouchers for fish and chip shops are a good idea?

Name ....
Address ....
....
....
Telephone ....

(All replies will be treated in confidence)